BREEDING BIRDS OF THE ALGARVE

BREEDING BIRDS OF THE ALGARVE

G. A. VOWLES and R. S. VOWLES

Centro de Estudos Ornithológicos no Algarve

Illustrations by

J. M. BENINGTON BSc (Hons)

Published by

Centro de Estudos Ornithológicos no Algarve
13 Brookside,
Newent,
Gloucestershire,
U. K.

ISBN 0 9523762 0 2

First published 1994 by Centro de Estudos Ornitológicos no Algarve,
13 Brookside, Newent, Glos., U.K.

Printed in Portugal by

Lithográfica do Sul, S. A.
8901 Vila Real de Santo António
Portugal.

CONTENTS

GLOSSARY and ABBREVIATIONS

GLOSSARY

Afrotropics: the tropical areas of the African continent.

Adult: birds mature enough for breeding.

Allopreening: mutual preening, or the preening of one sex by the other, often highly ritualized and forming part of pair-bonding.

Aquatic: living in water.

Arthropod: a member of the Arthropoda, a large group of animals containing insects, crabs, woodlice, centipedes, spiders and mites, amongst others. They are typified by having jointed limbs and bodies.

Barrocal: a limestone area, extending from Cape St. Vincent to Tavira.

Barlavento: the windward coast, starting just to the east of Portimão and extending to the west coast.

Bigamous: the pair-bond is between one male and two females.

Carpal (Carpal Joint): the wrist (wrist joint) of the wing.

Cervical air-sac: an inflatable part of the neck which, when expanded, enhances a pattern or colour.

Clearing: an open space in woodland or forest which has been made by man.

Copse: a small stand of trees, usually not larger than 5 ha.

Creche: several unfledged chicks are grouped under the protection of one adult.

Crest: elongated feathers on the top of the head which may usually be raised or lowered.

Dispersive: making random movements, lacking any definite directional trend.

Drumming: noise made by strking the bill against a, usually, hollow tree. Used by some species, particlarly woodpeckers, to advertise their breeding territory.

Ear-coverts: the small feathers covering the ear.

Emergent: plants which are rooted below water and project above the surface.

Feral: originally raised in captivity, escaped or released and living wild.

Fledge: to become able to fly.

Fledgling: a chick, feathered or partly feathered, which cannot yet fly.

Flight-feathers: the large feathers of a bird's wing, without which it cannot fly.

Flycatching: chasing and catching insects in flight.

Gape: the inner joint of the bill, (the commensural point).

Garigue: open, low-growing scrub, caused by burning or human interference, which include both bare patches and areas of grass/herbage.

Heath: dry, flat lowlands, with evergreen dwarf scrub plants.

Hedgehog scrub: a scrubland consisting mainly of low, rounded and often spiny plants.

Hovering: a method of hunting where the bird remains almost motionless above the ground by rapidly beating its wings and facing into the wind.

Immature: any bird which has not achieved adult plumage.

Juvenile: fledging or fledged birds which still retain the feathers that first replaced the natal down.

Lagoon: an enclosed coastal pool.

Littoral: coastal land less than 100m high.

4

Lores: the small feathers of the head immediately behind the **gape**.

Malar (malar stripe): usually a stripe running from the base of the bill towards the neck.

Maquis: dense scrub 1-3m high, often interspersed with broadleaf trees.

Mediterranean climate: hot summers with almost complete drought; mild winters with substantial rainfall.

Monogamous: the pair-bond is between one male and one female.

Monotypic: a species for which no races have yet been recognised. The opposite of **polytypic**.

Morph: a distinct colour form, determined genetically as opposed to racially.

Moustachial stripe: an obvious stripe running from the **gape** below the **ear coverts**.

Nidifugous: able to leave the nest and its vicinity soon after hatching.

Palearctic: Eurasia as far north as the main Arctic Ocean islands and east to Iraq; northern Africa as far south as the northern borders of the Sahel and of the Sudan.

Parkland: grassland with scattered mature trees.

Partial migrant: some populations migrate, some do not.

Passerine: the perching birds. Characterized by feet with a set of 4 toes jointed at the same level, suitable for gripping branches, 3 toes pointing forwards and 1 toe pointing backwards, and a **syrinx**, or 'song' chamber at the lower end of the **trachea**. All the species from page 186 to page 154 in this book are passerines.

pH: a measure of acidity and alkalinity. A pH of 7 is neutral, higher is alkaline, lower is acid.

Polyandrous: a female mating with more than one male.

Polygamous: the pair-bond is between one male and more than two females.

Polygynous: the pair-bond is between one male and two or more females.

Polytypic: a species for which there are recognised geographical races.

Promiscuous: there is a mating association of males and females without any pair-bond being formed.

Quartering: a method of hunting where the bird methodically flies low, backwards and forwards, over an area in search of prey.

Race: see sub-species.

Raptor: a bird of prey.

RAMSAR: the 'Convention on wetlands of international importance especially as water-fowl habitat', called the RAMSAR convention after the city of Ramsar, in Iran, where it was adopted in 1973. Portugal signed the convention in November 1980.

Ravine: a narrow, deep valley with rocky precipitous sides.

Resident: a species which remains in the same area throughout the year.

Rictal bristles: bare feather shafts around the bill.

Sahel: a zone of dry grassland south of the Sahara in western Africa.

Salt-marsh: coastal land which is regularly overflowed by the tide and is covered in vegetation.

Schist: foliated metamorphic rock.

Scrape: a depression, formed by the feet or by rotation of the body.

Scrub: area covered in bushes, generally less than 3m high, with or without low trees.

Sedentary: individuals do not usually move more than 50km.

Sequeiros: groves of fruit-bearing trees, planted commercially, which do not require irrigation, e.g. olive, carob, and almond.

Serras: hills and mountains.

Shield: a horny protrusion, bare of feathers, on the top of the bill where it meets the forehead.

Soaring: a rising flight on updraughts, used to gain height with little or no flapping.

Sotavento: the leeward coast east of Faro.

Stoop: to descend upon prey at great speed, on partly or nearly fully closed wings.

Sub-montane: hills more than 700m but less than 1200m above sea-level.

Sub-species: populations which inhabit separate geographical regions and which differ recognizably from one another, but which belong to a single species.

Summer migrant: a bird which comes to an area for the breeding season only.

Supercilium: the band of small feathers running back from the base of the bill above the eye, often of a distinctive colour.

Syrinx: the bird's voice or song organ situated at the base of the **trachea**. The equivalent of the human larynx.

Temperate: a mid-latitude climatic zone with a short cold season.

Trachea: the wind-pipe.

Trailing-edge: the rear edge of the wing in flight.

Wing-bar: a bar of contrasting colour, often white, across the wing.

ABBREVIATIONS USED IN THE TEXT

BBA	Breeding Birds of the Algarve
BWP	Birds of the Western Palearctic (Cramp 1977-1993)
CEMPA	Centro de Estudos de Migrações e Protecção das Aves
SNPRCN	Serviço Nacional de Parques, Reservas e Conservação da Natureza
S.E.	South-east
S.W.	South-west

INTRODUCTION

The Algarve region of Portugal, by virtue of its position at the extreme south-western corner of Europe and close proximity to Africa, forms a 'main highway' for migrating birds from both continents whilst still retaining its own special character and, thus, its own particular species of breeding birds. Until the 1960s, it was a region consisting of tiny fishing villages along the coast and small, family-owned farms and subsistance-level small-holdings inland. Portugal in general has long been overshadowed by its much larger eastern neighbour, Spain, which boasted a more developed economy and a much better road infra-structure, allowing access to areas away from the tourist resorts.

During the last 25 years, the increase in tourism, modernisation of agriculture and the introduction of new industries have all had their effect on changing the landscape of the region, particularly along the southern coastal strip. The Portuguese government and the local authorities have used the increased revenues from this economic development, as well as from EEC funding, to improve the infrastructure of the region, the new road-network making it possible, with a little effort, to reach parts of the Algarve hitherto accessed only on foot or by mule.

In the past, birdwatching throughout Portugal, and particularly in the Algarve, has been limited by the above historical factors. Until the beginning of this century, the only reliable records of Algarvian, and indeed Portuguese, birds were of specimens held in museum collections. The first book about birds in Portugal was W. C. Tait's 'The Birds of Portugal', published in 1924. This was closely followed, in 1931, by J. A. Reis Jr's 'Catálogo sistemático e analítico das aves de Portugal' and an undated publication by H.W. Coverley called 'Bird Notes - Portugal'. All three books are now long out of print but, at the time they were published, summarised all that was then known of the birds of Portugal. In addition to using data from the available collections of skins, they brought together the actual observations of both visitors to, and residents of, Portugal and, as such, could be considered the start of modern ornithology in the country. Unfortunately, nothing was then published specifically on the birds of Portugal for about 40 years.

During this time, the first of the increasingly popular field identification guides to the birds of Europe was published. Owing to the very small scale of map used, Portugal was, and still is in subsequent guides, shown as a very small part of the overall European map. As a result of this restriction, these guides provide inadequate, and sometimes totally mislead-ing, information as to both the presence and distribution of Portugal's bird populations.

In the 1970s, two new works appeared. The first, published in 1973, was R. Cary's 'A Guide to Birds of Southern Portugal', consisting of an annotated list of birds observed by the author and collaborators in that part of Portugal south of Lisbon but containing very few illustrations. 1977 saw the publication of the first of eight volumes of 'Handbook of the Birds of Europe the Middle East and North Africa', edited by S. Cramp, which is so important to our understanding of European birds that it is referred to as BWP throughout this book (BWP from its subtitle *'Birds of the Western Palearctic'*). Even BWP is restricted, however, when considering a small country like Portugal, by its geographical coverage of an area from Spizbergen in the north, Cape Verde Isles (off W. Africa) in the southwest and Kuwait in the southeast, but it will still form the basis of European ornithological studies for many years to come.

In 1989, the first atlas of Portugal's breeding birds, the *Atlas das Aves que nidificam em Portugal Continental*, was produced by the Centro de Migrações e Protecção de Aves (CEMPA), and is referred to as the national atlas thoughout this book. This atlas represented the only attempt thus far at mapping the distribution of Portugal's breeding birds and forms an excellent baseline for future studies. It was limited, however, by the number of observers able to participate and their time available, as well as by the large size of the squares in the grid used, each square covering 1280 sq. km.

The research for this present book took the atlas concept one stage further, to the southern-most region of Portugal, the Algarve, using a grid of 80 sq. km. blocks. It represents the results of 5 years' intensive fieldwork, by the authors and a team of volunteer helpers, during which 154 species of bird were found to breed in the region. Of these 154 species, 33 had not been shown to be breeding in the Algarve in the national atlas and a further 7 were not known to breed anywhere in Portugal. The habits, distribution, and status of each of these species are described in detail, with original illustrations by Michael Benington, an artist who has lived in the Algarve and who has depicted each species in the type of breeding habitat normally used in the Algarve. Distribution maps are included for all the confirmed breeding species, showing the areas where they most commonly occur. Brief notes, but with no illustrations or distribution maps, are included on 17 other species suspected of breeding but for which there is no confirmation. This book is not meant to be an identification guide to breeding species, but the quality of the illustrations is such that even a novice birdwatcher will find them of great assistance. Another feature of this book is a chapter on where to see birds in the Algarve. This is included for the benefit of both visitors and residents who would like to see more of the Algarve's birds but do not know where to go for the best results. Great care has been taken, however, to ensure that the nesting sites of rare or endangered species will not be disturbed and, although these are described in the text, the distribution maps have been edited to protect these species.

Particular attention is given in the text to any differences in the plumage or song of species that breed in the Algarve, compared with populations found in other parts of the Western Palearctic. For instance, Algarvian Long-tailed Tits are noticably darker than more northerly birds whilst the Green Woodpecker is duller and lacks the black mask.

One particular problem encountered in producing this atlas, referred to as the BBA throughout the book, resulted from the Portuguese love of exotic cage birds. From time to time these escape from captivity and often breed in the wild, finding the Algarve climate and environment ideal. The Common Waxbill, originally from east Africa but now a widespread breeding species and included as such as a normal breeding species, shows how easily these birds can start a viable population. To avoid any confusion, where single pairs or very small, local populations occur for an exotic species, these 'escapes' are given, together with various game birds which have escaped from hunting estates, under the heading of 'Feral Species' in Appendix II. Only time will tell whether or not these birds will be successful, resulting in future viable populations.

The order of species used in this book follows that used by Voous (1980) in the *'List of Recent Holarctic Bird Species'*. Much discussion is at present taking place in the ornithological world about the relationships between sub-species, species, and the families in which to include them, following the publication in 1990 of Sibley and Monroe's *'Distribution and Taxonomy of Birds of the World'*. This suggests a new classification of bird species based on DNA analysis and, in the future when more research has been done, may well become the accepted standard. In the meantime, we have continued to use the Voous order as that most widely used at present. There have also been several attempts recently to revise the common English names of species. In this respect we have continued to use traditional English names as they are the ones most people understand. Also included for each species is the official Portuguese name. This is not always the name in local usage, but, as different areas of the Algarve have different names for the same species, these have not been included in order to avoid confusion.

A summary of the methods used to obtain the information given in the text and the way in which the data were recorded and checked is given in Chapter 4. Throughout the book, only the common English names for plants and animals, including birds, have been used in order to make it more readable to the non-specialist. The scientific names for the plants and animals, except birds, are given in Appendix III and the scientific names for the birds are included in the Checklist, Appendix IV.

CHAPTER 1 - THE ALGARVE

An Introduction to the Region

GEOGRAPHICAL DESCRIPTION

The Algarve is the southernmost region of Portugal, the very name meaning 'the south' in the Moorish language. It is bounded to the west by the Atlantic, where the sheer cliffs and treeless heathlands receive the full force of the westerly winds; whilst to the south is also the Atlantic, but an Atlantic tempered by southerly breezes from northern Africa and protected from the full force of the ocean by the African continent. To the east lies the Guadiana River which, as one of the major rivers of the Iberian Peninsula, has long formed the border between the Algarve and Portugal's only neighbour, Spain. The northern boundary between the Algarve and the Alentejo, however, is less clearly defined in terms of geographical features. It starts in the east, following the River Vascão almost to its source, and from there taking an arbitrary route through the hills before following the River Seixe westwards to the Atlantic at Odeceixe. The area covers 3848km^2 of diverse habitat, ranging from the damp sub-montane climate of the Serra de Monchique, with a maximum annual rainfall of 2081mm, to the semi-arid town of Vila Real de Santo António, with a minimum annual rainfall of 23mm. It includes 651 water-courses, the most important of which are the Aljezur, Arade, Asseca, Beliche, Foupana, Odeleite, Odelouca, Odiáxere, Seixe, and Vascão. In addition, there are 4 major reservoirs - the Arade, which connects with the Funcho, the Beliche, and the Bravura, - and a further one on the Odelouca River is planned.

Fig. 1

A. River Seixe
B. River Aljezur
C River Odeáxere
D. River Odelouca
E. River Arade
F. River Vascão
G. River Foupana
H. River Odeleite
I. River Beliche
J. River Asseca

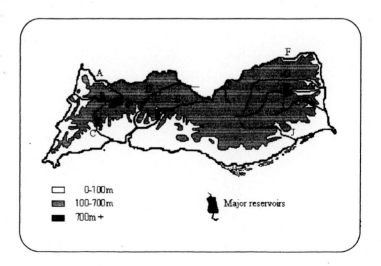

Although the Algarve has no volcanoes, it lies within an active earthquake zone with resultant minor damage to property every year. The mountain ranges of Monchique (with the highest peaks of Foia at 902m and Picota at 744m), Malhão, and Caldeirão run from west to east along the northern boundary, from which the land slopes gently down to the southern coastal strip.

PHYSICAL FACTORS DETERMINING BIRD DISTRIBUTION

The factors determining the distribution of birds are very complex; however, the primary factors are landform and climate which, together with soil, altitude, vegetation, and human action, create a recognizable environment in which certain fauna will normally be found. Those readers wishing to thoroughly understand the interaction between these various factors can do no better than to read "Algarve Plants and Landscape" by Mabberley and Placito (1993) which, although covering plants rather than birds, deals with this subject in depth. The following outline, however, may give a general idea of the factors involved.

Landform
Although the Algarve has many of the characteristics of the Mediterranean, the region in fact faces the Atlantic Ocean and so has been moulded over the years into a unique area with regard to both plant cover and wildlife. Three different landform types can be identified, see fig. 2.

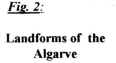

Fig. 2:

Landforms of the Algarve

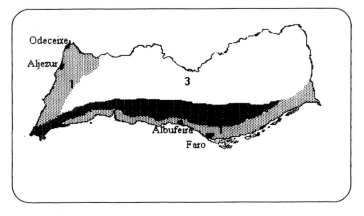

1 - the coastal strip. In the Algarve, the coastal areas have a character of their own and are even named after their relationship to the prevailing winds. That part east of Faro, known as the *sotavento* or leeward side, has extensive sand dunes and salt lagoons, together with a series of low-lying islands running from Faro almost to the Spanish border. That part of the coast west of Albufeira, known as the *barlavento* or windward side, is an area of rugged

11

cliffs, swept by the Atlantic winds. Between Faro and Albufeira is a region of extensive sandy beaches, with some fine woodland of the umbrella pine on an area of Pliocene sands. Behind the littoral, the Tertiary and Quaternary deposits are extensively cultivated, except in the extreme west where the windswept clifftops and heathland are used mainly for grazing. However, on the coastal plain between Aljezur and Odeceixe, where water is available for irrigation, a few large horticultural estates exist.

2 - the Barrocal or limestone area. This is a bow-shaped area, inland of the southern coastal strip, running from Cape St. Vincent almost to the Spanish border. It is formed of mainly Jurasic dolomites, limestones and marls and is nowhere more than about 20 km. wide. The rich brown soil, locally called *terra rossa*, is where the traditional Algarvian crops of almond, carob, fig and olive are grown. Where extensive irrigation is possible, mainly along the river valleys, orchards of various citrus fruits, mostly orange, occur whilst the few uncultivated hilltops are left to native scrubland.

3 - the inland hills or Serras. Almost three quarters of the Algarve is taken up by the Serras of the interior. The highest point of the Algarve is Foia (902 m), in the Serra de Monchique, and it is in the Monchique range that the only outcrops of syenite and foyaite occur. Patches of fertile land on the slopes are terraced for horticultural purposes whereas the more marginal ground is being taken over by eucalyptus plantations. There are, however, still some fine areas of native oak woodlands left. The rest of the Algarve's hills are formed mainly of carboniferous schists. Running south-west from Foia is the Serra de Espinhaço de Cão, a sparsely populated area now being increasingly taken over by forestry plantations of eucalyptus, whilst a few small farms line the deep valley bottoms. To the east of Foia lie the Serra do Malhão and the Serra do Caldeirão and this latter area gradually becomes a region of low, rolling hills towards the Spanish border. As with the other mountainous areas, these are being taken over by eucalyptus plantations, although north of Faro, around Barranco do Velho, are some of the most extensive remaining cork-oak woods in the Algarve.

Climate

Whereas the Algarve's coastline is washed by the Atlantic ocean, the climate is generally of the Mediterranean type, with hot, dry summers, mild winters and with well-defined rainy seasons. Even so, the total annual rainfall is rather low compared to the rest of western Europe. The weather, in simplified terms, is influenced mainly by two airstreams - that from the west, coming from the Atlantic, and that from the south-east, coming from North Africa. The weather of a country or region is often influenced by the presence of hills or mountains and the Algarve is no exception. Although none of the mountains is very high, the effect on the climate, when considered together with the prevailing airstreams, is absolute, dividing the region into four important climatic types (see Fig. 3):

12

Fig. 3

Climatic regions of the Algarve

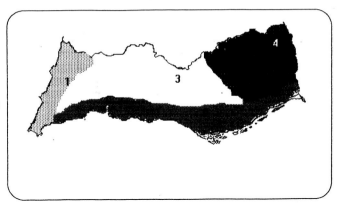

1 - the western seaboard. The Serra de Espinhaço de Cão, running from the Cape St. Vincent peninsular to the Alentejo border and joining with the Serra de Monchique, divides the western Algarve into 'Atlantic' and 'Mediterranean' climates. The cool, moisture-laden air coming from the northern Atlantic maintains a year-round temperate climate along the western seaboard, dropping its moisture on the mountains before reaching the rest of the Algarve. In summer the west coast is frequently blanketed in thick fog, especially early in the morning, and in winter it is common for the Monchique area to be covered with cloud, whilst the more eastern areas of the Algarve enjoy clear skies and sunshine. Fig. 4 compares the rainfall of the different areas.

2 - the southern coastal area. The southern coastal areas of the Algarve receive less rainfall than any other area (see Fig. 4). The Atlantic winds have already dropped their moisture over the mountains to the west whilst the warm, moisture-laden, southeasterly winds from north Africa, pass over the region and drop their rain on the Serra de Caldeirão to the north. This part of the Algarve enjoys a Mediterranean type of climate with long, hot, dry summers and mild winters.

3 - the inland mountains. The mountain ranges run from south west to north east across the Algarve and form a natural barrier to its northern neighbour, the Alentejo. These mountains receive most of the rain falling on the region, with Foia, not unexpectedly for the highest mountain, receiving the highest annual rainfall for the region with a maximum of over 2000mm. They are the source of all the Algarve's rivers, although most of the latter at least partially dry up during the hot summer months.

4 - the dry grassland area. In the extreme north-east of the Algarve, between the mountains and the Guadiana river, is an area of very dry, steppe-like land. By the time the westerly winds reach this area, all moisture has been dropped, whilst the south-easterly winds have to cross south-western Spain to reach this corner of the Algarve. It is an area characterized by low rainfall, rarely exceeding 300mm per annum, with 6-7 months per year of drought, and extreme daily and seasonal fluctuations in temperature.

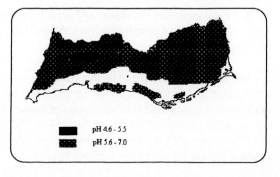

Fig. 4

Mean annual rainfall

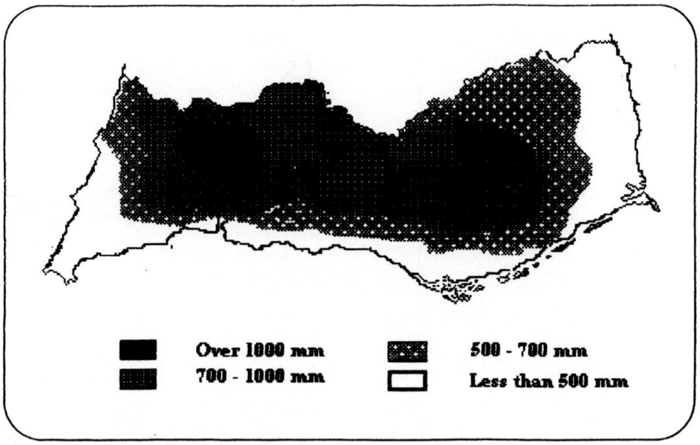

Over 1000 mm   500 - 700 mm

700 - 1000 mm   Less than 500 mm

Soil Type

The type of soil - the acidity or alkalinity - will affect the type of vegetation that can grow naturally in an area. Until recently, when modern, intensive agricultural methods became fairly widespread, it also determined the type of crops grown and the animal husbandry which could be practised. It will be seen from Fig. 5 that most of the Algarve, away from the south coast, has a mainly acidic type of soil, with a pH in the range 4.6 - 7.0. This area, curved along its southern edge and extending well into the Alentejo in the north, covers approximately two thirds of the region.

Fig. 5

Soil acidity

White areas represent alkaline soils.

pH 4.6 - 5.5

pH 5.6 - 7.0

Within the limestone area, which includes both the Barrocal and the surrounding coastal strips, the geology is extremely complex and beyond the scope of this work. It does, however, give rise to a mainly alkaline soil, although pockets of slightly acidic soil exist. The soil pH is in the range 6.5 - 8.5, with most areas within the 7.5 - 8.5 range. The underlying rocks provide excellent drainage and, in the past, the resultant shortage of surface water has limited farming to places in river valleys or near springs where water was easily accessible. Nowadays, extensive irrigation systems allow the full agricultural potential of these soils to be realised.

The hilly interior is an area of thin acid soil with a pH in the range 5.6 - 7.0. These soils are not generally used for agriculture although they are grazed, where possible, by

14

sheep and goats. The original forest cover has mostly gone, leaving a barren, scrub-covered landscape. Recently, large areas of the hills, particularly in the west, have been planted to non-endemic eucalyptus forests, and this is serving to increase the soil acidity, although it does help to prevent any further erosion of the sparse soil. It is this hill region where all the Algarve's rivers have their source, and several reservoirs have been built to harness the water for both domestic and agricultural purposes. Further reservoirs are planned for these river systems and there are arguments both for and against. Whilst there is no doubt that a further loss of habitat in wild, unspoilt countryside is to be regretted on environmental grounds there is a desperate shortage of domestic water in the region, with many towns having their water supply rationed in the summer months.

Altitude

The effect of altitude on plant communities, and therefore on animal communities, is closely tied to the previous factors - climate and soil type. The height of a mountain will not only affect temperature, there being an average fall of about half a degree Celsius per 100m rise in altitude, but also has an effect on the amount of rain that falls (as already discussed under Climate). Therefore, as may be expected, the mountain-tops maintain a different micro-climate to the littoral.

Lázaro e Ibiza (1920-1921) classified the altitude zones of the Iberian Peninsula, having regard for both the altitude of an area and its latitude. Following their classification, the altitude zones of the Algarve would be:

Littoral zone:	0 - 100m
Lower (hill) zone:	100 - 700m
Sub-montane (middle) zone:	700 -1000m

Fig. 6 shows the distribution of these three zones within the Algarve

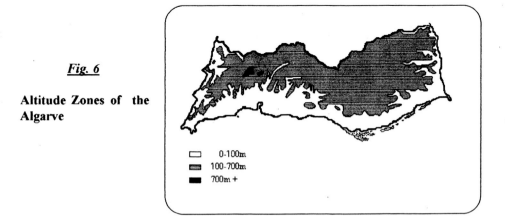

Fig. 6

Altitude Zones of the Algarve

☐ 0-100m
▦ 100-700m
■ 700m +

The Algarve's three zones of Littoral, Hill and Sub-montane are classified according to both the altitude and the type of plant community expected to be found in that partic-

15

ular habitat. It is these plant communities which determine the species of bird to be found in an area as they provide both nest sites and food, either directly in the form of fruits and seeds, or indirectly as the host plant for a bird's preferred insect diet or the general habitat for larger prey.

Vegetation

The Algarve is made up of an intricate patchwork of habitats, with no single tract extending more than a kilometre without some small intrusion of another habitat. For example, a eucalyptus plantation may have bramble in a gully or broadleaf trees alongside a track, a wilderness of scrub may have some orange trees by a ruin, and a cork-oak forest may have isolated patches of cereals. Therefore, although Fig. 7 shows the principal types of vegetation, there will be other types within them as well as many gradations.

Fig. 7

Dominant vegetative cover

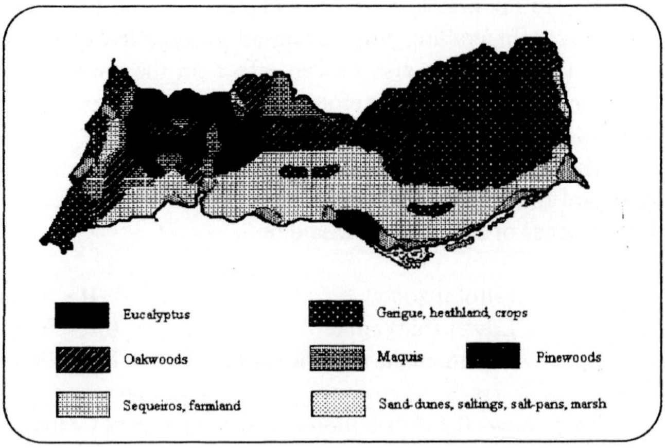

- **Eucalyptus.** The eucalyptus originated from Australia and was brought to the Algarve during the last century as a quick-growing softwood, able to thrive on poor soils in a Mediterranean-type climate. The trees are often planted very close together, preventing light from penetrating to the ground, so that there is little or no vegetation beneath the trees. It is planted extensively on hills, especially on the Espinaço de Cão and Monchique ranges. The principal species of birds using these plantations are Robin and Chiffchaff, on the sides of tracks and gullies, and Golden Oriole and Woodpigeon, which use the trees for nesting only.

- **Oakwoods.** Originally, the holm oak was the characteristic forest element to develop in a typical Mediterranean climate, on both acidic and alkaline soils. Today, this species exists only as scattered trees amongst the maquis or sequeiros. All the present-day oakwoods are cork-oak and have been planted by man as commercial crops on land not otherwise suitable for agriculture. By virtue of their broad crowns, the trees are spaced out and do not inhibit the growth of other plants. Where the woods are intensively managed, the ground beneath the trees is kept clear of vegetation and grass grows, producing a type of habitat which is generally termed 'parkland'. In less intensively managed or neglected woods, scrub quickly

16

grows beneath the trees, producing a mixture of woodland and maquis. The typical bird species for parkland are Orphean Warbler, Wryneck, and Lesser-spotted Woodpecker; whereas the typical species for the woods/maquis mix are Nuthatch, Crested Tit and Robin.

- Sequeiros. This is a Portuguese word, for which there is no adequate translation into English and which has been used throughout this atlas to describe a particularly Algarvian type of habitat. It means those groves which do not have to be irrigated yet produce commercial fruit. In the hills, it covers groves of olive or almond, sometimes with a carob or holm oak admixture. Beneath the trees can be garigue, cereals, or grass which has been closely-cropped by sheep or goats. In the littoral, where the soil is richer, the sequeiros contain mostly carob and olive with some fig. Beneath the trees, horticultural crops are normally grown, especially broad beans. The most common species of bird for this habitat are Short-toed Treecreeper, Hoopoe, Turtle Dove, Hawfinch, which particularly favour almond groves, Little Owl, Woodchat Shrike and Tree Sparrow.

- Farmland. In Fig. 7, it will be seen that sequeiros and farmland have been placed together. Agriculture in the Algarve is very fragmented with no extensive cultivation of single crops. Away from the coast, the areas of cultivation are too small to appear on this scale of map and in the littoral the very disparate types of agriculture are too interwoven with the sequeiros to separate them. Citrus groves are mainly to be found along the sides of rivers in the lowlands, owing to the need for large-scale irrigation through the hot, dry summer months. The only 'southern' species to be found on farmland is Serin.

- Garigue. Where the land is heavily over-grazed or continuously fired, trees will disappear and the scrub layer will consist of only a few extremely resistant species. It is very low vegetation, rarely more than 1 metre high, sparse, with large tracts of grass or bare earth. In the eastern Algarve, it is typically lavender and rock rose, interspersed with crops (mainly cereals and yellow lupin) and dry grassland. In the west, where the Atlantic winds further inhibit the growth of vegetation, there are distinctive species of dwarf rock rose and gorse, heather, thyme, lavender, and juniper. This habitat is only really exploited by Thekla Lark and, to a lesser extent, Short-toed Lark.

- Heathland. In the western Algarve, much of the garigue scrub takes the form commonly known as heathland. The vegetation is very low, usually not more than half a metre high, growing in dense and often impenetrable patches. It consists of the same species mentioned above for garigue in the west, with the addition of stunted holm and Kermes oaks (which form round bushes up to 2 metres high and 2-4 metres in diameter) and mastic. Stonechat and Rock Bunting are the two typical species.

- Crops. Under this heading are included grassland and cereals, but not other forms of agriculture (for which see Farmland). In the east, they are favoured by Quail, Little and Great Bustards, Corn Bunting, and Hen and Montagu's Harriers, whilst in the west they are favoured by Short-toed and Lesser Short-toed Larks and Tawny Pipit.

- Maquis. This is a dense, evergreen form of scrub which is common on the hills of the western Algarve. It is typically 3-4 metres high and so dense that it is almost impossible to force a way through it, consisting of tall species of broom, gorse, and rock rose, with numerous holm oak and strawberry tree. The most noteworthy species of bird is the Dartford Warbler, with Bullfinch and Nightingale in the gullies, and Great Grey Shrike on the fringes.

- Pinewoods. Although there are small pockets of pinewoods throughout the lower altitudes of the Algarve, the only area large enough to appear on this scale map lies between Albufeira and Faro. It consists entirely of umbrella pine on sandy soil, with little ground cover. Most of these woods contain urban developments, however it is still possible to see Azure-winged Magpies and Serin.

- Sand-dunes. There are extensive sand-dunes at Aljezur, Carrapateira and Alvor in the west, and running intermittantly from just west of Faro to the Spanish border. Kentish Plover, Short-toed and Crested Larks, and Stone Curlew are the most noteworthy species of bird.

- Saltings and Salt-pans. Apart from small areas fringing the Alvor estuary and the banks of the tidal zone of the Arade, all the Algarve's saltings and salt-pans lie within the Ria Formosa and Castro Marim reserves (see Chapter 3). As well as the 'sand-dune species', which also nest on the dry parts of saltings and salt-pans, there are Black-winged Stilt, Avocet, and Little Tern.

- Marsh. There are small freshwater marshes to be found at Aljezur, Carrapateira, Budens (Boca de Rio), Lagos (near the aerodrome), Fontes (between Estômbar and Silves), and on the urban developments of Vale de Parra and Vilamoura, all holding Great Reed Warbler. However, the extensive reed bed at Ludo and the specially-made lake at Quinta de Lago (both at the western end of the Ria Formosa) are outstanding, with Night Heron, Purple Heron, Little Bittern, Baillon's Crake, Penduline Tit, Purple Gallinule, Red-crested Pochard, Gadwall, and all three Algarve grebes.

Human Interference

Until comparatively recently, in terms of evolution, the use to which man put the countryside was greatly dependent upon the first four factors already discussed: landform, climate, soil, and altitude. However, over the last few centuries, human ingenuity has made many changes to the environment, especially in the reduction or complete destruction of native flora and in the draining of swampland.

Originally, the evergreen oak forests of holm oak *Quercus ilex* were the climax vegetation of the Algarve, but so extensive has been the destruction of these forests that today there remain only scattered holm oaks of the closely related *Quercus rotundifolia*. On poor, hilly soils they have been replaced by cork oakwoods, which have in turn been replaced by maquis, eucalyptus, and garigue over much of the region. On poor, lowland soils, such as the Barrocal, the land has been cleared for the planting of sequeiros, leaving islands of rocky hill tops covered in 'hedgehog' scrub composed of rounded clumps of Kermes oak, gorse, and mastic. On fertile lowland soils and on the banks of rivers, man has removed all vestiges of forest, ploughing the land for crops or planting it with citrus groves. Most of the trees which are now accepted as an integral part of the Algarvian landscape were originally introduced by man, e.g. the olive was brought from the Middle East and the various citrus species were brought from the Far East, whilst the newly-introduced eucalyptus from Australia has already taken over much of the western serras. Although the planting of eucalyptus is generally to be deplored, the present patchwork of cultivation and forest/groves provides a great diversity of flora and fauna, far in excess of that which the original evergreen forests could have sustained. Providing the present levels of trees (wild and cultivated) and maquis are maintained, with no further increase in eucalyptus, the Algarve will remain a much more interesting place than if there were vast tracts of monotonous uniformity.

During the last twenty years or so, there has also been a tremendous surge in tourism, leading to large numbers of touristic complexes along the south coast. This has led to the wholesale destruction of marshes and reed-beds for building or for the construction of golf-courses, which has had a disasterous effect on an important sector of wildlife - an effect which is accelerating every year. Those few marshes that remain are under threat and are being systematically destroyed, with the exception of the protected Ria da Formosa. Sand-dunes and the barrier islands off Faro have been illegally colonised by fishermen and people wanting cheap holiday homes, which is destroying a very fragile ecosystem as well as polluting the water. Tourism and wildlife need not be mutually exclusive, as can be seen at Quinta de Lago, but too often there is no incentive for developers to consider the environment and already a lot of the coastline is beyond recovery.

Some habitats created by man have in fact been to the benefit of certain birds, e.g. the salt-pans to the south of Tavira, which support large numbers of breeding and migrating waders. Other habitats have helped to increase certain species, e.g. grasslands (Corn Bunting and Larks), chimneys (White Stork), and buildings (House Sparrow, House Martin and Swallow). Indeed, the Swallow, which was originally a cave-dweller, is not now thought to nest naturally anywhere in the world. In addition, man's agriculture and husbandry has brought about a richer and more diverse avifauna, thereby increasing the number of bird species in the Algarve. It is only comparatively recently that his greed, and his technical ability to satisfy that greed, has begun to reduce the variety of habitat and, therefore, to threaten some species to the point of extinction.

CHAPTER 2 - CONSERVATION

Until the revolution in 1974, sweeping the dictator Salazar from power, the Algarve was a quiet backwater seemingly forgotten by the authorities in Lisbon. There were very few tarmac roads, just those linking the main towns, and most villages could be reached by foot or mule only. Farms and small-scale industry were mainly centred around Faro and Portimão, the remainder of the province being given over to cork-growing and to peasants growing just sufficient food for their own needs. Therefore, poisoning of the atmosphere, pollution of rivers, pesticides, destruction of cork-forests in favour of eucalyptus, draining of marshes, and touristic over-development of the coast were all things of the future.

During the 1970's and early 1980's, all these horrors came suddenly to the Algarve, as money was put into development of the region and the package-holiday companies discovered the charms of 'the quaint, unspoiled Algarve'. At that time, the coast between Faro and Albufeira was very rapidly turning into a continuous belt of villas, apartments, and tourist complexes, with every indication that the remainder of the coast would shortly follow suit. Inadequate provision was made for sewerage disposal, so that effluent was allowed to enter streams or run untreated into the sea, and marshes were being drained as 'worthless land' to become golf-courses. Water was pumped in ever-increasing quantities by bore-holes from underground, with no thought given to depletion of the water-table, so that the water level dropped drastically allowing the entry of sea-water. Scrub and herbage removed from clifftops, for building or for access by car for tourists or fishermen, has resulted in up to one metre of land being lost annually from some parts of the coast. Initially, the government's priorities were to re-structure the country's economy and to modernise the Algarve as quickly as possible, so that the ruination of the Algarve continued unchecked. However, with the spectre of Spain's even more desecrated coastline always in view, the Portuguese government quickly realized that a halt had to be called to indiscriminate urbanization and that an overall policy for protecting the environment had to be drafted.

The principal State department for the environment is the Ministry for the Environment and Natural Resources, under whose auspices lies the SNPRCN - the Department for Parks, Reserves and Nature Conservation. The SNPRCN is responsible for a wide range of activities, including the formulation and implementation of a national plan for conservation, the ratification of agreements with other countries on relevant proposals, the setting up and management of reserves and other protected areas, the promotion of studies into eco-systems, and the education of young people into the need for conservation. Under the umbrella of the SNPRCN is CEMPA - the Centre for the Study of Migration and Protection of Birds - which, as the name suggests, deals solely with studies envolving birds.

Portugal's only national park (not to be confused with 'natural park'), in the extreme north of Portugal, was set up prior to the revolution, in 1971. Since then, a further twenty protected areas have been created, totalling more than 5% of the land surface of Portugal. These protected areas can basically be divided into two categories: 1) the 'Natural Parks' and the 'Areas of Protected Countryside' and 2) the 'Natural Reserves'.

1) The first category is intended not only to protect the countryside and conserve the environment but also to promote countryside recreation and to preserve traditional rural life-styles. The SNPRCN has the power to acquire property, public or private, if necessary

to maintain the traditional rural character of the zone and it can dictate as to how the land is to be used.

2) The second category is intended to protect all aspects of Nature, preventing anything whatsoever that would endanger the ecosystem. The SNPRCN has the power to declare all or part of a natural reserve closed to the public, except for administrative or scientific purposes.

Portugal's second protected area, the 'Sapal de Castro Marim e Vila Real de Santo António', was the Algarve's first. This Natural Reserve was created in 1975 and covers an area of salt-marsh important for both flora and fauna. Since then a further two protected areas have been created in the Algarve, the Natural Park of the 'Ria Formosa' and the Area of Protected Countryside of 'Sudoeste Alentejano e Costa Vicentina' (see Chapter 3, Where to watch breeding birds, page 26, for a map showing these three areas).

In order to conserve the remainder of the region, not protected under one of these zones, the Portuguese government passed legislation in 1991 under the heading of Plano Regional de Ordanimento do Território do Algarve (regional plan for the development of the Algarve), commonly referred to as PROTAL. Until this legislation was passed, each local authority had the power to sanction any urbanization or any change in land-use that it wished, without any reference to Lisbon (i.e. the central government). PROTAL decrees that all local authorities have to produce an overall development plan, which has then to be submitted to Lisbon for approval. If the plans are approved, they have to be placed on show to the public at the council offices for three months, during which time anyone has the right to object. While these plans are being drawn up, it is virtually impossible for any new project to obtain authorization and even developments which already had authorization before PROTAL, but were not yet completed, have had their licences revoked. By the end of 1993, only the local council of Lagos had succeeded in producing an approved development plan and placing it on show.

While long stretches of the coastline were being polluted and urbanized, the interior of the Algarve did not escape the attention of those for whom quick profits meant more than the environment or the national heritage. Any area not suitable for intensive agriculture, including cork-oak woods where the trees were old or needed replacing, was considered of no value and therefore suitable for planting with the quick-growing but non-endemic eucalyptus. In addition to the speed with which this tree grows to maturity, reaching commercial value in 15 years as opposed to nearly 30 years for the cork-oak, there is the bonus to the grower of his rarely having to replant the tree as it regrows from the root after cutting.

The clearance of the cork-oak forests, in favour of the eucalyptus, is threatening not only many of the Algarve's more interesting species of breeding bird, such as the Orphean Warbler, but also the very structure of the land on which they grow. The eucalyptus consumes three times the amount of water that the cork-oak requires - an important consideration in a region with severe water shortages. It also has a longer tap root and so is able to lower the water table below that reached by native trees. Planted close together, as is the norm in these plantations, the trees prevent light penetrating to the ground so that there is no herbage or scrub beneath them. In addition, the eucalyptus is very prone to fire, causing the destruction of large areas of the Algarve every year, yet rarely destroying itself as it can almost always grow again from the root.

The Forestry Service, which comes under the jurisdiction of the Ministry of Agriculture and Fisheries, is well aware of the dangers of extensive planting of the eucalyptus and has the power to prevent any further planting. Broadly speaking, any proposal for a new eucalyptus plantation must satisfy the following requirements:
1) the land to be planted must be over 400m above sea level.
2) no destruction of either cork oak or holm oak, or any other protected species, must be involved.
3) the council in which it is proposed to have the plantation must not be already more than 25% covered in eucalyptus.
4) there must be no objection to the proposal from the council.
5) there must be no reasonable objection from the people living or working on the fringes of the proposed plantation.
6) the proposed plantation must not endanger or destroy any site of scientific or cultural interest.

The Forestry Service has wide powers over private forests, preventing the premature cutting of eucalyptus, the premature removal of cork from cork-oaks, and the removal of native hardwoods. Even the cutting down of dead or diseased trees requires permission and the trees are carefully examined by the Service before a licence is issued. Apart from advising various authorities and individuals on forestry matters, it also provides technological data on water resources and soil management.

As well as its role in controlling and advising other bodies, the Service owns forests of its own, which it manages both commercially and with conservation of the national heritage in mind. In the Algarve, the Service has three divisions - Portimão, Faro, and Tavira. The Portimão division owns three forests - P.F. de Vila do Bispo, Mata National de Barão S. João, and Mata National de Herdade de Parra; Faro division owns none; and Tavira owns two - Mata National de Conceição de Tavira and P.F. das Terras de Ordem. Although all these forests hold a wide variety of flora and fauna, none of them is particularly outstanding for birds except the Herdade de Parra, north of Silves, which includes some wild unspoiled hill-country.

Hunting also comes under the jurisdiction of the Forestry Service, controlled by the semi-autonomous Hunting Department. In Portugal, there is the tradition that anyone can walk - and by extension hunt - on any unfenced land, providing no damage is caused. Although no shots may be fired within 250m of a dwelling, a hunter may legally shoot across fields and public ways, and until recently the owner of unfenced land (the majority of land in the Algarve) could not prevent hunting. Today, it is not difficult for an owner to declare his land a no-hunting area on the grounds that hunting would hinder or endanger his work. It has also become possible for a group of landowners to create their own hunting preserves or for a land-owner to make a touristic hunting zone where no-one unauthorized by him may hunt or even enter - none of which was possible when the BBA was started.

Generally speaking, hunting is not a threat to the birds of the Algarve. Inevitably there are individuals who shoot at 'anything that moves' and others who kill raptors or owls to protect game species or domestic livestock. Large raptors make particularly easy targets and, as these species are slow to reproduce, such killing can take a heavy toll of eagles and vultures in particular. However, this is strictly illegal and the list of legal quarry for hunters is shorter than for many other countries. Every year the Hunting Department decides the period within which each quarry species may be hunted, having considered the breeding success or otherwise of resident species and making sure that hunting finishes well before the birds are likely to start breeding. The hunting season is normally from October to

January and shooting is allowed only on Sundays, Thursdays and public holidays. Enforcement of the hunting laws is carried out by the hunting police, who are employed by the Department, as well as by the civil police.

A further threat to birds is the illegal trapping and netting of small birds for eating. Although trapping is mainly directed at migrating birds, the method is indiscriminate in the species it takes and many resident birds are killed. In addition, trapping often continues into the early spring when most resident species start breeding. Trappers regard the law against trapping as foolish, as their fathers and generations before them always trapped. So, trappers regard themselves as hunters carrying on a traditional pastime and, until recently, some authorities perhaps sympathized with them. Today, however, both the civil police and the hunting police will prosecute trappers, imposing heavy fines with the possibility of imprisonment.

Apart from the State bodies involved with conservation, there are numerous small groups or societies, mostly run by universities, whose objectives are the preservation of Nature in general or of some particular species. None of these is large enough to have the resources necessary to have any impact and their formation or termination tends to depend on the personalities of the people involved. The two exceptions to this are Quercus (a name taken from the scientific name for oak) and the Liga para a Protecção da Natureza (League for the Protection of Nature), abbreviated to LPN. Quercus is the smaller of the two and, although active elsewhere in Portugal, is not very involved with the Algarve. The LPN was created in 1948 and continued as a very small society until about a decade ago, when it became the unofficial conservation society for Portugal. Since then it has grown rapidly and has become powerful enough to negotiate with councils and to influence new legislation. The Algarve has its own branch, which holds monthly walks for members and non-members, and which has been instrumental in gaining government approval of the Alvor estuary as a protected area.

As with every 'civilized' country in the world today, pesticides and the pollution of the environment are a major problem for Portugal. Fortunately for the Algarve, industrialization and intensive farming came late to the region, and so legislation was already in place before irrevocable damage could occur from these activities. Portugal's entry into the EEC has further strengthened legislation. There are still several problems facing the Algarve, however, which have yet to be resolved.

- In the Monchique area, pig-farming has become increasingly popular. Owing to the steep slopes of the area, the effluent from the styes runs straight into the streams and from there into the rivers. This, together with the extensive planting of eucalyptus (see Fig. 7, Page 16, for map showing eucalyptus distribution), is causing high acidity in the rivers, with resultant loss of a wide spectrum of flora and fauna. The species of bird which have declined most noticeably on the Serra de Monchique are those which seemingly cannot adapt to eucalyptus plantations, e.g. the Lesser Spotted Woodpecker and the Nuthatch, and those which feed directly from the water-courses, e.g. the Kingfisher and the Common Sandpiper.

- The summer months in the Algarve are very hot and receive little or no rain. Frequently the temperature rises to 45^0 C and it is not uncommon to have no rain from April to October. The land immediately adjacent to rivers is heavily cultivated or planted to citrus, as this land is easiest to irrigate. Although the ground immediately below a citrus tree or around vegetables is well-watered, and therefore soft, the remainder of the orchard or field is baked as hard as rock. When the heavy rains occur in late October or early November, the water rushes straight off the land into the rivers, carrying with it all the pesticides and artificial fertilizers that have remained on the surface all summer. The dangers of pesticides in the river systems are obvious, but a high level of artificial fertilizer is also harmful as these fertilizers are rich in phosphates, which further raises the level of acidity in the water.

- The various councils buy land from time to time for a wide range of purposes, such as rubbish tips, with seemingly little thought to the suitability of the land for the purpose for which it was purchased. Several rubbish tips have been sited close to urban developments and one council's recent attempts to provide a site were firstly adjacent to a proposed hospital and then next to a major water-course! Fortunately, the LPN and local residents were vigilant and protested forcefully enough to have both sites abandoned.

An unforeseen influence on the environment in the Algarve has been the influx of foreigners now residing in the area, anxious to escape the inclement weather of their native countries. Many have made their homes on the coast, increasing the problems caused by tourism, others have bought cottages or smallholdings in the country, increasing the migration of rural populations away from traditional peasant-farming. Counteracting these adverse effects, however, is the fact that these foreigners are used to thinking about wild-life and conservation. They are also, generally, more willing to 'make a fuss' over environmental matters and, now that Portugal is in the EEC, to protest as far as the EEC courts if necessary. It is estimated that there are some 15,000 foreigners resident in the Algarve, owning property worth at least £200 million and spending about £60 million a year, according to AFPOP (Association of Foreign Property Owners in Portugal). Not only are they a vital part of the region's economy but, with a vote in local elections, they have a vital voice in its conservation.

During the 1970's and 1980's, the Algarve underwent a period of rapid change - partly because of the revolution ending the Salazar regime and partly because of the expansion in tourism. With Portugal's entry into the EEC, phased over the late 1980's and early 1990s, the face of the Algarve was altered irrevocably. New roads, including a motorway linking Spain with the west coast (to be finished by the end of this century), have been constructed with EEC funding but with no proper environmental impact studies having been made beforehand. Small farms and villages have been abandoned as uneconomic, the rural populations moving into the towns, whilst large plantations and intensive farming take over. By and large, Portugal is tackling the problems already mentioned in a sensitive manner and the Algarve is fortunate in having a sympathetic Governor. Of course, there are always a few officials, as in every country, who regard conservation as hampering progress and who will try to avoid environmental issues. These people are finding it more and more difficult to continue this way, however, in the face of increasingly stringent legislation and the increasing awareness of the general population of the need for conservation. Without doubt, pressures on the environment will continue to increase but, it is to be hoped, not unchecked in the future.

CHAPTER 3 - BIRDWATCHING IN THE ALGARVE

When to watch breeding birds.

The Algarve enjoys a sub-tropical, Mediterranean-type climate, with winter temperatures rarely falling below 6^0 C, so that the breeding season for most resident passerines extends from February to August with many individuals breeding throughout the year. Even summer migrants, such as the House Martin, often return to the Algarve in January and have produced their first brood of chicks by the end of March.

With no clearly-defined breeding season, it is important to realize the different strategies used by birds in their breeding cycles. Large birds, such as raptors, need several months from nest-building to the fledging of their young and so have time for only one brood before the hot summer months, June-August. For example, the Eagle Owl starts its courtship in October/November and lays in December/January. Medium-sized birds, such as the Hoopoe, require less time to produce fledged young and can therefore raise more than one brood in a single breeding season. Incubation can take up to 3 weeks and a further 3-4 weeks to care for the young. In order to have more than two broods whilst food is most plentiful, these too must start nesting in January or earlier. Small passerines, such as the Sardinian Warbler, take about 2 weeks to incubate the eggs and 2 weeks to fledge the young and generally have 3 broods. As they and their nests are particularly vulnerable to bad weather, they can afford to wait until the February/March rains have finished to start their first brood. Some small passerines, such as the Common Waxbill, regularly have 2 broods in the spring, rest during the extremely hot summer months, then have a further brood in September/ October; whereas the truly southern species, such as the Rufous Bush Robin (Chat) and Red-necked Nightjar, do not arrive until May and breed through the hottest months when other species choose not to.

As this book deals exclusively with breeding birds, some warning is not out of place about the vulnerability of nests. Normally, under natural conditions, if a predator finds a nest then the eggs or chicks will be eaten and the nest-site will be a dangerous place for the adult. As a wild bird cannot distinguish between predators and friendly humans, the close approach of an observer to the nesting area often results in the adult abandoning the nest. The nests of the following groups of birds should be particularly avoided:
- Raptors, which are renowned for their tendency to desert nests even when the observer is some way off.
- Waders, which make a great deal of noise when a predator approaches. Gulls especially are attracted to the commotion and will eat both eggs and chicks when the intruder has left. In addition, eggs and chicks are superbly camouflaged, with the result that they can be trodden on without the observer knowing.
- The young of most small passerines will jump from the nest when disturbed, from about half-grown onwards, even though they can neither fly nor walk properly, and become easy prey for passing predators. Careless walking by the observer through vegetation will leave a trail to the nest, which also attracts the attention of passing predators.

Where to watch breeding birds.

In the text of each of the confirmed-breeding species, there is a detailed description of the preferred nesting habitat in the Algarve, together with helpful hints on when and where to find the species. In addition to this, in the following section, particularly good bird-watching areas are shown and details are given as to which require authorization to enter and how to obtain it. The law in Portugal is basically that the public may enter unfenced/ ungated land on foot, provided no damage is caused. Orchards and horticulture should never be entered without permission, however, as there are irrigation systems which are easily destroyed. Some forms of land-usage have their own laws, such as salt-pans where it is prohibited to walk in the water or on the earth walls dividing the pans, and entry is also forbidden into some hunting reserves. If there is someone nearby, it is polite to ask permission to walk even through scrub - if no Portuguese is spoken, a bird-book and a mime of walking in a particular direction is more than sufficient to convey what is being asked.

The following map shows not only the legally protected zones but also the best areas in which to see particularly Algarvian species. These are intended to help visitors with little time available and to encourage residents to leave their usual, well-tried bird-watching routes and explore further afield. Each area contains a description of habitat, access, and the birds special to to that area.

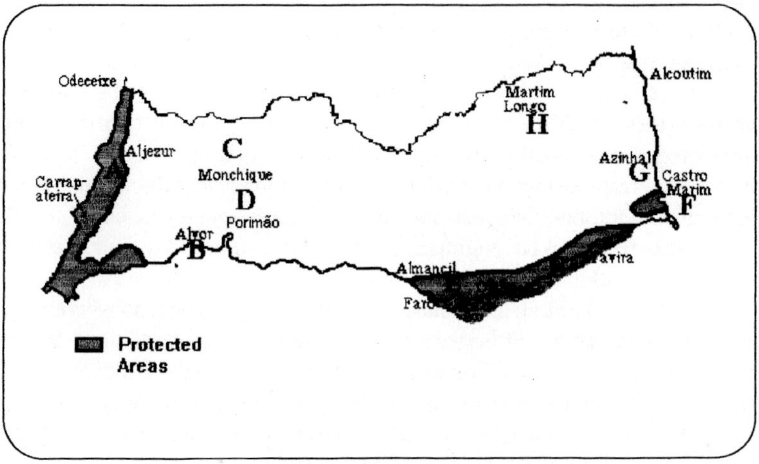

Fig. 8

Birdwatching areas of the Algarve.

A. Paisagem Protegida do Sudoeste Alentejano e Costa Vicenta.

This protected area extends from just south of Sines, in the Alentejo, down the west coast to Cape St. Vincent and east to Burgau. The part which is contained within the Algarve starts at Odeceixe in the north and covers a spectacular stretch of Atlantic cliffs and wind-swept heathland. The whole park is easily accessed by footpaths and tracks from the main roads and there are no restrictions on entry. In Vila do Bispo there is a warden who will willingly help with any problems. Species of special interest all along the cliffs are both Kestrels, all three species of Swift, all Algarvian larks, Tawny Pipit, Blue Rock Thrush, Black Redstart, Raven, and Chough.

26

Although the whole area is worthy of exploration, the following are of particular note:

- Odeceixe to Aljezur. Coastal horticulture is good for Cirl Buntings. The beach road to the north of the Aljezur River passes marshland, saltpans, and sand-dunes, with a good selection of typical species.
- Carrapateira. A small area of marsh and extensive sand-dunes. From here, several good tracks lead to the coast, enabling a car to be taken right to the cliff edge.
- Salema. A kilometre east of the road to Salema, by Budens, a track leads to a medium-sized reed-bed, running down to a stony beach known locally as Boca do Rio, with Reed and Great Reed Warblers, Little Bittern, and Common Waxbills.

B. Alvor Estuary

Although it had no protection during the course of fieldwork for this book, the law enabling this to become a protected zone was about to be passed at the time of publication. It covers approx. 10km^2 of sand-dunes, salt-marsh, and disused salt-pans. As far as is known, access will not be restricted. To reach the estuary, take the road from Portimão to Lagos and turn left at Mexilhoeira Grande, at a crossroads immediately after the road to the station (Estação). The estuary is at the very end of this road. About half-way down the road on the right is A Rocha Christian Field Study Centre and Bird Observatory, signposted Cruzinha, where the resident staff can answer questions on the local breeding birds. Species of particular interest are Black-winged Stilt, Kentish Plover, Stone Curlew, Little Tern, and Short-toed Lark.

If time permits, a short excursion can be made from here to Lagos. There is an easily-viewed Egret colony at the Ponte da Piedade, due south of Lagos off the Sagres road. Also, at the entrance to Lagos, there is a White Stork's nest at the side of the road on a chimney.

C. Monchique

The mountains west of the town are the highest in the Algarve and have the only sub-montane vegetation in the region. The road signposted Foia will take the visitor almost to the highest point. Shortly before reaching the top, there is a drop to the left covered in scrub, where Spectacled Warbler and Rock Bunting can be found.

In many places around Monchique the traditional cork oak has been replaced by the eucalyptus. Many fine stands of oak are still to be found, however, on the north side of the Monchique-Casais-Marmelete road, where Crested Tit, Nuthatch, and Lesser Spotted Woodpecker can be seen.

D. Odelouca valley

North of Portimão in the direction of Monchique, a road forks to the right to Silves at Porto de Lagos. After 2kms, immediately before a river-bridge, a dirt road goes to the left which follows the Odelouca River. Azure-winged Magpies can be expected anywhere along this road. After a little over 1km there is a view over the river, with the chance of Little Egret, Bee-eater, and Melodious Warbler by the river itself. About 3kms further on there is a fork in the road, the right-hand arm of which leads back to the river where it is shingly and Little Ringed Plover and Common Sandpiper can be seen. Many of the surrounding hill-tops are covered in dense scrub where Dartford Warblers breed.

If time permits, the track can be followed over quite high hills through scrub and eucalyptus to Monchique, with possible views of hunting Short-toed Eagles on the way.

E. Parque Natural da Ria Formosa

This is an important wetland reserve, cited by RAMSAR, of 16,000ha and extending from the Quinta do Lago development in the west to Manta Rota in the east. As well as an almost continous belt of salt-pans and marshes along the coast, there are numerous islands - both sandy and salt-marsh - offshore. Some of the sandy islands are inhabited and can be reached by ferry from Olhão or Tavira.

Those species of bird to be expected in this habitat can be found throughout the park, however the following sites are worthy of particular note:

- Quinta do Lago. Turn south in Almancil and follow signs until the development is reached, then continue as straight as possible to the coast - where there is a pay car-park. From here eastwards, between the golf-course and the salt-marsh, runs a way-marked footpath to a hide from which can be seen Little Bittern, several species of grebes and duck, Purple Gallinule, and Great Reed Warbler. The only recorded Red-crested Pochard breeding in the Algarve were found here. In the trees just past the hide, there are often Azure-winged Magpies. Booklets about the flora and fauna to be seen from the path and hide can be obtained from Reception, which is sign-posted from the entrance to the development.

- Ludo. This is a specially protected area of salt-pans and extensive reed-beds, which is closed to the public. In addition to the species at Quinta do Lago, there are Night Heron, Baillon's Crake, Black-winged Stilt, Kentish Plover, and Penduline Tit. To enter, written authorization must be obtained from the park's offices at Quinta de Marim, Quelfez, which is between Faro and Olhão. Whilst at the offices, it is worth taking a way-marked trail to a hide which faces a Bee-eater colony.

- Faro to Olhão. Approximately half-way between Faro and Olhão, on the right hand side, there is a radio mast in a fenced enclosure. A track runs along the western boundary, from which can be seen Collared Pratincoles flying from and to their colony within the enclosure. It is strictly prohibited to enter the fenced area, which ensures the safety of the only thriving colony of Pratincoles in the Algarve.

- Tavira. There are extensive salt-pans to the south of the town, where Black-winged Stilt, Avocet, Kentish Plover, and Little Tern breed. Numerous tracks lead through the network of pans, however excellent views can be had of all the species, without disturbance to the birds, from the road to the Tavira Island ferry.

F. Reserva Natural do Sapal de Castro Marim e Vila Real de Sto. António

This reserve, established in 1975, was the second of Portugal's protected areas to be created and the first for the Algarve. It covers an area of salt-pans and salt-marsh, where Black-winged Stilt, Avocet, Kentish Plover, and Little Tern breed. White Storks are especially prolific, nesting on trees, ruined buildings and chimneys throughout the reserve. Leaflets on the wild-life of the area, as well as helpful information on the best access routes, can be obtained from the Information Office in the castle of Castro Marim.

G. Azinhal

The small town of Azinhal, lying 8 kms to the north of Castro Marim, is the access point to an area of oak, marsh and scrubland which contains a wide spread of species. The following sketch map shows the tracks/paths and habitat zones.

Fig. 9

Azinhal area.

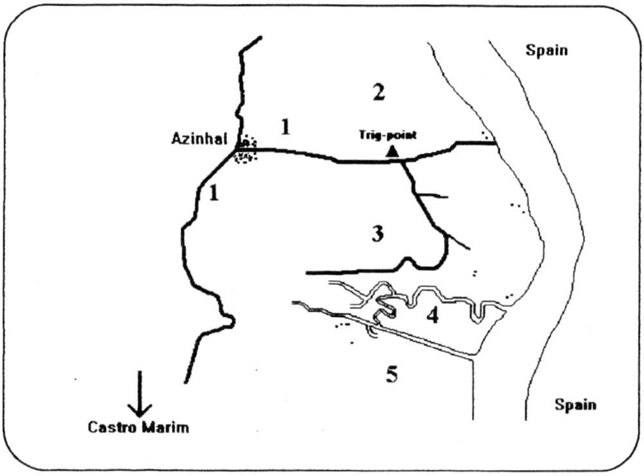

1. Low, open scrub: Thekla lark.

2. Open Oakwoods and grassland: Crested Tit and Orphean Warbler.

3. Thick scrub: Dartford Warbler (higher parts), Rufous Bushchat,Woodlark, Spotted
   Flycatcher (lower parts).

4. Marshland, channels, and riparian vegetation: Spectacled Warbler, hunting harriers
   (marshland); Little Grebes (channels); Nightingale, Cetti's Warbler,
   Great Reed Warbler (riparian).

5. Dry grassland: Little Bustard and Great Bustard.

H. Martim Longo to Vaqueiros
      This area has extremes of weather, with cold winters and very hot dry summers.
Most of the original trees and large bushes have been removed for grazing and agriculture,
leaving rolling dry grasslands with rocky ravines. During the breeding season, the rivers
partially dry out with only the hardiest of native vegetation growing along the banks. The
following map shows an area which is easily worked and which can form a starting point for
further exploration, as all the approach roads have interesting and varied habitats.

Fig. 10

Martim Longo area

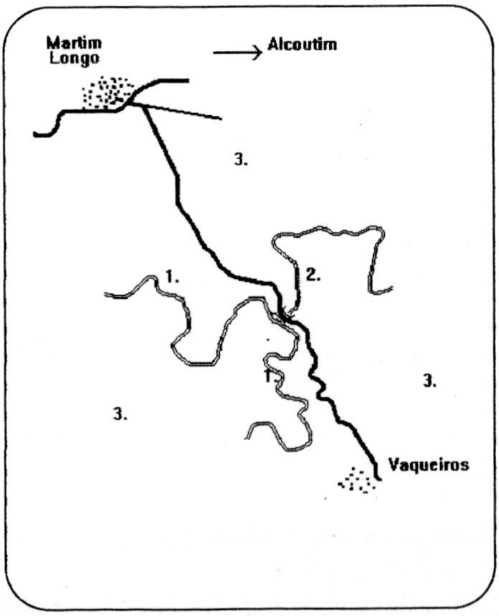

1. Small water-course and ravine.
   Rufous Bush Robin (Chat), Blue RockThrush, Rock Bunting.

2. Large, wide water-course.
   Little Ringed Plover, Common Sandpiper, Red-rumped Swallow

3. Dry grasslands.
   Thekla and Short-toed Larks.

CHAPTER 4.

Atlas techniques

This atlas of breeding birds of the Algarve was undertaken in response to the inaccuracies of available publications and to the numerous enquiries from friends and strangers for a book able to guide them when looking for birds breeding in the Algarve district of Portugal.

Planning

In response to the above, to the inaccuracies of the various publications available at the time, and to the anticipated shortcoming of the national Atlas, it was decided in 1987 to produce a distribution atlas of the breeding birds of the Algarve. The aims of the project were:

- To determine the accurate distribution of all bird species breeding in the Algarve.
- To provide a basis from which future range expansion or decline could be estimated.
- To provide an indication as to the scarcity or abundance of each species in all parts of the Algarve.
- To record as much as possible about the breeding habits of Algarvian birds in the Algarve. Many species do not follow normally-accepted breeding/migration patterns, owing to the Algarve's benign climate, and local populations often choose different habitats or have different nesting behaviour to their northern counterparts.
- To guide both amateur birdwatcher and professional ornithologist towards the best sites in which to find any particular breeding species. This would include a habitat map, and maps showing roads and tracks to a suggested series of itineraries taking in good bird-watching areas.
- To provide an illustration for each breeding species, with both male and female depicted where the sexes are very different, showing clearly the characteristics of local races and the local breeding habitat.

A time-span of five years for the field-work, commencing in 1988, was allocated, which allowed one year for exploration into unknown areas to find access paths and for determining possible problems, three years for basic field-work, and one year for in-filling gaps in coverage and for checking on scarce breeders. This was thought to be long enough to ensure adequate coverage of remote areas whilst short enough to freeze distributions.

It was decided to keep to the national maps of 1/50.000 as a basis for the Atlas rectangles, partly because these were the only large-scale maps readily available at the time, and partly because this enabled easy comparison with the national atlas. Each map was divided into eight, by subdividing the quarters already marked on the maps, and each division was numbered 1 to 8 (see fig. 11, Chapter 5), making 88 rectangles of 10 x 8 kms for the whole of the Algarve. Some maps, for example those with large expanses of sea, did not make eight rectangles.

The methods to be used were those recommended by the European Ornithological Atlas Committee (EOAC), with modifications in accordance with the experiences of other Atlases - in particular the Atlas of Breeding Birds in Britain and Ireland (BTO, 1976).

Recording Methods and Data Collection

The first year of fieldwork was undertaken solely by the organizers and close associates, to accurately assess the problems which would be faced by volunteer observers. In order to overcome the principal problem, access to the interior, a Land Rover was used to explore every remote rectangle and sketch-maps were made of all serviceable tracks. On the border between the Algarve and the Alentejo, there was often only a small area, which was part of the Algarve, within the rectangle and frequently there was not even a path. For these areas, access had to be found from the Alentejo, including fords where a river formed the boundary. Although the maps available show relief and watercourses accurately, the most recent survey of these maps was 1965 except for map 49A, which was based on a 1:25 000 map and published in 1981. Since 1965, the Algarve has changed out of all recognition - not only the over-developed coast but also the mountains. On the one hand, the majority of small villages in the interior have vanished together with their access routes; on the other hand, since joining the EEC many councils have pushed brand new roads, using new routes, to the surviving villages. In addition, many areas have been afforested or have been turned into touristic hunting zones, both of which contain many serviceable tracks, but note that access is restricted for the latter.

For the subsequent three years of field work, volunteers were designated one or more rectangles each - usually in areas with which they were already familiar - and asked to visit each type of habitat for each of the three years. Where the same habitat occurred in several fragments throughout a rectangle, observers were asked to visit as many fragments as possible for at least one season. Although the breeding season was defined as February-July, the following guidance was given to the observers:

- Some species are easier to find in the winter, e.g. the Eagle Owl, which calls mainly in November.
- Many species, especially passerines, are easier to prove breeding when they are carrying food to chicks later in the season than when they are sitting on eggs earlier in the season.
- Winter and passage birds often sing well into the breeding season. Care was advised in recording these as some individuals may stay to breed whereas some may migrate, e.g. the Robin.

Sheets were produced in three formats for each observer:
1) an explanation of the codes to be used.
2) a sheet for casual sightings, where an observer could record any sightings outside his/her designated area.
3) a list of species, with two columns to be completed with the appropriate codes. One list would cover one rectangle for one season, the highest code-number for each species for the season being recorded only. Observers were advised to use their own judgement on completing the abundance column, bearing in mind the species concerned - e.g. three pairs of Golden Eagle in one rectangle would be abundant by anyone's standards, whereas only three pairs of Sardinian Warbler would be scarce for the Algarve. Observers were also advised to classify the abundance of a species within its habitat only, e.g. if Mallard were abundant on lakes covering 10% of the rectangle but absent on bare mountain-tops covering

32

90%, this species would be recorded as abundant for that rectangle. Check surveys were made by the authors to ensure standardization of the various individual assessments of abundance.

In addition, each observer was given a photocopy of the map or maps for which he/she was responsible. Although the 1:50000 maps are the most readily-available large-scale maps, they were during the course of the fieldwork for this Atlas only available in one shop in Faro and it was seldom possible to obtain all the maps for the Algarve at any one time. The photocopy was marked with appropriate new roads and divided into the eight rectangles, numbered on the reverse.

Some rectangles along the boundary with the Alentejo contain only small areas of Algarve. Observers were instructed to record only those species which occurred within the Algarve. Where the actual nest was not found, observers should also be careful as to which side of the border breeding was most likely to take place, e.g. small chicks of Little Ringed Plover would normally be proof of breeding, but if the only area of suitable nesting shingle was on the Alentejo side of a boundary-river, then this species had to be ignored or reduced to 'possible' only.

Lastly, the volunteers were cautioned on two aspects of the project:
- The safety of any nests located was the primary consideration. The British Trust for Ornithology's instructions for its Atlas included: "In most cases, breeding can be proved without ever approaching the nest", and this was held as a general maxim for the BBA. The volunteers were asked to concentrate on the distribution of species in their rectangle rather than possibly disturbing birds at the nest, particularly in the case of threatened species, such as raptors, and easily disturbed species, such as waders whose cries might be noted by watchful predators. Observers were assured that the breeding localities of rarities would be kept strictly secret.
- Although the law in Portugal allows pedestrians to cross unfenced land, as long as no damage is caused, it is always best to ask permission when there is someone available to ask. Even when a volunteer can speak no Portuguese, a smile and a mime are always better than walking straight past, and often a country-person can recognise species from a bird-book and offer advice on the direction in which to go. In no case was a volunteer met with hostility, and in many cases the volunteer was escorted many kilometres to the secret nesting place of a rare species and offered bountiful hospitality on the return.

After the first year's concentrated fieldwork, i.e. at the end of the second year, it could be seen where coverage was likely to be thin. It had been shown during the course of the British Trust for Ornithology's Atlas that ornithologists experienced in atlas work can cover a rectangle in a day at the right time of year. With this in mind, those rectangles which were undercovered and which were near the coast were allocated to the more skilled observers, in addition to the rectangles for which they had already volunteered, to be covered by day trips. However, this still left large areas in out-of-the-way places which could not be covered by day trips. For these, expeditions by Land Rover were made by the organizers, with a caravan or tents as mobile bases, and a total of six months was spent in this way in the remotest parts of the Algarve during 1989 to 1992.

By the end of the penultimate year, it was clear that some species were still under-covered, especially nocturnal species. The organizers examined the species list for each rectangle, together with maps and habitat surveys, and estimated which species were missing from each rectangle but which 'ought' to be there. Each observer was then handed a list of 'missing' species for his/her rectangles and asked to particularly search for these species, whilst still attempting to prove breeding for those species which had yet to be confirmed.

33

Observers were also asked to check on their previous estimates of abundance for every species already found in their rectangles, as population densities can quickly increase or decrease. For the nocturnal species, as well as some easily-identified species (e.g. Golden Oriole) and difficult-to-find game species (e.g. Quail) observers were asked to enlist the help of local people as much as possible.

For the raptors, it was fortunate that a survey was carried out by the Algarve University, headed by Senhor Luís Palma, during 1987 to 1992. This atlas is deeply indebted to the resulting exchange of data and to the wealth of information which was made freely available.

Checking and Final Analysis of Data

At the end of each season, all records were scrutinized by the organizers for possible errors. The identification of unlikely species was carefully checked with the observer and, in the case of doubt, checked during the following season. If the species in question was not found in the same area and there was reasonable doubt as to the correct identification, it was either disregarded (in the case of a rarity) or designated as a 'possible breeder' (in the case of a species in the 'wrong' habitat).

Some species were queried where the breeding activity was in doubt. Many species, such as the Robin, are common winter and passage migrants, often remaining and singing strongly until well into the breeding season of the Algarve. The Robin, does in fact breed in good numbers in the north-western Algarve, but is not known to breed on the south coast where it is common on passage. Other species, such as the Dunnock *Prunella modularis*, are not known to breed anywhere in southern Portugal but do breed in northern Portugal, so that possible breeding could not be dismissed without investigation; and others, such as the Willow Warbler, had not been thought to breed south of the Cantabrian Mountains, in Spain, prior to the field-work for the BBA.

After these checks were made, the data from individual record-sheets were computerized and transferred to master records for each rectangle and onto provisional maps for each species. Comparison between the master-records and the distribution of species shown on the provisional maps highlighted dubious breeding and initiated a further check where appropriate.

At the end of four years of fieldwork, data sheets were drafted for each observer with the highest code given for each species for the whole period in each of his/her rectangles, regardless of who had originally submitted the records. The observers were asked to check these against their notebooks and to notify the organizers of any additions or to query anything which seemed unusual to them. Any additions or queries were verified during the final season's fieldwork.

The main purpose of this publication is to show the breeding distribution of the Algarve's birds, but under the individual species in Chapter 5, details are given of each species' breeding status: Possible, Probable, and Confirmed Breeding. These categories were determined according to guidelines laid down by the EOAC.

CHAPTER 5 - BREEDING BIRDS OF THE ALGARVE

EXPLANATION OF TEXT

The text for each species begins with the scientific name of that species, followed by the most commonly used English and Portuguese name. Within the text, the authors have tried to simplify various descriptions as much as possible, in order to make them more readable. Where a bird usually undertakes a particular activity, e.g. it **usually** mates for life or it **usually** feeds its young on caterpillars, it is simply stated that the bird undertakes the activity. This should not be taken to mean that it **always** does things that way, as inevitably there are individuals who 'break the rules' and do things differently. All information given applies to the Algarve only, unless otherwise stated.

Within the text there are sub-headings, which cover various topics as follows:

Distribution: World-wide distribution, including introductions by man.

Status in the Western Palearctic: Increasing, decreasing, or stable in the Western Palearctic in general and in Portugal in particular, together with probable causes of any change. Whether migrant or resident and whether migrants may be present at other times of the year.

Preferred habitat: Firstly the preferred habitat is given, followed by habitats used sometimes and habitats avoided. The species' relationship with man is usually given also.

Food: The preferred food and hunting or gathering techniques are given, as well as other foods and techniques. Where the food fed to the chicks is different to that eaten by the adults, this is stated.

Breeding: The month when territorial displays or songs begin is important because birds are more easily found at that time and because the timing of all other activities can be approximately calculated. Following this are descriptions of: song-flight, courtship displays, nest, rôle of the sexes, incubation and fledging times, age of first breeding, and status of the pair-bond.

Hints on recognition: A general description of the bird perched and, where relevant, in flight. Comparison is made only with species likely to be found in the Algarve, other species being ignored. Differences in plumage or song in the Algarvian birds to other races are specified. This should be read in conjunction with the illustration.

Hints on finding: General help on how to find each species. Exact locations are rarely given, as it would be detrimental to have hundreds of birdwatchers at one place. This should be read in conjuncion with Preferred habitat and thought given to the best time for the observer within the bird's breeding cycle.

Confirmation of breeding: Any difficulties in obtaining confirmation of breeding are stated, as well as information on the map where necessary, followed by the number of rectangles in which the species was observed and the degree of confirmation of breeding in each rectangle. An explanation of the way in which this was obtained is given in Chapter 4.

EXPLANATION OF MAPS

The fieldwork for the BBA was carried out over a period of five years, 1987-1992, by a number of enthusiastic residents and visitors to the Algarve. For this purpose, the Algarve was divided into 88 rectangles, 10km x 8km, based on the national cartographical series of 1:50,000 (see Chapter 4 for a more detailed account of the methods used for data collection and interpretation). The following diagram shows the reference numbers of the maps which cover the Algarve and the way in which each was divided to make the rectangles. The thick lines show the outline of each map, the thin lines show the divisions already printed on the maps, and the dotted lines show the further divisions which were made for the purposes of the BBA.

Fig. 11 - **Index to 1:50,000 scale maps used**

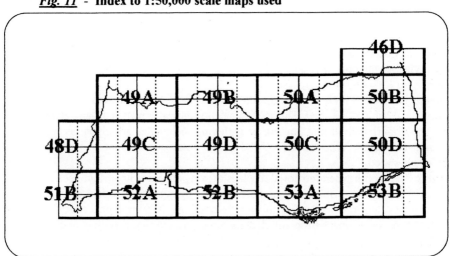

In order to locate each map in relation to a known point, the principal town or village for each is as follows:

46D- Monte Vascão
48D- Bordeira
49A- Odeceixe
49C- Monchique
50A- Ameixal
50C- S.Braz de Alportel
51B- Sagres
52A- Lagos and Portimão
53A- Loulé and Faro

49B- S.Marcos da Serra
49D- Silves and S.B. de Messines
50B- Alcoutim
50D- Vila Real de S.António

52B- Lagoa and Albufeira
53B- Tavira

36

Distribution map

 The map shown for each species gives the breeding distribution only; records for non-breeding birds have been ignored. Rare or vulnerable species are represented by a single blank map with the breeding information written in a centralized box. Species with large territories, crossing the boundaries of rectangles, have been represented by equal shading for every rectangle in which they have been seen. The remaining maps show the 88 rectangles shaded to show the relative abundance of the species within its breeding area (see Chapter 4 for further details on the methods used to determine abundance).

Fig 12. Shading used on Distribution Maps

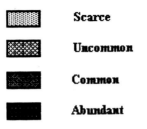

Scarce

Uncommon

Common

Abundant

TACHYBAPTUS RUFICOLLIS

LITTLE GREBE

Portuguese name: Mergulhão-pequeno.

Distribution: The Little Grebe is to be found throughout temperate and southern Europe and Asia, as well as northern, equatorial, and all the southern portion of Africa. It is more common in the southern half of Portugal than in the north (CEMPA).

Status in the Western Palearctic: There has been some decline in Europe since the 1950s, probably owing to pollution and the destruction of habitat by drainage. There is insufficient data to assess whether it has generally declined in Portugal or not. With the steady draining of coastal marshland and an increase in private reservoirs in the Algarve, there has been a colonization of the interior and a reduction in coastal breeders in recent years. It is mainly resident, although there is some dispersal to the coasts in winter.

Preferred habitat: Well-vegetated fresh water with some open areas, e.g. coastal lagoons, marshy ponds, and reservoirs. It particularly favours open water, where it can swim and dive freely, with areas of dense aquatic vegetation, where it can nest and hide from intruders. It is tolerant of human disturbance and often uses water-hazards on golf-courses.

Food: Mainly insects and larvae, but molluscs and small fish are also eaten. Most of its prey is caught by shallow diving, at up to 1m below the surface of the water. It will also search for food by swimming with its head and neck immersed, or take it from plants, the air, or the surface of the water.

Breeding: Pair-formation takes place in late summer or during the winter. In February, the pair leaves the winter feeding area and occupies a territory; established pairs remain on the same territory throughout the year if possible. Courtship display occurs when the pair-bond is being formed and just before nesting. Both sexes, together or individually, trill loudly whilst swimming together or occasionally whilst pattering side by side over the water with wings waving in the air. In March, the pair makes several floating platforms of water weeds, attached to submerged vegetation or to the branches of a bush growing in the water. One platform is then completed as a nest, by the pair piling more aquatic plants onto it. The birds form a cup-shape in the vegetation, in which 4-6 eggs are laid. Incubation is by both sexes and takes about 3 weeks. The young are semi-nidifugous but are cared for and fed by both parents, often riding on the backs of the parents. When the young of the first brood are about 2 weeks old, a second clutch is laid and often the older chicks will help feed their siblings from the second clutch. Fledging takes 6-7 weeks and the young become independent 4-5 weeks later. The pair-bond is monogamous and lasts for life if the pair can maintain a year-round territory.

Hints on recognition: This tiny grebe is easily the smallest water-bird to be found in the Algarve. Typically, it swims with a hunched posture, the neck and tail hardly visible and the wings slightly raised, making it seem very round. Care should, however, be taken with distant views as it sometimes stretches its neck, affording confusion with the Black-necked Grebe (for which, see that species). When it is seen well its chestnut-red cheeks, throat, and under-neck are unmistakable. It rarely flies, preferring to dive and swim under water to a place of concealment.

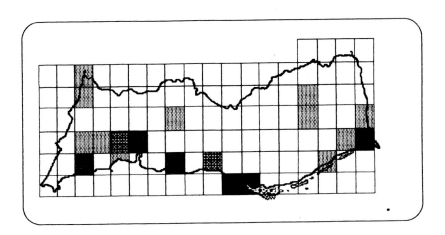

Hints on finding: Excellent views can be obtained of this species from the hides at Quinta da Marinha and Quinta do Lago (see Where to watch breeding birds, E). Elsewhere, its loud cry of "dee-dee-dee- dee" ringing across the water or the sharp metallic "tick" from the water-weeds instantly draws attention to its whereabouts.

Confirmation of breeding:

Number of rectangles in which recorded:	19
Possible breeding:	0
Probable breeding:	5
Confirmed breeding:	14

PODICEPS CRISTATUS

GREAT CRESTED GREBE

Portuguese name: Mergulhão-de-crista.

Distribution: The middle latitudes of Europe and Asia, except the Far East, as well as a few scattered sites in Africa and Australasia. Apparently it was not breeding in Portugal in the early part of this century (Coverley), although in the national atlas it was recorded breeding at several sites in the southern half of the country and along the eastern border with Spain. In the Algarve, the only known breeding site is at Ludo, where it breeds spasmodically.

Status in the Western Palearctic: In the latter half of the nineteenth century, this species was brought to the verge of extinction in Europe, at least partly because of its slaughter for the plumage trade. During this century, the population has recovered with protection and, in some areas, has increased owing to the formation of man-made lakes and reservoirs. The first recorded breeding of this species in southern Portugal was in 1973 (BWP 1977). Those birds breeding in Portugal are probably resident, dispersing to the coast and to large lakes outside of the nesting season.

Preferred habitat: Large (at least 1ha per pair) but shallow (less than 5m deep) areas of fresh-water with plentiful aquatic vegetation, both around and in the water. It avoids rocky, very narrow stretches, and deep water with no shallow areas. It will tolerate forests, brackish water, and a limited amount of human disturbance.

Food: Mainly fish, but it will also take aquatic invertebrates. Fish are normally caught by diving, although it will also search for small prey by swimming with its head below the water. Insects are taken from the surface of the water or from vegetation, or are snatched from the air.

Breeding: Pair-formation commences in the wintering quarters, before a territory is occupied. The courtship displays are varied and elaborate, but all involve both sexes erecting the feathers around the head to form a ruff. The most distinctive display is when both birds dive and re-emerge together with beakfuls of weed, then face one another upright, heads turning rigidly from side to side, appearing to stand on the surface of the water by paddling their feet rapidly. In March, the pair chooses a site and builds a substantial nest of aquatic vegetation in the water, either floating, tethered, or built up from the bottom. Finer material is placed around the rim for covering the eggs. One clutch of 3-5 eggs is laid; incubation is by both sexes equally and takes about one month. Sometimes a second clutch of 1-2 eggs is laid when the first brood is about 6 weeks old, in which case a new nest is made. For the first 2-3 weeks, the young are cared for and fed by both parents, riding on the back of one adult while the other catches food. When the young are about 5 weeks old, the brood is split between the two parents and each parent cares exclusively for its own share of the chicks. Fledging takes about three months and the young become independent immedieately or shortly afterwards. The pair-bond is monogamous and lasts only until the brood is divided.

Hints on recognition: Its size and shape make it unmistakable in the Western Palearctic. The calls are variously described as barking, growling, and snarling.

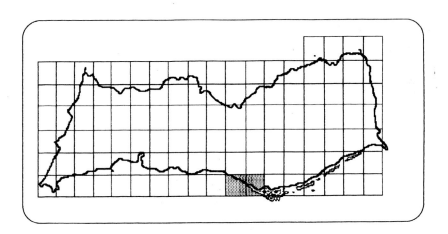

Hints on finding: The only known breeding site in the Algarve is at Ludo, although it can frequently be seen at Quinta do Lago (see Where to watch breeding birds, E).

Confirmation of breeding:

Number of rectangles in which recorded: 2
Possible breeding: 1
Probable breeding: 0
Confirmed breeding: 1

PODICEPS NIGRICOLLIS

BLACK-NECKED GREBE

Portuguese name:
Mergulhão-de-pescoço-negro.

Distribution: The Black-necked Grebe breeds in most of the middle-latitudes of Asia and north-west America, and at scattered sites in Europe, southern and central Africa, and the Middle East. There was no recorded breeding in Portugal, prior to the BBA. This species is migratory in part of its range, and migrants can be seen passing through the Algarve in the autumn and winter. Those breeding in the Algarve are probably resident.

Status in the Western Palearctic: The status of this species is difficult to determine because it changes breeding sites frequently and is particularly sensitive to changes in habitat. During the last 100 years, it has increased in the north and west of its range, but has decreased in most of southern Europe and probably no longer breeds anywhere in northern Africa. The species fluctuates in numbers from year to year, possibly because of human interference. Breeding was proved in the first two years of fieldwork for the BBA only and the continued destruction of marshland makes the future breeding of this species very uncertain. During the preparatory year for the BBA, it also bred at Ludo.

Preferred habitat: Small, shallow ponds, with plentiful vegetation, often close to man. It particularly favours areas of freshwater which increase during the winter but dry out in the summer months. In both of the confirmed-breeding rectangles in the BBA, small pools in pocket-sized marshes amongst housing developments were used.

Food: Mainly insects and larvae, but also some molluscs, amphibians, and small fish. Prey is taken by skimming or pecking from the surface of the water, by snatching from the air, by diving, or by swimming with the head and neck below water.

Breeding: In courtship display, which can be seen from February onwards, both sexes raise the crest and the head-feathers to form a facial ruff. Both birds stand upright on the water, side by side and touching, paddling rapidly with the feet to keep afloat, and then dashing across the surface of the water together in this position. During late March or early April, both sexes build several floating heaps of water-weed, anchored to aquatic vegetation, one of which will be the final nest. A hollow is formed in the heap by either bird sitting on it and piling more vegetation around it. There is usually only one clutch of 3-4 eggs; incubation is by both sexes and takes about 3 weeks. The young are semi-nidifugous and are cared for by both parents. When they are small, they ride on the backs of the parents, but from 2-3 weeks onwards they may be cared for in crèches or the brood may be split between the adults (see also Great Crested Grebe). Should there be more than one brood, the young of the first brood often help to feed their younger siblings from the second brood. Fledging takes about 3 weeks and the chicks become independent shortly afterwards. The pair-bond is monogamous and may last for one season only.

Hints on recognition: Both sexes of this beautiful little water-bird are unmistakable in breeding plumage, having a black head, neck and back with a bright chestnut stripe along the side of the body and a spray of bright chestnut feathers behind the eye. In the distance or in silhouette, it can generally be distinguished from the Little Grebe by its more upright neck posture and up-turned beak (however, see also that species).

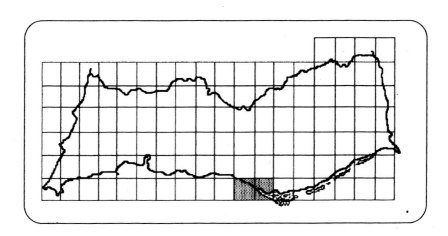

Hints on finding: There are several small marshy pools near the coast, between Ludo and Albufeira, including at Quinta do Lago, which may contain this species. At the start of the breeding season, both sexes are particularly vocal, calling a plaintive "coo-ee" or trilling loudly during courtship displays.

Confirmation of breeding :

Number of rectangles in which recorded:	2
Possible breeding:	0
Probable breeding:	1
Confirmed breeding:	1

PHALACROCORAX ARISTOTELIS

SHAG

Portuguese name:
Corvo-marinho-de-crista.

Distribution: The Shag breeds and winters entirely within the Western Palearctic. In Portugal, it occurs in the southern half of the country only, extending as far north as Berlenga (CEMPA).

Status in the Western Palearctic: There have been some decreases in recent years in the northern part of its range and this species is particularly susceptible to oiling from tanker spillages.. However, it has increased substantially in most of its range, possibly owing to a reduction in human persecution. Comparing the accounts of Coverley and recent estimates (Teixeira 1984), it would seem that the Portuguese population is stable. This species is mainly resident, breeding on the coasts and wintering at sea close to shore within territorial waters.

Preferred habitat: This species is essentially marine, but seldom ranging far from the coast at any time of the year. It is dependent on rocky coastlines for breeding but favours sheltered bays or channels for feeding. It generally avoids fresh or brackish water, shallow water, estuaries, etc.

Food: Almost entirely fish, which is caught below the water and brought to the surface to be eaten. Food intended for the young is carried in a special pouch inside the lower mandible. Unlike the Cormorant *Phalacrocorax carbo*, it takes a high proportion of fish which is not desired by man.

Breeding: Older, experienced birds return to the nesting colonies in January or February and re-use their sites from the previous year. Young birds arrive later, in April or May, in which case the male chooses the site and starts to build the nest. Pair-bonding follows shortly afterwards with courtship displays involving ritualistic bowing and stretching by both birds. The most distinctive display is performed by the male, who throws his head backwards, touching his fanned tail, and then repeatedly darting his head upwards and forwards, showing his gape. The pair. constructs a heap of vegetation, with coarse material as a base and finer material on top, to which more material is added throughout incubation and the rearing of the young. The site is usually a rocky ledge just above high water, either in a sheltered cove or in a cave, but it can also be underneath a large boulder on a boulder-beach. One clutch of 1-6 eggs is laid. Incubation is by both sexes equally and takes about one month. The young are cared for and fed by both parents. Fledging takes 7-8 weeks and the young become independent 3 or more weeks later. Although young birds sometimes pair at one year old, most first-time breeding males are two years old and females three years old, and breeding is rarely successful until they are three and four years old respectively. The pair-bond is generally monogamous, but bigamy can occur. Most birds separate from their mates when the young become independent, but they reunite when they return to their nest-site in the following breeding season.

Hints on recognition: This all-black, crested sea-bird can only be confused with the larger Cormorant, which occurs in the Algarve as a non-breeder. However, the Cormorant lacks the crest and has a white throat.

44

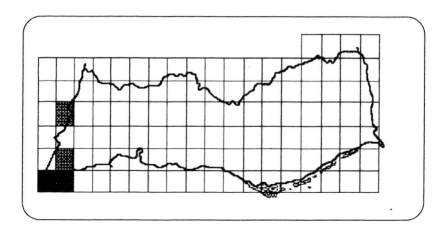

Hints on finding: From the cliff-tops on the west-coast, a scan over the water will usually produce a Shag, either flying low over the waves or bobbing on the surface of the sea.

Confirmation of breeding:

Number of rectangles in which recorded:	4
Possible breeding:	0
Probable breeding:	0
Confirmed breeding:	4

IXOBRYCHUS MINUTUS

LITTLE BITTERN

Portuguese name: Garça-pequena.

Distribution: The Little Bittern breeds in most of Europe except the north and north-west, as well as in temperate western Asia, the northern Indian sub-continent, central and southern Africa, and Australia. In Portugal, it is more common in the centre than anywhere else, (CEMPA).

Status in the Western Palearctic: It is decreasing almost everywhere in Europe, probably because of pollution and destruction of habitat. It no longer breeds at many traditional sites, including most of those in north Africa. Owing to the secretive nature of this species and to the type of habitat in which it is found, there is inadequate data with which to estimate its status in Portugal. However, as with other wetland species, it would appear to be declining in the Algarve. It is normally a summer visitor to Europe, wintering in eastern and central Africa, but a few sometimes over-winter in the Algarve.

Preferred habitat: Freshwater marshes and pools with dense stands of tall emergent vegetation. It can also be found along the sides of rivers and ditches, and in water-hazards on golf-courses where there is sufficient cover. It is tolerant of human presence providing that there is adequate vegetation in which to hide.

Food: Mainly fish, amphibians, and insects, but it will also take small mammals, molluscs, and the young and eggs of birds. It catches its prey by standing motionless, waiting for something to pass, or by stalking slowly through the water. The species is primarily crepuscular, but is also active during both the day and the night.

Breeding: This species is not colonial. In April, the male arrives at the nesting grounds and chooses a site in dense vegetation. Shortly afterwards he starts building a compact pile of dead reed stems or similar material, to which he attracts a female by repeatedly calling with deep barks or croaks. If he fails to attract a female to this nest, new ones are built until he is successful. The courtship display has not been fully observed but it is thought to include the raising of the back, neck and crown feathers, and the showing of the red lower mandible. Only one clutch of 5-6 eggs is laid. Incubation takes 2 1/2 to 3 weeks and is by both sexes, with the female incubating mostly at night and the male mostly during the day. Both parents care for the chicks and feed them by partial regurgitation. The young are able to move about the vegetation close to the nest about one week after hatching, but will not wander far unless disturbed. Fledging takes about one month, although the young leave the nest completely at 3 weeks old. The chicks become independent shortly after fledging and immediately leave the breeding area. The age of first breeding is one year old. The pair-bond is monogamous and lasts for at least one season.

Hints on recognition: This small heron, when seen well, has very distinctive plumage. When seen standing or climbing, the male has all black upperparts and creamy underparts, whilst the female and juveniles are streaked brown. In flight, both sexes show dark bodies and dark trailing edges to the wings, with striking pale patches on the fore part of the wings. It can only be confused with very rare vagrants to Europe not yet recorded in Portugal.

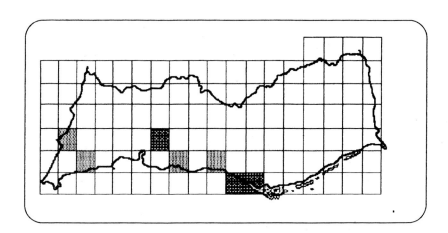

Hints on finding: The easiest place to see this species is from the hide at Quinta do Lago (see Where to watch breeding birds, E). Patience is required to obtain a glimpse of this very secretive bittern, however, and often a quick flash of black and white in flight is all that is seen.

Confirmation of breeding:

Number of rectangles in which recorded: 5
Possible breeding: 2
Probable breeding: 1
Confirmed breeding: 4

NYCTICORAX NYCTICORAX

NIGHT HERON

Portuguese name: Goraz.

Distribution: The Night Heron breeds in all parts of the world except the most northerly latitudes and Australasia. In Portugal, it is restricted to the southern half of the country only. The sole known breeding site in the Algarve is Ludo.

Status in the Western Palearctic: This species declined drastically during the latter half of the last century but has recovered to a certain extent since the 1940s. Although CEMPA estimates that there are some 300 breeding pairs in Portugal, it is scarce in the Algarve. It occasionally overwinters in Europe but is primarily a summer visitor, wintering in tropical Africa where it joins resident populations.

Preferred habitat: Shallow freshwater, especially pools, lagoons, and swamps, with dense emergent vegetation and some trees - the latter being important for both roosting and nesting. It is sometimes found by rivers or ditches with suitable vegetation on the banks, which accounts for all the Algarvian records outside of Ludo. It is tolerant of human disturbance and can often be seen away from water.

Food: Mainly fish, amphibians, and insects, although it will also take small mammals and young birds. It catches its prey by remaining motionless in the water or on land, or by stalking slowly through the water, until something suitable comes near enough for it to snatch. It is essentially a nocturnal and crepuscular feeder.

Breeding: Colonial, sometimes mixed with egrets or other herons. Both sexes arrive at the breeding grounds simultaneously, in mid-March or early April. Shortly after arrival, the bare parts of both sexes begin to change colour - in particular the legs become bright red. The male establishes a nesting territory within the colony, as well as a feeding territory which can be as much as 20kms away. A short distance from the nesting territory, the male selects a temporary territory on which to display to the females. The pairing display is initially hostile towards all approaching birds, including females, and consists of calling whilst bobbing, stretching the neck and lifting the feet as though dancing. The pair formation takes about 2 weeks, after which the nest-platform is built. The female sits on the nest site, which is usually in a tree, whilst the male brings her twigs with which to construct the nest. Normally one clutch of 2-3 eggs is laid, but sometimes there are two clutches. Incubation is by both sexes, the female taking the larger share, and takes about 3 weeks. The young are cared for and fed by both parents. They leave the nest at 2-3 weeks old, sometimes returning to the nest to be fed, although they do not fledge until 3-4 weeks later. The young become independent shortly after fledging. The pair-bond is monogamous and lasts for the breeding season only.

Hints on recognition: It is a stocky heron, larger than the Cattle Egret and with a relatively short neck. Both sexes are alike, appearing all white and pale grey except for a black crown and back. Two long white plumes reaching from the head to the back (which are raised erect during courtship or during disputes with rivals) can be seen when the bird is observed closely. In flight, this species appears totally grey above except for the black crown and two black oval patches on the back.

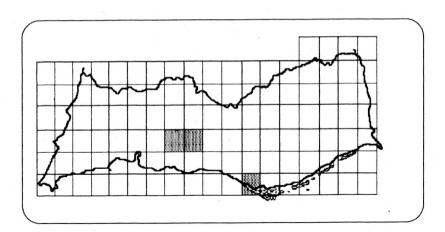

Hints on finding: The only known nesting area in the Algarve is Ludo, which requires permission to be entered (see Where to watch breeding birds, E).

Confirmation of breeding: Although all sightings of this species in suitable habitats have been included as 'possible breeding', it is unlikely to breed anywhere in the Algarve outside of Ludo.

Number of rectangles in which recorded: 3
Possible breeding: 2
Probable breeding: 0
Confirmed breeding: 1

BUBULCUS IBIS

CATTLE EGRET

Portuguese name: Garça-boieira.

Distribution: The Cattle Egret is to be found in all the warm regions of the world. In Europe, it is restricted to the Iberian Peninsula and the Camargue (France).

Status in the Western Palearctic: There has been a considerable increase in the range of this species over the past 50-60 years. In 1930 it spread from Africa to British Guiana in S. America and then to the rest of the American continent. It reached Australasia in 1948 and was introduced into Hawaii in 1949. The first recorded breeding in the Camargue was in 1969. In Portugal, it expanded north of Lisbon in the 1940s and apparently is still spreading northwards (CEMPA). It is resident in Portugal.

Preferred habitat: Most colonies in the Algarve are situated on sea-stacks, although it will also use reed-beds, trees, etc. for nesting. Feeding can be as far as 60kms from the nest and for this it particularly favours agricultural land, where it can be seen following animals or tractors. It will feed on the banks of rivers and ponds or on the margins of marshland, but rarely wades and avoids entering deep water or swamps. It is indifferent to man, allowing the close approach of herdsmen/shepherds and field-workers.

Food: Mainly insects, which are caught on the ground. It commonly rides on the backs of animals, from which it will swoop onto its prey. Amphibians, reptiles, and small mammals are also occasionally taken. In a colony in southern Spain, it was found that almost 80% of the food given to the chicks was grasshoppers and crickets (Herrera 1974).

Breeding: Colonial, often with other herons. In late February or early March, the plumage of both sexes changes colour, becoming orange-buff on the back, head plumes, and breast. Shortly afterwards, the male chooses and defends a pairing territory, which may be separate to the prospective nest-site. During this time, he marches up and down aggressively, with feathers erected, calling loudly, or leaps into the air to flap his wings together with a thud. This display attracts several females which, at first, he attacks, until eventually one is allowed to stay. The nest is a pile of twigs brought by the male and laid on a grassy ledge on a stack (or in the branches of a tree) by the female. The first clutch of 4-5 eggs is laid in April and the second clutch in June, and sometimes there is even a third clutch. Incubation is by both sexes equally and takes about 3 weeks. The chicks are cared for and fed by both parents and leave the nest at about 3 weeks old. Fledging takes one month and the young become independent about 2 weeks later. First breeding is usually at 2 years old. The pair-bond is monogamous and is of seasonal duration only.

Hints on recognition: The only two species with which this egret can be confused in the Algarve are the Squacco Heron and the Little Egret (for which, see that species). The former has a white breast, buff back, dark head-plumes, blue/black bill and is rare in Portugal. The Cattle Egret has long orange-buff plumes on the otherwise white breast, back and crown in breeding plumage. Its habit of feeding on dry ground, or following animals and ploughs, distinguishes it from other herons and egrets. In flight, only the feet protrude beyond the tail and it flaps its wings more shallowly and quickly than the Little Egret.

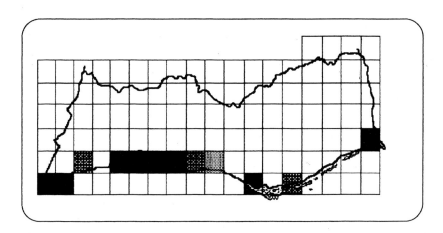

Hints on finding: Colonies along the coast can easily be found in the evening by following adults flighting in to roost. Good views can be had, without disturbance to the birds, at the colonies of Ponte da Piedade (south of Lagos) and from the coast between Benagil and Albufeira.

Confirmation of breeding: This species can be observed feeding almost anywhere in the Algarve, at a considerable distance from the nest-site. Therefore, only probable and confirmed breeding are shown on the map.

Number of rectangles in which recorded: 12
Probable breeding: 1
Confirmed breeding: 11

EGRETTA GARZETTA

LITTLE EGRET

Portuguese name: Garça-branca-pequena.

Distribution: The Little Egret breeds in most of the warm and temperate latitudes of the world, except the Americas. It breeds only in the southern half of Portugal (CEMPA). Most European birds are summer migrants, wintering in northern subtropical Africa, but those that breed in the Algarve are apparently resident.

Status in the Western Palearctic: This species declined almost to the point of extinction during the 19th century, owing to extensive slaughter for the plumage trade. It is now recovering, following protection, and is spreading in the north of its range. It has recently bred for the first time in Brittany (France) and there has been a significant increase in spring migrants arriving in Great Britain. Numbers appear to be stable or slightly increasing in the Algarve.

Preferred habitat: Most colonies in the Algarve are on sea-stacks, with the Cattle Egret, but those in the Sotavento use trees and reed-beds for nesting. It feeds in both freshwater and saline water, favouring rivers, salt-pans, estuaries, and marshes, commonly up to 20kms from the nesting colony. It is tolerant of human presence, but does not associate with man as does the Cattle Egret and is rarely found in dry situations.

Food: Mainly small fish, amphibians, and insects, but it will also take small reptiles and mammals, crustaceans, and birds. It catches aquatic prey either by stalking and chasing through the water, or by standing motionless, occasionally stirring the water with one foot. Other prey is generally caught on the margins of water, e.g. reptiles from the banks of rivers.

Breeding: Colonial, usually with Cattle Egrets. It arrives at the nesting area in February and the male establishes one or more pairing-territories. During this time, he walks up and down the site, calling loudly, plumes erect, occasionally leaping into the air and clapping his wings together with a thud. Several females and males are attracted by the display and at first the male is antagonistic towards both sexes. . One female is eventually allowed to remain and mutual displays of bowing and stretching, with plumes erected, are performed. The nest is on a ledge on a stack, on piles of dead reeds in reed-beds, or in a tree, and is built mostly by the female from twigs brought by the male. One clutch of 3-5 eggs is laid in April. Incubation is by both sexes and takes about 3 weeks. The young are cared for and fed by regurgitation by both parents. Fledging takes about 6 weeks, although the chicks leave the nest when 3-4 weeks old and move about the colony. The young become independent shortly after fledging, although siblings will remain together for some time after leaving the colony. Age of first breeding is probably one year. The pair-bond is monogamous and is of seasonal duration only.

Hints on recognition: The only species with which it can be confused is the Cattle Egret (for which, see that species). It is larger than the Cattle Egret and all white, with long head-plumes. It has long black legs with greenish-yellow feet and a long neck, often held in a snake-shape. It is usually solitary, standing or wading in water. In flight, the legs protrude noticeably beyond the tail and the yellow feet can be observed when the bird is seen closely. The wing-beats appear deeper and more leisurely than those of the Cattle Egret, resembling the flight of the Grey Heron.

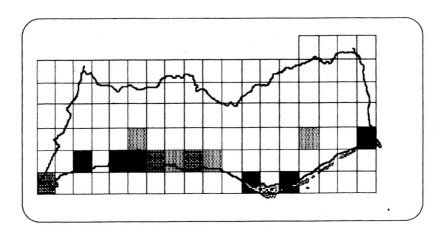

Hints on finding: Good views of this species can be had at the nesting colony of Ponte da Piedade (south of Lagos) and at the two small colonies off the coast between Benagil and Albufeira. Feeding birds can be found by quiet pools on the larger rivers (see Where to watch breeding birds, D) or on coastal marshes and salt-pans, especially in the Ria Formosa.

Confirmation of breeding: As with the Cattle Egret, this species can be observed feeding almost anywhere in the Algarve, at a considerable distance from the nest-site. Therefore, only probable and confirmed breeding are shown on the map.

Number of rectangles in which recorded: 13
Probable breeding: 2
Confirmed breeding: 11

ARDEA CINEREA

GREY HERON

Portuguese name: Garça-real.

Distribution: The Grey Heron is to be found in most of the temperate and warm regions of Europe, Asia, and Africa. The national atlas proved breeding at six sites in Portugal and the BBA added a further site at Ludo in the Ria Formosa.

Status in the Western Palearctic: It has expanded its range in northern Europe and has also established new colonies in Spain. This is counteracted, however, by a general decrease in the south. Coverley mentions this species nesting on the cliffs in the western Algarve, but these colonies have since disappeared. The only known breeding site in the Algarve is at Ludo, where it breeds spasmodically.

Preferred habitat: This species prefers nesting in trees rather than in bushes, reed-beds or on rocks, although it will use these, and therefore trees are an important feature of most colonies. It shuns extensive or dense woods, however. It requires wetlands or rivers for feeding, preferring marshes, shallow freshwater, salt-pans, or estuaries. It is tolerant of human presence where it is not persecuted.

Food: Mainly fish, amphibians, reptiles, small mammals, and invertebrates. It will also take molluscs, birds and some plant material. It catches its prey mainly by stalking slowly through the water or standing motionless near the edge of water, snatching unwary prey. It has also been known to swim and dive for food (Lowe 1954).

Breeding: Colonial, with other herons, or solitary. Both sexes arrive at the same time at the breeding grounds, but only the male takes up and defends a display-site, which is often an old nest. The display consists initially of the male stretching his neck upwards and calling loudly. When a female approaches, he stretches upwards then bends the body forward, his beak still pointing straight upwards. Finally, if the female remains, he bows the head downwards, crest erect, and makes a snapping sound with his bill. This is repeated rapidly several times, appearing like dancing. In February or March, the pair constructs a nest of twigs, lined with leaves and grass, the male bringing most of the material while the female builds. One clutch of 4-5 eggs is laid. Incubation is by both sexes equally and takes nearly 4 weeks. The young are cared for and fed by both parents. Fledging takes 6-7 weeks and one of the adults always remains with the chicks for the first 4 weeks. The young become independent 2-3 weeks after fledging and usually breed for the first time at 2 years old. The pair-bond is basically monogamous, although the male is often promiscuous and will try to rape other females whilst maintaining a firm pair-bond with his mate. Occasional cases of bigamy also occur. The pair-bond is of seasonal duration only.

Hints on recognition: Adults cannot be confused with any other European species, although the juveniles can be mistaken for Purple Herons. It is a mainly grey-and-white bird, grey on the back and white on the neck and underparts, with a yellow bill and legs, and black head plumes. In flight, the wings appear all grey above and below with an all-white body, whereas the Purple Heron appears to be grey above and brown/dark grey below (see that species). Some juveniles can be slightly brownish, but most are grey and white and all are much paler and greyer than juvenile Purple Herons.

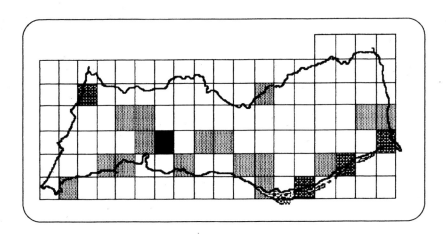

Hints on finding: The only known breeding site in the Algarve is at Ludo, for which authorisation to enter is required (see Where to watch breeding birds, E). However, feeding birds (presumed to be non-breeders) can be readily seen on the larger rivers, e.g. the Arade, and on salt-pans and saltings.

Confirmation of breeding: Non-breeders are commonly seen in the Algarve at all times of the year. The map shows abundance and should not be considered as the actual breeding distribution.

Number of rectangles in which recorded: 21
Confirmed breeding: 1

ARDEA PURPUREA

PURPLE HERON

Portuguese name: Garça-vermelha.

Distribution: Southern Europe, south, S.W. and S.E. Asia, southern and eastern Africa, and a few sites in north-west Africa (including the Cape Verde Islands). It breeds in scattered localities along the length of the Portuguese coast, as well as a few in the interior of the Alentejo (CEMPA). The only site at which it has been proved to breed in the Algarve is Ludo.

Status in the Western Palearctic: In central and eastern Europe there has been a slight expansion in range since the mid-1900s, although it is decreasing in some areas. Breeding was not proved in the Cape Verde Islands until 1951 (Bourne 1955). It is nowhere common in Portugal, where it is estimated to number 100-1000 birds (CEMPA), and breeding is spasmodic in the Algarve. It is a summer visitor to Europe, wintering in Africa south of the Sahara, although individuals can occasionally be seen in Europe during the winter months.

Preferred habitat: Shallow freshwater with extensive tall stands of dense vegetation such as reeds or Tamarisk. It avoids vegetation with numerous trees, although it will tolerate and use willows. It is not tolerant of human presence and readily deserts the nest if disturbed.

Food: Mainly fish and insects, which it catches in the evening or early morning by remaining motionless in shallow water and snatching the prey as it passes. It also fishes, by wading in deeper water and grabbing its prey with its beak, and stalks amphibeans, small mammals, and reptiles.

Breeding: Colonial, often with other herons. In Ludo, it nests with the Grey Heron. Both sexes return to the nesting colony in late March or early April and shortly afterwards the male chooses a nest-site in a clump of dead reeds or in a bushy tree close to open water. The pair-forming display for this species is not known but is probably the same as for the Grey Heron (for which, see that species). The pair constructs a nest of dead reeds or twigs, in which one clutch of 4-5 eggs is laid. In addition, they build a platform of dead reeds, on which the off-duty adult may rest and where the chicks can be fed, later. Incubation is by both parents, although the female does the larger share, and takes almost one month. When the adults change places during incubation, bill-clapping can be heard, similar to that performed by White Storks. The young are cared for and fed by regurgitation by both parents. Fledging takes 6-7 weeks, although the young are able to leave the nest at 8-10 days old, and the chicks become independent about a fortnight after fledging. First breeding is at one year old. The pair-bond is monogamous and of seasonal duration only.

Hints on recognition: This species can only be confused with juvenile Grey Herons (for which, see that species). When the bird is standing, the chestnut neck, black crown, and black belly are distinctive; whereas the Grey Heron has a white belly, neck, and crown (although the crown can be black outside of the breeding season). In flight, the uppersides of the two species are similar; when seen from below, however, the black belly and the chestnut leading edges to the wings (instead of white) are apparent.

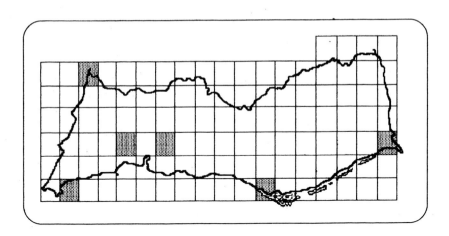

Hints on finding: The only known breeding site is at Ludo. Outside of Ludo, individuals can frequently be seen feeding on the River Arade, between Estômbar and Silves, and on salt-pans and saltings in the Ria Formosa.

Confirmation of breeding: Non-breeders are frequently seen in the Algarve, as well as individuals feeding away from the nesting colony. The map shows abundance and should not be considered as the actual breeding distribution.

Number of rectangles in which recorded: 6
Confirmed breeding: 1

CICONIA CICONIA

WHITE STORK

Portuguese name: Cegonha-branca.

Distribution: Outside of the Western Palearctic and the bordering regions of Asia, the White Stork breeds only in the Far East. In Europe, it is mainly restricted to the Iberian Peninsula and Central and Eastern countries, although a few breed in France. It is well distributed throughout Portugal, except for the north-west (CEMPA).

Status in the Western Palearctic: This species has declined drastically everywhere in Europe since the mid-1900s, probably owing to changes · in the environment, destruction of wetlands, and the increasing use of pesticides. In most European countries, the population has reduced to between one tenth and one fortieth of the population at the turn of this century, and it has become extinct in several regions. In Portugal, too, numbers have been steadily declining since 1959 (CEMPA). However, there has been a recovery in numbers in the Algarve owing to protection of nest-sites and prohibition of the most dangerous pesticides, and there were more pairs breeding by the end of the field-work for the BBA than there were at the beginning. Most European Storks are summer visitors, but those that breed in the Algarve usually remain all year, often using their nests for roosting during the winter months.

Preferred habitat: Open damp meadows, marshes, salt-pans, banks of tidal rivers, etc., for feeding. Most Algarvian Storks use buildings or chimney stacks for nesting, although in the east they often use trees and on the west coast they use the cliffs and sea-stacks. It is tolerant of human presence, often nesting on buildings in the middle of cities, but avoids tall vegetation, fast-moving water, and dry or cold regions.

Food: Mainly mammals and insects, but also earthworms, reptiles, amphibians, birds' eggs or young, and other small animals. It catches the prey by stalking or probing.

Breeding: Most males, and often the pair, with an established nest remain all year, defending it against rivals. He stays on the nest for a large part of each day, often displaying by throwing his head over his back and bill-clattering, leaving only briefly to feed. Sub-adult males, breeding for the first time, choose a site and begin to build a nest, to which they attract a female with the same display. The pair constructs a large pile of branches and twigs, lined with grass or rubbish such as clothing, paper, plastic, etc., to which more material is added throughout the nesting season. One clutch of 4 eggs is laid in March or April, although young birds rarely lay in their first year after pairing. Incubation is by both sexes and takes nearly 5 weeks. When the adults change places at the nest, both sexes perform the head thrown over the back display and bill-clatter. The young are cared for and fed by regurgitation by both parents. Fledging takes 8-9 weeks, although the chicks can stand at 3 weeks old. The young become independent and leave the area 1-3 weeks later. Sub-adults usually do not start breeding until 3-5 years old, although they will pair and occupy a nest before this. The pair-bond is monogamous and often lasts for life, owing to the site-fidelity of both sexes.

Hints on recognition: This large black and white bird cannot be confused with any other species inhabiting Europe. It has a red bill and long red legs. In flight, the legs protrude well beyond the tail and the neck is stretched forward - unlike the herons and egrets which fly with the neck doubled back on itself.

58

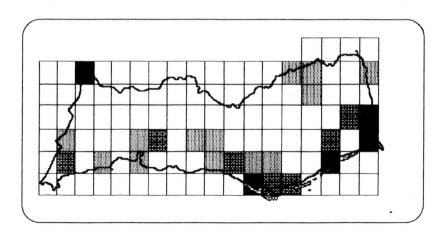

Hints on finding: Prominent nests can be seen at the eastern entrance to Lagos, at the start of the Praia da Rocha road west of Portimão, in Silves, on the chimney stack in Almancil, several in Olhão and Tavira, and numerous nests in and around Vila Real and the Castro Marim reserve.

Confirmation of breeding: As with the egrets, only probable and confirmed breeding are shown on the map, owing to this species feeding away from the nest-site.

Number of rectangles in which recorded: 25
Probable breeding: 0
Confirmed breeding: 25

ANAS STREPERA

GADWALL

Portuguese name: Frisada.

Distribution: The Gadwall breeds throughout the middle latitudes of Europe, Asia, and North America. Neither Coverley nor BWP shows this species as breeding in Portugal, but the national atlas recorded it in six areas in southern Portugal. In the Algarve, the only recorded breeding sites are Ludo and Quinta do Lago.

Status in the Western Palearctic: It has spread its range westwards and northwards, especially during this century, reaching as far as Iceland. In Portugal, it is presumed by CEMPA to be a recent breeder and increasing, as there is no mention of it at all by Coverley. In the Algarve it is certainly increasing, from no recorded breeding in the national atlas to approximately 40 pairs by the end of the field-work for the BBA. Those breeding in the Algarve are resident.

Preferred habitat: Shallow fresh water, either standing or slow-moving, with plenty of cover. It avoids marine or brackish waters, but is tolerant of human presence where it is not persecuted.

Food: Mainly underwater plants, which it obtains by swimming with its head under the water. Apparently, it grazes sometimes and parasitises other species of duck as well as Coot, although these forms of feeding behaviour have not been observed in the Algarve. Aquatic insects, small amphibians and fish, and molluscs are also taken, but probably by accident.

Breeding: Pair-bonds are usually formed whilst flocking during the winter prior to breeding and pairs can commonly be seen already bonded at Quinta do Lago in October-November. Groups of males display to watching females by variations on head/ tail bobbing, whilst calling loudly. Courtship flights may also be observed, where one or more females are chased by one or more males. By March, the pair has established a nesting territory, often based upon the female's nest-site of the previous year. The pair may also have preferred feeding and loafing areas, which will be defended as territories. The female makes a slight hollow in dense vegetation on the ground, close to water, and lines it with grass and leaves to form a low rim. During late April, she lines the nest with her own down and lays one clutch of 8-12 eggs. The male usually deserts his mate shortly after the completion of laying, and certainly by mid-incubation, so that incubation and the care of the young are carried out by the female alone. Incubation takes about 3 1/2 weeks and fledging 6-7 weeks. The chicks are able to swim and self-feed from hatching and become independent upon fledging. First breeding is at one year old. The pair-bond is mainly monogamous, although there is some promiscuity, and lasts until the first clutch is complete. If the clutch is lost, the female seeks a new mate for the replacement clutch.

Hints on recognition: It has the same general shape as the Mallard, but is slightly smaller. The male appears to be mid-grey all over, with some brown feathers on the back, jet black under the tail, and a panel of chestnut, black, and white on the side of the wing. The female is very similar to the Mallard female, but is greyer and lacks the blue and white panel of the Mallard (see that species). In flight, the Gadwall is the only duck in this region to show a broad white band covering the rear-half of the wing next to the body.

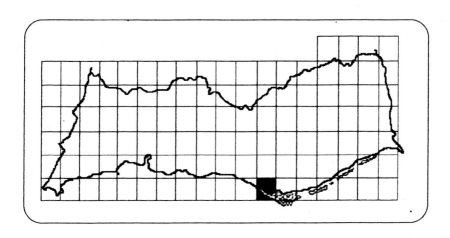

Hints on finding: This species can readily be seen at any time of the year from the hide at Quinta do Lago (see Where to watch breeding birds, E).

Confirmation of breeding: It is not known to breed outside of Ludo and Quinta do Lago.

Number of rectangles in which recorded: 1
Possible breeding: 0
Probable breeding: 0
Confirmed breeding: 1

ANAS PLATYRHYNCHOS

MALLARD

Portuguese name: Pato-real.

Distribution: The Mallard is to be found throughout the Northern Hemisphere, including Greenland and northern Alaska to the north and Hawaii to the south. It was introduced into Australasia in the 1860s. It bred in the Azores earlier this century, but has not been reported recently. In mainland Portugal, it breeds wherever there is a suitable habitat (CEMPA).

Status in the Western Palearctic: Although there have been some local increases, most populations are declining, probably owing to drainage of wetlands and to hunting pressures. In the Algarve, the eggs and young are often stolen by man to raise for food so that, together with its being extensively hunted in the winter, the species is restricted to areas which have difficult access or which are protected. It is resident in Portugal.

Preferred habitat: All kinds of slow-moving fresh and salt water, but it requires fairly still and shallow water for feeding. It avoids very deep water, fast-flowing rivers, water that is out of sight of land, and dry or rocky places. It is tolerant of human presence where it is not persecuted and will readily use artificial ponds.

Food: Almost anything, including vegetation, crops, invertebrates, small birds and mammals, fish, molluscs, etc. It will take plants and prey from water by swimming with its head below the surface, by diving, or by floating and picking food from the surface. On land, it will graze like geese, dig with its beak into the ground, and strip invertebrates and seeds (including cereals) from plants.

Breeding: Pair-formation occurs during the autumn and most birds are paired by October. The courtship display consists of variations on head and tail bobbing/shaking and is frequently performed by several males together, even when some are already paired. Courtship flights may also be observed where one or more males pursue a female, sometimes forcing her down and raping her. The female chooses the nest-site, which can be in a variety of habitats, including vegetation, ruined buildings, and holes high up in trees (10m or more), sometimes far from water. She makes a shallow nest of grass and leaves, lined with her own down, from February onwards, in which one clutch of 9-13 eggs is laid. Incubation is by the female alone and takes almost one month, during which time she is harassed and often raped by passing males everytime she leaves the nest to feed. The care of the young are also by the female alone, as the male deserts the nest and his mate shortly after the clutch is complete. Fledging takes 7-9 weeks, although the chicks are self-feeding and leave the nest within 24 hours of hatching. The young become independent shortly after fledging and breed for the first time at one year old. The pair-bond is basically monogamous, although the male is often promiscuous and will attempt to attract or rape other females whilst maintaining a firm pair-bond with its mate. Replacement clutches and pairing in subsequent years may or may not be with the same mate.

Hints on recognition: The male is unmistakable, with an emerald green head, white ring around the neck, chestnut breast, generally grey body, and bright red legs. The female is brown all over, except for a patch of white-blue-white on the side, and she also has red legs. In flight, both sexes show bands of white-blue-white on the wings.

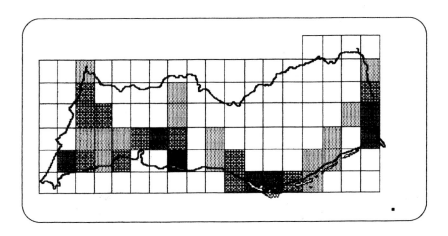

Hints on finding: Good views of this species can be obtained all year round from the hide at Quinta do Lago (see Where to watch breeding birds, E).

Confirmation of breeding: The map shows the species' preference for low-lying coastland and lowland rivers, with little colonisation of mountain reservoirs.

Number of rectangles in which recorded: 34
Possible breeding: 1
Probable breeding: 9
Confirmed breeding: 24

NETTA RUFINA

RED-CRESTED POCHARD

Portuguese name: Pato-de-bico-vermelho.

Distribution: The Red-crested Pochard breeds in Central Asia and at a few scattered sites in Europe. BWP showed no birds present in Portugal and the national atlas showed breeding in only one area, with about 30 pairs, just north of Lisbon. During the fieldwork for the BBA, successful breeding was proved at Quinta do Lago in the Ria Formosa Reserve.

Status in the Western Palearctic: It is so sparsely distributed in Europe that long-term variations in population density are difficult to assess. BWP (1977), however, states that numbers possibly declined during the last century but are now definitely increasing. Coverley makes no mention of this species. It is probably resident.

Preferred habitat: Small pools of fresh or saline water, with submerged vegetation as well as stands of emergent plants, e.g. reeds. It avoids water with trees in close proximity and prefers lowland regions. The site used in the Algarve was an artificial water-hazard, fringed by dense reeds, on a golf-course. It is tolerant of human presence.

Food: Mainly vegetative, including leaves, stems, seeds, and roots. It obtains the food by diving, swimming with its head below the surface, or up-ending. It also occasionally takes insects, amphibians, small fish, and molluscs.

Breeding: Pair-formation takes place during the autumn or winter, while the birds are still flocking. The courtship display is communal, involving several males to one female. It consists variously of bobbing, shaking, and flicking the head and tail, accompanied by wing flapping and loud calls. The male raises its crest and points the bill downwards, to present a rounded red head to the female. Males will also chase females in pursuit-flights. In spring, when the pair-formation is complete, the male further courts the female by bringing her food or twigs and this continues even after nesting has started. In April, the female makes a nest on the ground in deep cover close to the water. She forms a depression, which she then lines with fine plant material and her own down. One clutch of 8-10 eggs is laid. Often, the female lays her eggs in the nest of another female or in the nest of a different species of duck, especially the Mallard or the Gadwall. Incubation takes 4 weeks and is by the female alone, although unlike most ducks, the male helps to guard the nest and accompanies the female when she feeds. The female cares for the young, which are nidifugous, as the male deserts her and the nest shortly after the eggs have hatched. Fledging takes about 7 weeks, after which the young become independent. First breeding is at 1-2 years old. The pair-bond is monogamous, although there is often promiscuity and the males will rape unattended females. It lasts only until the chicks have hatched.

Hints on recognition: The male is unmistakable with his rounded reddish head, bright red beak, black chest and tail, brownish back, and white sides. The female is a soft brown on the upperparts, darker on the crown and nape, streaked brown on the underparts, and has a distinctive white throat and cheeks. In flight, the male shows a broad white band along the entire trailing edge of the wing, as well as one along the leading edge. The female also shows a broad white band on the trailing edge, the only brown duck breeding in this area to do so.

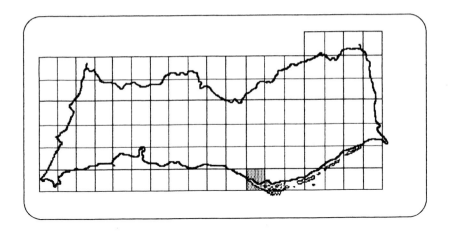

Hints on finding: This species can be observed throughout the year from the hide at Quinta do Lago (see Where to watch breeding birds, E), although they are difficult to see during the summer months when they remain amongst the reeds.

Confirmation of breeding: It has not been recorded away from its nesting area in the Ria Formosa.

Number of rectangles in which recorded: 1
Possible breeding: 0
Probable breeding: 0
Confirmed breeding: 1

ELANUS CAERULEUS

BLACK-SHOULDERED (BLACK-WINGED) KITE

Portuguese name: Peneireiro-cinzento.

Distribution: The Black-shouldered Kite is widely distributed in Africa, the Indian sub-continent, and South-east Asia. In the Western Palearctic, it breeds in small numbers in the Iberian Peninsula and in North Africa. In Portugal, it is to be found primarily in the central portion of the country, especially in the Alentejo where the habitat is particularly favourable for the species (CEMPA).

Status in the Western Palearctic: In North Africa, this Kite has declined considerably and is no longer to be found at many of its traditional breeding sites. As is so often the case with raptors, this decline has probably been caused by persecution and pesticides. This is counterbalanced, however, by an increase in numbers and expansion in range in both Spain and Portugal. From Coverley's accounts it would appear to have been very rare earlier this century, whereas it should now be considered not uncommon in the greater part of the Alentejo. In 1991, during the preparation of the BBA, breeding was proved for the first time in the Algarve. The species is mainly resident throughout its range.

Preferred habitat: This is without doubt open grassland, with scattered mature oaks for nesting and 'look-out posts'. It avoids forests and mountains, but will use cropland and marshes for hunting. The species is very sedentary and stays within the same habitat throughout the year.

Food: This Kite hunts by hovering or quartering the ground and dropping onto its prey of small mammals, birds, or reptiles. It will also use trees or fence-posts from which to drop onto prey or to catch large insects in flight. In Portugal, the Corn Bunting is apparently a favoured item of food (BWP 1980).

Breeding: Unlike most raptors, which have elaborate courtship displays, the pair of this species simply circles the chosen nest-site with slow, exaggerated wing-beats or 'plays tag' from tree to tree. In January or February, both sexes help to build the nest on the branch of a tree, although the male provides most of the material and the female constructs most of the nest. Each year, a completely new nest is made consisting of twigs, lined with roots and grass, which is added to throughout incubation. One clutch of 3-4 eggs is laid in early March, is incubated mainly by the female and takes nearly a month to hatch. The young are brooded by the female for the first week or so, after which both sexes hunt for food. Although the food for the young is caught by both parents, it is always the female who gives the food to the chicks, bill-to-bill, until they are able to feed themselves from what is brought to the nest. Fledging takes 7-8 weeks, but both parents continue to feed the young for some weeks afterwards. The age at which the young first breed is not known. The pair-bond is monogamous and continues after breeding, probably lasting for life.

Hints on recognition: It is barely larger than a Kestrel and has the same habit of hovering. It is mostly pale grey, however, with black shoulder-patches (seen from above) or black wing-tips (seen from below). Its colouring and method of hunting by quartering the ground resemble the male Hen Harrier, but its small size and short, slightly-forked tail, together with its persistent hovering, distinguish it.

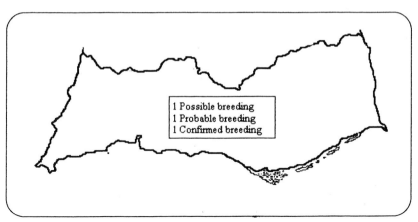

Hints on finding: Owing to the rarity and vulnerability of this species in the Algarve, no assistance is given in this section.

Confirmation of breeding: There is one confirmed breeding record for the western half of the Algarve and one probable breeding record for the eastern half. A further pair, which could possibly be breeding, was observed near the confirmed western nest-site. For reasons of security, the map shows only centralized information.

Number of rectangles in which recorded:	2
Possible breeding pairs:	1
Probable breeding pairs:	1
Confirmed breeding pairs:	1

MILVUS MIGRANS

BLACK KITE

Portuguese name: Milhafre-preto.

Distribution: The Black Kite breeds in most of Europe, Asia, Africa, and Australia. It is well distributed throughout Portugal, (CEMPA). Both BWP and the national atlas show this species breeding only in the north-eastern corner of the Algarve, whereas the fieldwork for the BBA found it also in the northern mountains.

Status in the Western Palearctic: There has been some recent extension in the range of this species to the west and north of Europe, possibly owing to pollution provid-ing more dead fish, possibly owing to more extensive protection, but it has decreased markedly in some parts of south-eastern Europe. In Portugal, Coverley refers to the Red Kite as the more common of the two kites, although it is apparently quite the reverse today (CEMPA). It is a summer migrant, wintering mainly in Ethiopian Africa.

Preferred habitat: Lakes, rivers, and wetlands with some trees. It will also use small reservoirs and sheltered coastal waters, and even open country far from water. It avoids the open sea, high moun-tains, and dense forests. It is particularly tolerant, for a raptor, of human disturbance and will ignore most human activities whilst feeding.

Food: The traditional food of this raptor is carrion, including dying or diseased animals or fish, but it will eat virtually any animal matter. It will harass other birds, including large eagles, until they drop or disgorge their food; it will steal fish from the nests of herons; it is adept at snatching small prey from the ground or from water; it will search on foot for insects, small rodents, nestlings, reptiles, etc.; and it will take scraps and offal from fishing-boats.

Breeding: Individuals return to the breeding grounds in March, older birds re-uniting with their mates from the previous year on their old eyries..Unpaired males soar and call over prospective nest-sites until a female is attracted. Courtship displays include flying close together, the male above the female, then the female rolls onto her back and briefly touches talons with the male. Some-times the pair grasps talons more firmly in flight, resulting in their tumbling and spirally downwards until just above the ground or trees. In April, the male builds a new nest, or refurbishes an old one, in a tree or on a ledge of a cliff. It is made from twigs and lined with rubbish, such as paper, plastic, clothes, etc. One clutch of 2-3 eggs is laid. Incubation is mainly by the female and takes 4-5 weeks, the male bringing food to the female while she incubates. The young are cared for by both parents and fledging takes 6 weeks. During the first week after hatch-ing, the young are brooded and fed by the female, the male bringing the food. Later, both sexes hunt. The young become inde-pendent 6-7 weeks after fledging and breed for the first time at 3 years old or later. The pair-bond is monogamous and is re-formed each year at the eyrie.

Hints on recognition: This raptor is slightly larger in body-length than the Buzzard ,with which it is most likely to be confused, but has almost 50% greater wing-span and a longer tail. When perched, it appears to be entirely medium-brown, whereas the Buzzard is always pale, almost white, with streaking on the throat, chest, and under the tail. The tail of the Kite is forked when perched and bow-shaped when in flight.

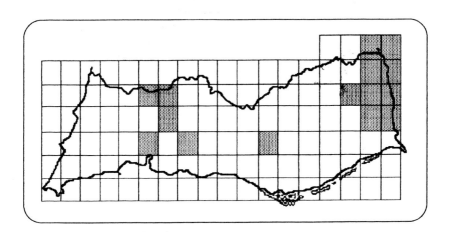

Hints on finding: This Kite can almost invariably be seen on the Guadiana River at Alcoutim. A tarmac road runs southwards from Alcoutim, along the bank of the Guadiana to Odeleite, from which several birds can usually be seen hunting together with the Red Kite *Milvus milvus*.

Confirmation of breeding: As with most raptors, the territories for this species cross the boundaries of the BBA rectangles. Therefore, every rectangle which is used by breeding birds, regardless of whether it contains an eyrie or not, is marked equally on the map. This also helps to conceal the whereabouts of eyries and to protect the species.

Number of rectangles in which recorded: 15
Confirmed breeding: 2

CIRCAETUS GALLICUS

SHORT-TOED EAGLE

Portuguese name: Águia-cobreira.

Distribution: The Short-toed Eagle breeds in all temperate latitudes of the Western Palearctic, the adjoining regions of Central and S.W. Asia, and the Indian sub-continent. In Europe, it is restricted to the south and east. It is well-distributed throughout the southern two-thirds of Portugal (CEMPA).

Status in the Western Palearctic: It has declined drastically in Europe during the last century and is still declining, becoming extinct in many regions, possibly due to persecution and environmental changes. In Portugal, however, it would appear to be more common now than it was in the first half of this century (CEMPA). In the Algarve, the population is estimated to be about 50 pairs (L. Palma). It is mainly a summer migrant, wintering in the northern tropics of Africa, although individuals can be seen throughout the winter.

Preferred habitat: The lower to middle altitudes of the Serras, avoiding the littoral, the Barrocal, and the tops of mountains. It favours fairly open terrain with some mature trees for nesting, but it will use forests where there are sufficient clearings in which to hunt. It is tolerant of occasional human presence on its hunting grounds, but leaves the nest readily.

Food: Mainly reptiles, especially snakes. Occasionally, it will also take small birds, mammals, invertebrates, and fresh carrion (it has been seen to take dead fish and even the leg of a kid). It catches its prey by hovering or by quartering the ground, but will also use a perch from which to strike.

Breeding: Established pairs return in late January or early February to the nesting grounds of the previous year and re-unite at the eyrie, although a new nest may be built subsequently. Sub-adults return a little later. The male chooses and defends a territory, which includes a feeding area and a potential nest-site. Both sexes perform courtship displays, involving swooping and dipping flights, calling repeatedly, during which the male will often carry a snake or twig. The nest is sited in a tree, usually hidden at the top although it has been recorded on a low exposed branch and even on the ground. It is constructed of twigs, with a deep cup lined with vegetation, the male bringing most of the material whilst the female builds. One clutch of one egg is laid. Incubation takes nearly 7 weeks and is by the female alone, although the male occasionally helps. The chick is cared for by both sexes and fledging takes 10-11 weeks. Both parents hunt and bring food to the nest, although only the female feeds the chick. The young is dependent upon the parents for several weeks after fledging and associates with them until the winter, when it migrates separately. First breeding is probably at 3 or 4 years old at least. The pair-bond is monogamous and is renewed each year.

Hints on recognition: In Europe, this species can only be confused with the Osprey (for which, see that species), but habitat and feeding methods are different and it is noticeably larger if both species are seen together. When perched, it appears to be mostly brown, including the throat and breast, with no markings on the head, contrasting with a pale streaked belly. In flight, when seen from below, it appears all white with fine horizontal stripes over the entire bird and a prominent 'hood' effect from the dark head, neck and breast. Its call resembles that of a gull. It is the only large raptor to hover frequently, often appearing to hang in the air over the hills.

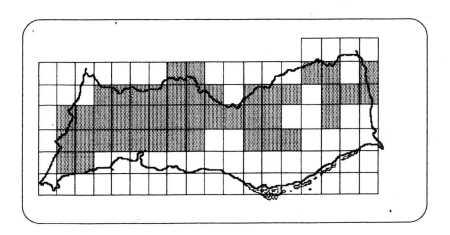

Hints on finding: It is far more common in the western Algarve than in the east, especially on the southern slopes of the Serra de Monchique. The roads running south to north, such as the one skirting the Bravura (Odiaxere) Barragem, the one from Penina to Casais, and the one from Odelouca to Alferce, cross suitable country. A scan of the sky with binoculars from a vantage point will often produce good views of this eagle.

Confirmation of breeding: See the Black Kite for a general explanation of the map. There are approximately 50 pairs breeding in the Algarve (L.Palma).

Number of rectangles in which recorded: 44
Confirmed breeding: 16

71

CIRCUS CYANEUS

HEN HARRIER

Portuguese name: Tartaranhão-azulado.

Distribution: The Hen Harrier breeds in the middle and upper latitudes of Europe and North America, the south and west of South America, and in northern Asia. Although the national atlas proved breeding in N.W. Portugal and probable nesting in the Alentejo, no breeding had been proved in the Algarve prior to the BBA.

Status in the Western Palearctic: This species has declined considerably during the last century in Europe and appears to be still declining, probably owing to pesticides and human persecution, the latter because of this bird's tendency to eat young game birds. It is stable or increasing, however, in some parts of northern Europe. In Portugal, it is less common than it was formerly, when Coverley mentions nests at Coimbra and in the Alentejo. It is resident but dispersive in the Iberian Peninsula, with numbers augmented in the winter by migrants.

Preferred habitat: Open terrain with short herbage. It avoids woodlands, steep mountains, and marshland, although it will feed along the edges of these habitats. In the Algarve, it particularly favours the steppe-like grasslands of the north-east.

Food: Small or young birds, and rodents. It hunts its prey by quartering the ground, pouncing on voles and songbirds. It often uses the edges of habitats to catch its prey unawares and will sometimes take flying birds in active pursuit. Large insects, such as locusts, and other animal-life are very occasionally taken.

Breeding: Both sexes return to the breeding grounds in March, the males arriving slightly earlier than the females. The male displays by swooping flights and aerial switchbacks, over a suitable nesting habitat until a female is attracted. Later, courtship displays include aerial passing of food from the male to the female. The female, flying lower than the male, rolls onto her back and either takes food directly from him, talons to talons, or he drops it for her to catch. In April, the female constructs a pile of vegetation on the ground in thick cover, in which one clutch of 4-6 eggs is laid. Incubation takes 1 month and is by the female alone, the male bringing food to the nest. Fledging takes 5-6 weeks, the female brooding and feeding the chicks, whilst the male catches all the food at first. Later both parents hunt. The young become independent a few weeks after fledging and breed for the first time at 2 or 3 years old. The pair-bond is mainly monogamous, although there is a strong tendency for the males to be polygamous. It is of seasonal duration only and often the male deserts the young when they are large enough for the female to leave them and hunt.

Hints on recognition: The male and female look totally different from one another, but both look very similar to the counterpart sexes of the Montagu's Harrier (for which, see that species). The female is dark brown above with a white rump and prominent black bands on the tail. When seen in flight from below, the overall colour is buff with heavy streaking on the body, whereas the female Montagu's Harrier has greyer flight-feathers. The male is very pale grey with a white rump and black tips to the wings, above and below. Harriers have long slender wings and tail, are about one third larger than a Kestrel, and have particularly bouyant flight, with long powerful wing-beats. They almost always hunt by quartering.

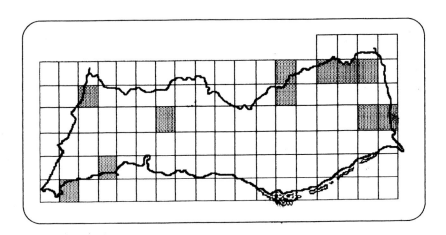

Hints on finding: The easiest place to see this species is near Azinhal (see Where to watch breeding birds, G), although the most common Harrier in the area is the Montagu's and therefore care should be taken in identification.

Confirmation of breeding: See the Black Kite for a general explanation of the map.

Number of rectangles in which recorded: 11
Confirmed breeding: 1

CIRCUS PYGARGUS

MONTAGU'S HARRIER

Portuguese name: Tartaranhão-caçador.

Distribution: The Montagu's Harrier breeds in the temperate latitudes of the Western Palearctic and Central Asia only. It is well distributed throughout Portugal, wherever there is suitable habitat.

Status in the Western Palearctic: This species has declined in many parts of its range, probably owing to pollution, pesticides, climatic changes, persecution, and habitat destruction. It was considered by Coverley to be not common anywhere in Portugal, whereas it is in fact fairly common today in the Alentejo, despite the increasing mechanization of farming (CEMPA). The national atlas did not prove breeding in the Algarve, but there were two 'probable' areas shown in the north-east and the BBA has confirmed breeding there. It is a summer migrant, wintering in Ethiopian Africa.

Preferred habitat: Open grassland or low sparse scrub, with few or no trees. It particularly favours the flat or gently rolling grasslands of the north-eastern Algarve and will frequently use corn-fields. It will also use damp areas, such as broad river valleys and marshes, but avoids swamps and open water. It is not tolerant of human presence and readily deserts the nest if disturbed.

Food: Mainly small mammals and birds, especially larks and the Corn Bunting, but also eggs, reptiles, and large insects (Hiraldo et al 1975). It hunts by quartering the ground and then swooping onto its prey or catching it in fast pursuit. It will occasionally hover briefly or hunt from the ground.

Breeding: Individuals return to the breeding grounds in March, sometimes the males before the females but often the pairs arrive together. The male displays over the nest-site by soaring quite high (up to 1km), then dropping in a series of spirals or plunges, with the wings and tail spread, until he reaches the nest. The courtship display includes the pair flying close together, the male higher than the female, then the female rolling onto her back and touching talons with the male. In April, the female constructs a nest, on the ground amongst tall vegetation, from locally available plant-matter. One clutch of 4-5 eggs is laid. Incubation takes 4 weeks and is by the female alone, the male bringing food to her. The chicks are cared for and fed directly by the female, the male bringing the food to the nest at first then later both sexes hunting. Fledging takes 5-6 weeks and the young become independent soon after. The age of first breeding is 2 years old for females and 3 years old for males, although breeding may be attempted before that. The pair-bond is monogamous, but polygyny often occurs. It is of seasonal duration only, although the pair may re-unite owing to site-fidelity.

Hints on recognition: This Harrier is very similar to the Hen Harrier (for which, see that species). The male is entirely light grey, with black tips to the under and upper sides of the wings. It differs from the Hen Harrier in having a narrow black horizontal band along the upper wing, two bands on the under wing, and no white on the rump. The female is dark brown above with a white rump and a strongly banded tail. She is virtually indistinguishable from the female Hen Harrier except when seen closely in flight from below, when a slight contrast can be observed between the greyish flight feathers and the buff body and fore-wing. Both sexes have the long narrow wings and tail typical of Harriers, but, when seen with Hen Harriers, are slimmer and have a more buoyant flight.

M

F

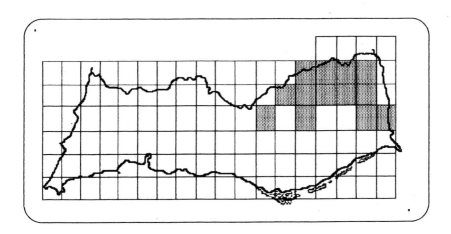

Hints on finding: Several birds can almost always be observed hunting near Azinhal (see Where to watch breeding birds, G, on the channel between areas 4 and 5). Also, any of the tracks leading north or south through the grasslands along the Martim Longo to Alcoutim road will often produce hunting harriers.

Confirmation of breeding: See the Black Kite for a general explanation of the map.

Number of rectangles in which recorded: 13
Confirmed breeding: 3

ACCIPITER GENTILIS

GOSHAWK

Portuguese name: Açor.

Distribution: The Goshawk breeds throughout the upper and middle latitudes of the Northern Hemisphere. It is mainly confined to the northern half of Portugal, although the national atlas confirmed breeding at two localities in the Alentejo and the BBA suspected breeding in the Algarve.

Status in the Western Palearctic: It has declined drastically in Europe during the last century and the early part of this century and, despite recoveries in some areas, is still declining. These declines may be due to pollution in the north and to reduction in prey in Spain, whereas the recoveries have been helped by afforestation. In Portugal, Reis Jr. and Coverley referred to this species as rare or scarce and BWP shows it as entirely absent except in winter. The national atlas found breeding in 9 areas and it is thought that 5 pairs breed in the Algarve (L.Palma). It is resident in Europe.

Preferred habitat: Forests, including eucalyptus. It favours woodlands with some open areas, such as clearings, breaks or tracks, streams, and fields, and will tolerate extensive close forests where such open areas are present. It avoids open country. It is tolerant of some human presence in its feeding area, but not near the nest-site.

Food: Mainly birds and mammals, but it will also take fish and insects. In many areas, the most commonly caught prey is the Wood Pigeon and this is probably the case in the Algarve. It catches its prey by swift aerial pursuit, taking advantage of close cover to approach and take the passing animal by surprise. It will also stoop onto its prey from a great height like the Peregrine or swoop from a hidden perch.

Breeding: The female tends to stay near the eyrie all year, whilst the male moves away for the autumn and winter months. In March the female advertises her territory by calling loudly and performing aerial displays, spiralling high and then dropping in loops or plunging with wings closed to the nesting area. Older males return to the mate and nest-site of the year before, whilst young ones are attracted to unmated advertising females. Both sexes help to build or repair a nest of branches and twigs, lined with soft greenery, high in a tree. Established pairs may have two or more nests which are re-used in succession. One clutch of 3-4 eggs is laid. Incubation takes just over 5 weeks and is mainly by the female, whilst the male brings her food. The young are cared for and fed by the female alone, the male provisioning the nest, although the female will hunt when the chicks are large if the male brings insufficient food. Fledging takes 5-6 weeks and the young become independent at about 10 weeks old. First breeding is at 2-3 years old. The pair-bond is monogamous and of seasonal duration, although the pair usually re-unite at the eyrie in successive years.

Hints on recognition: This hawk can only be confused with the female Sparrowhawk (for which, see that species). Both species have short rounded wings and relatively long tails, which are diagnostic for the hawk family, and are heavily barred over the entire undersides. The female Goshawk is much larger than the male, being almost as large as a Buzzard and therefore readily identifiable. The male Goshawk, however, is about the same size as a female Sparrowhawk. If seen clearly from below, note the deep 'pigeon' breast of the Goshawk, the wavy 'S' shape to the trailing edge of the wing, and broad black ear-coverts.

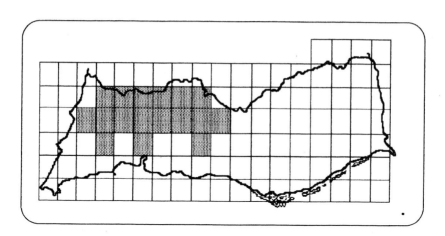

Hints on finding: This is probably one of the most difficult species to find, owing to the speed with which it moves through deep forests. The optimum time to look for it is early in the morning in March, when the females are advertising. Her call, which has been described as 'chattering' and 'wailing', can be heard as much as a kilometre away.

Confirmation of breeding: See the Black Kite for a general explanation of the map. Although breeding was not definitely proved during the fieldwork for this book, it is believed that 5 pairs probably breed in the Algarve

Number of rectangles in which recorded: 17
Probable breeding: 5

ACCIPITER NISUS

SPARROWHAWK

Portuguese name: Gavião da Europa.

Distribution: The Sparrowhawk breeds in most of Europe, the north coast of Africa, northern Asia, and the Himalayas. It is apparently more widely spread in northern Portugal than in the south (CEMPA).

Status in the Western Palearctic: It decreased drastically during the last century and the early part of this century, mainly as a result of persecution by game interests. Although protection has aided recovery in many areas, this has been offset by pesticides killing the adults and reducing hatching success. In Portugal, Coverley stated that this species was common, especially around Oporto, whereas the national atlas shows none breeding there now. It is still not uncommon in the Algarve (L. Palma). It is resident.

Preferred habitat: Woodlands with numerous open areas, e.g. clearings, rides and wide tracks, as well as open terrain with copses or belts of trees. It avoids both unbroken forests and treeless countryside. It will tolerate marshland, mountains, and agricultural land where there are sufficient trees for its needs.

Food: Almost entirely birds, especially small passerines. Despite the prejudices of game interests, BWP (1980) states that game species have accounted for less than 1% of the prey taken in various studies. Small mammals are also occasionally taken. When hunting, it either perches in a hidden place or flies low along the edge of trees, relying on surprise to catch unwary birds. If the prey tries to avoid capture by rising quickly, the hawk may roll upside down and catch it from beneath, or if it goes into ground cover it may be pursued on foot. This hawk also stoops from a great height onto prey below.

Breeding: In April or earlier, both sexes return to the traditional nesting area. The female chooses the nest-site and advertises it by calling loudly and performing aerial displays, which may include spiralling high and then dropping in loops or plunging with wings closed to the nesting area. The male answers her calls, forming a courtship duet. The pair builds a new nest of twigs each year, in the main canopy of a tree. One clutch of 4-6 eggs is laid in late April or early May. Incubation takes 6 weeks and is by the female alone, the male bringing her food. The young are cared for and fed by the female, the male provisioning the nest. The male hunts alone until the young are at least well-grown, although the female will also hunt near the end of the fledging period. Fledging takes about a month and the young become independent 3-4 weeks later. First breeding is at 2 years old. The pair-bond is monogamous and of seasonal duration only, although the pair will often re-unite at the nest-site in subsequent years.

Hints on recognition: This species is a typical hawk, having short rounded wings, a relatively long tail, and strong horizontal bars over the entire underside. The female is much larger than the male (as much as 25% bigger), being about as long as a Tawny Owl, whereas the male is barely larger than a Blackbird. When perched, the male is distinctive, being blue-grey to slate-grey on the upperparts, rufous-and-white barred on all the underparts. In flight, the rufous and white body and under-wing, contrasting with light grey flight feathers barred with brown, is distinctive. The female strongly resembles the male Goshawk in size and plumage (see that species for differences).

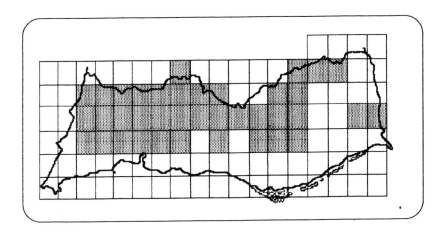

Hints on finding: This species is frequently observed in the hills in winter, spiralling on a thermal or hunting low over the ground, but is rarely seen during the breeding season. It may most easily be found in the early morning in April, when the female is advertising, although the call is rather similar to that of the Goshawk.

Confirmation of breeding: See the Black Kite for a general explanation of the map. It is believed that there are approximately 100 pairs breeding in the Algarve, mostly in the western half (L.Palma).

Number of rectangles in which recorded: 38
Confirmed: 4

BUTEO BUTEO

BUZZARD

Portuguese name: Águia-de-asa-redonda.

Distribution: The Buzzard breeds throughout Europe and northern Asia, except the extreme north, as well as in south-west Asia and the Atlantic archipelagos of the Azores, the Canaries, Madeira, and the Cape Verde Islands. It is well distributed in all parts of Portugal (CEMPA). The BBA found it in all suitable habitats in the Algarve.

Status in the Western Palearctic: It declined drastically during the last century and the first half of this one, owing to heavy persecution by game interests. There have been recoveries recently in some areas with protection, but it is still extensively (and illegally) shot or trapped, preventing full recovery. In Portugal, it is fairly common everywhere, being most common in the Alentejo (CEMPA). It is widespread in the hills of the Algarve, especially in the north-east, and numbers would appear to be stable. It is resident but dispersive.

Preferred habitat: Mixed woodland and open country, such as woods with numerous large clearings or grassland with copses. It prefers oakwoods but will also use conifers or eucalyptus. It avoids treeless terrain and areas which are difficult for its hunting techniques, e.g. tall crops. It is tolerant of human disturbance where it is not persecuted.

Food: Almost any animals, including carrion. In most studies of its diet, rodents form the predominant quarry, followed by birds (mainly young ones), then lizards and invertebrates. When hunting in flight, it soars over open terrain until an animal is seen, then swoops onto it. It will also use a perch from which to scan the ground or will search for invertebrates on foot.

Breeding: The male, shortly joined by the female, re-asserts or takes possession of a nesting area by circling high over the tree, frequently dropping vertically or rolling in undulating flight. The pair perform these mutual courtship displays, calling loudly to one another, until the nest is complete. The pair builds a bulky nest of branches, lined with greenery, in a tree or occasionally on a rocky ledge. An established pair will have several nests, which are changed each year or may be used in successive years. One clutch of 2-4 eggs is laid in March. Incubation takes about 5 weeks and can be by both sexes or by the female alone. The young are cared for and fed mainly by the female, who never leaves them alone for the first 2 weeks. At first the male hunts and provisions the nest, then, when the young are about half-grown, both parents hunt. Fledging takes 7-8 weeks and the young become independent 6-8 weeks later. First breeding is at 3 years old. The pair-bond is monogamous and often lasts for life.

Hints at recognition: In size it is smaller than the eagles, although it is superficially similar in colour and behaviour. It has relatively broader wings and a shorter tail than any of the small eagles and frequently "mews" like a cat. The plumage is very variable, but is most commonly medium-brown on the upperparts and lighter brown on the underparts with paler throat and belly. In flight, when seen from below, the body and fore-part of the wings appear brown whilst the flight-feathers and tail appear light grey, often with a prominent dark patch on the carpal joint. Note that the similar Honey Buzzard *Pernis apivorus* never raises its wings above the horizontal when soaring, unlike the Buzzard.

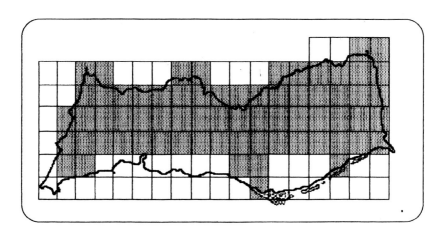

Hints on finding: This species can be found in any broken woodland in the hills, but it is more common in the east than in the west. A drive in the Serra de Caldeirão to a good vantage point in March or April will usually find displaying adults. The plaintive mewing call can be heard at some distance and pinpoints the presence of these birds.

Confirmation of breeding: See the Black Kite for a general explanation of the map. It is more common in the east than in the west.

Number of rectangles in which recorded: 68
Confirmed: 27

AQUILA RAPAX

STEPPE EAGLE

Portuguese name: Águia-rapace.

Distribution: There are two distinct racial groups for this species, the Tawny Eagle *Aquila r. rapax* (and other subspecies) and the Steppe Eagle *A. r. orientalis* (and other subspecies). As the pair breeding in the Algarve belong to the second group, only the characteristics of the Steppe Eagle are discussed in the BBA. The Steppe Eagle breeds in eastern Europe and Central Asia. The Algarvian pair are 'escapes' from the Falconry Centre - first the adult female escaped, then the young male was released. There are no other birds of this species known to be breeding in western Europe.

Status in the Western Palearctic: In its natural range, it has retreated eastwards and is now only found in the extreme east of the Western Palearctic. It is normally a summer migrant, wintering in eastern and southern Africa. The Algarvian pair appears to be sedentary, although the young do not appear to remain in the region.

Preferred habitat: As its name suggests, this Eagle normally breeds on the Steppes. In the Algarve, hoever, the preferred habitat is mountainous country with broken woodlands or scattered trees, possibly because this habitat affords protection from persecution. The female is tolerant of human presence and will approach, although not very closely, when called by her name. The male avoids humans and is rarely seen.

Food: It takes a wide range of animal food. It has been observed taking small mammals, birds, reptiles including snakes, freshwater fish, invertebrates, and amphibians. It hunts fish and land-dwelling prey mainly by soaring and dropping on to it, although it will also hunt on foot or from a perch.

Breeding: The nest in the Algarve had not been discovered by the end of the fieldwork for this book, therefore the following details of breeding have been taken mainly from BWP (1980) and may not apply to the Algarve. The male advertises his territory by soaring and undulating flight over the eyrie, while calling loudly. In March, the pair builds a nest of twigs, lined with grass, fur and hair, in a tree or on a crag. The male provides most of the material with which the female constructs the nest. One clutch of 1-3 eggs is laid in April. Incubation takes 6 1/2 weeks and is by the female alone, the male bringing her food. The young are cared for and fed by the female only, the male provisioning the nest. When the young are well-grown, the female will also hunt, although it is rare that more than one chick survives to this stage owing to sibling canabalism. Fledging takes 8-9 weeks and the young become independent about 6 weeks later. The age of first breeding is not known, but is probably at least 3 years old. The pair-bond is certainly monogamous and for life in the Algarve.

Hints on recognition: The adults are the only raptors in this region to be totally dark brown when seen from above or below, with no markings whatsoever. The species is typical of soaring raptors, having long broad wings and a short tail. It is larger than a Buzzard, having approx. 50% greater wingspan, and slightly smaller than Golden and Imperial Eagles. The juveniles and immatures are distinctive, when seen from below, having a broad white band separating the rufous brown body and fore-wing from the black flight-feathers and tail. This race is totally different in appearance from the smaller North-African race, the Tawny Eagle *A. r. belisarius*, which is tawny-brown and black.

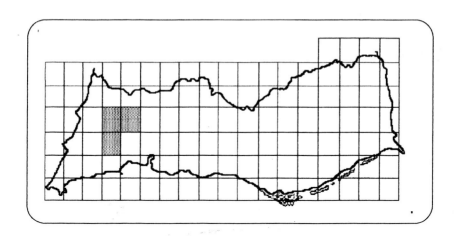

Hints on finding: Owing to the scarcity and vulnerability of this species in the Algarve, no help is given in this section.

Confirmation of breeding: Although no nest was found during the fieldwork for this book, a juvenile has been observed in the area which is known to contain the pair. See the Black Kite for an explanation of the map.

Number of rectangles in which recorded: 3
Confirmed breeding pairs: 1

AQUILA HELIACA

IMPERIAL EAGLE

Portuguese name: Águia-imperial.

Distribution: The Imperial Eagle breeds in the Iberian Peninsula, eastern Europe and Turkey, occasionally in Israel, and Central Asia. It is to be found in the southern half of Portugal only (CEMPA).

Status in the Western Palearctic: The range of this species has shrunk drastically during the last 100 years and is still decreasing, mainly owing to habitat destruction, pollution, and pesticides, as well as myxomatosis killing its favoured food the rabbit. It has become extinct in many areas where it formerly bred and is classified as an endangered species in Europe. In Portugal, the national atlas found signs of breeding in only five locations. In the Algarve, one pair bred annually until the fieldwork for the BBA commenced. It is thought that the pair is still in the area, although further breeding has not been proved (L.Palma). The Iberian population is resident.

Preferred habitat: Open parkland or areas with mixed grassland and woodland. It normally avoids mountains and extensive forests, but in the Algarve it has been forced by human pressures to accept these habitats. It will not tolerate treeless terrain, but it is fearless of man and freely enters agricultural areas, which leads to its persecution.

Food: Medium-sized mammals, especially rabbits. It will also take carrion and medium-sized birds, and occasionally reptiles. It hunts by soaring or by swooping from a perch. The prey is killed on the ground as this eagle is not agile or fast enough to catch it in aerial pursuit.

Breeding: Pair-formation occurs whilst the birds are still in sub-adult plumage, i.e. before their fifth year. The male advertises the potential eyrie by soaring and calling loudly over the site. When a female is attracted, he performs undulating displays over his whole territory, as well as plunging and rolling with wings closed, dropping almost to the trees. The female often joins him and the pair displays together, including mutual touching of talons. In January or February, the pair builds a large nest of branches and twigs, lined with greenery, fur, and debris, in a large tree. Established pairs may have several nests which are used and re-used in different years. One clutch of 2-3 eggs is laid. Incubation takes 6 weeks and is by both sexes, although the female takes the larger share. The young are cared for and fed by both sexes, the female brooding when the chicks are small, whilst the male hunts. Fledging takes 9-11 weeks and the young remain a further 2-3 weeks near the nest. Usually only one chick survives to fledge, owing to sibling rivalry, but two will often survive if food is abundant. The pair-bond is monogamous and lasts for life.

Hints on recognition: When perched this dark-brown eagle shows conspicuous light cream on the upper part of its head and neck as well as a prominent white band on its 'shoulders'. In flight, it appears all black when observed from below; however, from above the cream head, white shoulders and pale-grey rump are diagnostic. The juvenile, when seen in flight from below, is tawny brown on the body and fore-wings, contrasting with black flight-feathers and tail. When seen soaring at a distance, it can be distinguished from the Golden Eagle by the way it holds the wings absolutely horizontal instead of a very shallow 'V'. Only the Iberian race *A. h. adalberti*, often called the Spanish Imperial Eagle, has the prominent white shoulder patches.

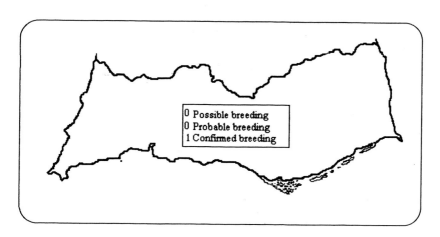

| 0 Possible breeding |
| 0 Probable breeding |
| 1 Confirmed breeding |

Hints on finding: Owing to the extreme vulnerability of this threatened species, no help is given in this section.

Confirmation of breeding: See under 'Status'. A further sub-adult pair was seen near the border of the Algarve, but it is not known whether it bred within the Algarve. The map is shaded with information centralised to protect the whereabouts of this species.

Number of rectangles in which recorded: 3
Confirmed breeding pairs: 1

AQUILA CHRYSAETOS

GOLDEN EAGLE

Portuguese name: Águia-real.

Distribution: The Golden Eagle breeds almost everywhere in the Northern Hemisphere. In Europe, it is well-distributed wherever there is suitable habitat and sufficient protection. BWP and the national atlas show this species breeding in the extreme north of Portugal only.

Status in the Western Palearctic: There was a marked decline in this species during the last century, owing to persecution. It has recovered recently in some area, following protection, but has become extinct or is still declining in other areas. According to Reis Jr., it was more common and widespread in Portugal in the early part of this century than it is today. The BBA proved breeding for two pairs in the Algarve, with the probability of a further pair. It is resident.

Preferred habitat: Remote mountains, largely inaccessible to man. It avoids wetlands and dense forests, as well as narrow gorges where it cannot make use of thermals to soar and gain height. It is generally not tolerant of human disturbance and will desert the nest if approached too often.

Food: Mainly mammals and birds, but it will also take reptiles and carrion, as well as fish and insects occasionally. It usually hunts by quartering the ground methodically and pouncing on its prey in a quick rush. It rarely takes birds in aerial pursuit or by stalking on foot, but it will use a perch from which to swoop onto passing animals.

Breeding: The male establishes a territory whilst still in sub-adult plumage, by soaring and calling loudly over the prospective nest-site. It may be a year or more before a female is attracted, during which time the male stays within the territory, which is usually about 50 km^2 but can be as much as 600 km^2 or more. The courtship display consists of the pair soaring and swooping together, as well as aerial play and mock attacks. The female chooses a site for the eyrie on a cliff-ledge, or occasionally in a tree. The pair builds the large nest from branches and twigs, lined with greenery and wool. Established pairs have several nests, which are used and re-used in successive years, all of which may be refurbished before one is chosen. One clutch of 2 eggs is laid in February or March. Incubation takes 6 weeks or more and is mainly by the female, the eggs being left unattended while she hunts. The young are cared for and fed by both parents, although almost always only one chick survives to fledge as the elder usually kills and eats the younger sibling. Fledging takes about 10 weeks and the young become independent about 3 months later. The age of first breeding is probably 3 or 4 years old. The pair-bond is monogamous and lasts for life.

Hints on recognition: This is the largest eagle in Europe, having the body 50% larger and the wings 75% longer than the Buzzard. It is dark brown, almost black, except for a light brown band across the middle of the wings and light brown (golden) on the upper part of the head and neck. In flight, when seen from below, it appears all dark except for a light brown patch at the base of the tail. When seen soaring at a distance, it can be distinguished from the Imperial Eagle (for which, see that species) by the way it holds the wings slightly above the horizontal in a very shallow 'V', instead of horizontal.

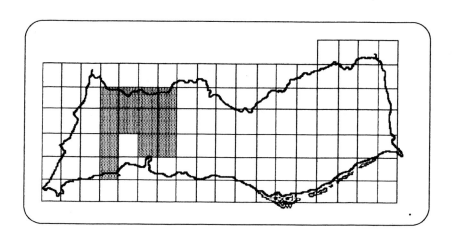

Hints on finding: Owing to the vulnerability of this species, no help is given in this section.

Confirmation of breeding: The map is shaded, centralised on the western Algarve, to protect the whereabouts of this species.

Number of rectangles in which recorded: 12
Probable breeding pairs: 1
Confirmed breeding pairs: 2

HIERAAETUS PENNATUS

BOOTED EAGLE

Portuguese name: Águia-calçada.

Distribution: The Booted Eagle breeds in most of southern and eastern Europe, as well as Central Asia, northern Africa and South Africa. In Portugal, it is mainly confined to the centre of the country, especially in the Alentejo (CEMPA).

Status in the Western Palearctic: In some areas it is increasing whilst in others it is decreasing, for reasons apparently unknown. In Spain there are about 9000 pairs and the population is believed to be increasing (BWP 1980). The status in Portugal is not clear, although it would appear to be fairly common in the Alentejo (L.Palma). There has not yet been any proved breeding in the Algarve. It is a summer migrant, wintering in Africa south of the Sahara.

Preferred habitat: Open oakwoods in hilly countryside. It favours areas with mixed scrub, grassland, and woods, avoiding extensive unbroken forests and treeless terrain. It is tolerant of human activity within its hunting territory.

Food: Mainly birds, lizards, and small mammals, but it will also take insects. It hunts birds by diving into the trees or bushes and chasing the prey through the branches. It will also soar over more open country, attacking its prey on the ground.

Breeding: Birds arrive in the Algarve in March, on migration to more northerly sites or to take up territory. Either the male or the female will advertise the territory by soaring and calling over the potential nest-site. Mutual courtship displays are conspicuous and noisy, including aerial loop-the-loops, undulations, rolls, talon-touching and wing-shaking. The pair constructs a large flat nest of branches and twigs, lined with greenery, in a tree, although a crag is sometimes used. Old nests, either their own or those of other species, are often re-used in successive years. One clutch of 2 eggs is laid in April. Incubation takes 5 1/2 weeks and is mainly by the female, the male bringing her food. The young are cared for and fed by both parents, although the female carries out the major share of duties whilst they are small. Two chicks are sometimes reared, but usually only one survives owing to sibling rivalry and canabalism. Fledging takes 7-9 weeks and the young become independent about 2 weeks later, staying within the home-range until migration in August-September. The age of first breeding is not known. The pair-bond is monogamous and of seasonal duration only, although the pair may reform in successive years because of fidelity to the eyrie.

Hints on recognition: This species is only slightly larger than the Buzzard and has a flight silhouette closer to that than to the large eagles, but with a longer tail and narrower wings. It has two distinct morphs, a light and a dark, but the light morph is the norm in the Algarve.
Light morph: When perched, it appears to be a very light brown on the upperparts, with a blackish wing-bar, and white on the underparts. When seen from below, the body, tail, and all the fore-part of the wings appear to be pure white, contrasting with black flight-feathers.
Dark morph: When perched, it can superficially resemble a Golden Eagle, being medium-brown with a prominent 'golden' band across the wing. There is, however, no gold on the head and nape and it is much smaller than the Golden Eagle. In flight, when seen from below, it appears to be pure black all over except for a light reddish-brown tail.

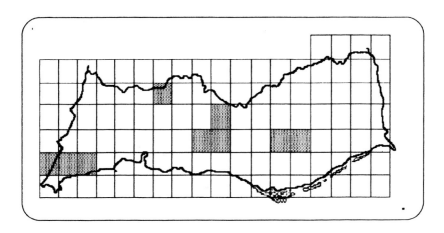

Hints on finding: No help is given in this section, owing to the scarcity of this species in the Algarve.

Confirmation of breeding: See the Black Kite for a general explanation of the map. There has not yet been any proved breeding in the Algarve, but two pairs held territory throughout the period of fieldwork for the BBA and may have nested. A third pair took up territory in the final year of fieldwork and may have subsequently bred.

Number of rectangles in which recorded: 9
Possible breeding pairs: 1
Probable breeding pairs: 2

HIERAAETUS FASCIATUS

BONELLI'S EAGLE

Portuguese name: Águia-de-bonelli.

Distribution: The Bonelli's Eagle breeds in the Mediterranean Basin, southern Africa, a few sites in equatorial Africa, and southern Asia. Although BWP shows this species absent from Portugal, except for one site near Lisbon, the national atlas proved breeding in most parts of the country.

Status in the Western Palearctic: This species has declined and is still declining throughout the Western Palearctic. The reasons for the decrease are not fully understood. Whereas the original decrease may have been due to pollution, pesticides, and persecution, there has been no recovery following protection and environmental controls. In Portugal the population is estimated to be about 50 pairs, the greatest density being in the north-east (CEMPA). As Coverley appeared to regard this species as a rarity, there may be an increase in the Portuguese population. It is resident.

Preferred habitat: Open country with trees and crags or cliffs, such as that found in the western serras. It avoids unbroken forest and marshland, but is tolerant of some garigue or maquis and will hunt on the edges of cultivated areas. It is not tolerant of human disturbance.

Food: Mainly mammals, especially rabbits, and medium-sized birds, e.g. the Red-legged Partridge and pigeons. It hunts its prey in a variety of ways: by quartering the ground, by swooping from the cover of trees to catch birds on the ground or in flight, by stooping from a soaring position, and by chasing on foot. It will also take reptiles occasionally.

Breeding: Both sexes, together or separately, advertise the territory by circling high over the potential eyrie. The courtship display includes mutual talon-grasping and aerial loop-the-loops, with sudden steep plunges. Sometimes a twig is dropped by one of the pair to its mate, who chases it and catches it almost on the ground. During the winter months the pair constructs a nest of branches, lined with greenery, on a cliff-ledge or in a tree. The same nest, refurbished, may be used in the subsequent year, or several nests may be made and used in turn. One clutch of 2 eggs is laid at the end of January. Incubation takes about five and a half weeks and is mainly by the female whilst the male brings her food. The young are cared for and fed by both parents, although the female stays with them for the first 1-2 weeks whilst the male provisions the nest. Usually only one chick survives to fledge, owing to sibling rivalry starving the smaller one to death. Fledging takes about 9 weeks and the young remain with the parents for at least 8 weeks afterwards. The age of first breeding is not known, but is probably at 2 or 3 years old. The pair-bond is monogamous and lasts for life.

Hints on recognition: This small eagle is barely larger than the Buzzard. When seen in flight from below, the body and head appear to be all white, contrasting with dark wings. If seen closely, note the narrow, white leading edge to the black wings with medium-grey flight-feathers, and the light-grey tail with a black terminal band. If it is seen from above, note the prominent white 'collar' on the back of an otherwise dark bird and the grey tail with a black terminal band. When perched, it has noticeably pale underparts, heavily streaked on the neck and breast, with medium-brown crown, nape, and wings.

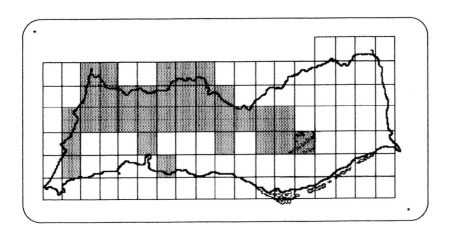

Hints on finding: Owing to the intolerance of this species to human disturbance, no help is given in this section.

Confirmation of breeding: See the Black Kite for a general explanation of the map.

Number of rectangles in which recorded: 33
Confirmed breeding: 6

PANDION HALIAETUS

OSPREY

Portuguese name: Águia-pesqueira.

Distribution: The Osprey breeds in Europe, Asia, North and Central America, almost as far south as the Equator, and south-east Asia and Australia. In Europe, it is mainly confined to the north-east. According to BWP (1980), the pair breeding in the Algarve was the only one known to breed on the mainland of the Iberian Peninsula. The national atlas, however, found a further site in Portugal.

Status in the Western Palearctic: This species declined drastically during the 1800s and the early part of this century, mainly because of persecution by fishing interests, and became extinct in many parts of Europe. More recent declines, especially in the Mediterranean, are probably owing to tourism and pollution. According to Tait (1924), it used to be more common in Portugal than it is today. Coverley states that is was probably fairly common in the 17th century and mentions several eyries in the Algarve, including one as far east as Carvoeiro, that were occupied earlier this century. The present population of Portugal is three pairs only (CEMPA). The Algarvian birds are resident, although migrants from northern Europe can be seen passing Cape St.Vincent in the autumn.

Preferred habitat: Marine cliffs and waters. It will also fish in freshwater lakes, such as the larger reservoirs (barragens).

Food: Fish, which are caught in the talons, as feet are thrown forward at the last moment, in a shallow dive. The bird may dive from a soaring height or from close to the water, and can hover over the water searching for its quarry.

Breeding: The male advertises the prospective eyrie during the winter by aerial loop-the-loops, whilst calling loudly, and by soaring over the site. The courtship displays are similar to other raptors except for the 'fish-display', where the male rises steeply into the air with a fish in his talons, hovers with his legs dangling to show the fish, dives almost to the eyrie, then repeats the display. The pair builds a bulky nest of twigs, often lined with greenery, on a sea-stack (or tree in other parts of its range). The male brings the greater part of the base branches, whilst the female brings most of the small twigs and greenery. The same nest is used in successive years unless it is unsuccessful, in which case another nest is built. In March, one clutch of 2-3 eggs is laid. Incubation takes 5 weeks and is by both sexes, although the female does the greater share. The chicks are cared for and fed by the female only, whilst the male hunts and provisions the nest. Fledging takes 7-8 weeks and, unlike most other large raptors, there is little inter-sibling rivalry. The young birds become independent 1-2 months after fledging and breed for the first time at 3 years old. The pair-bond is monogamous and lasts for life in the case of the Algarvian birds.

Hints on recognition: When perched, this bird is distinctive in being all brown on the upperparts, contrasting with white underparts and head. If seen well, the black streak through the eye and shaggy crest at the back of the head are diagnostic. When seen in flight from below, it can look similar to the Bonelli's Eagle (for which, see that species), which can be found in the same habitat. The Osprey, however, has almost all the underwing white, with only a narrow black band ending in a round black patch on the carpal joint before the flight feathers. In addition, the tail is barred and has no terminal black band.

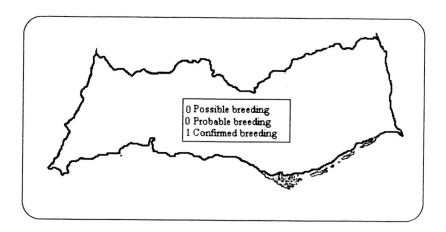

0 Possible breeding
0 Probable breeding
1 Confirmed breeding

Hints on finding: Owing to the intolerance of this species to human disturbance, no help is given in this section.

Confirmation of breeding: The established pair bred successfully only once during the fieldwork for the BBA. A further pair attempted to take possession of a territory but did not breed. The Algarve is shown with the breeding information given centrally, to protect this vulnerable species.

Number of rectangles in which recorded: 5
Confirmed breeding pairs: 1

FALCO NAUMANNI

LESSER KESTREL

Portuguese name: Peneireiro-das-torres.

Distribution: The Lesser Kestrel breeds in the middle latitudes of the Western Palearctic and Central Asia. In Europe, it is confined to the Mediterranean and Black Sea regions. It is to be found in most parts of Portugal (CEMPA).

Status in the Western Palearctic: There has been a massive decline in this species in every area, except France, since the turn of this century. For example, BWP states that the population of Spain has crashed from 100,000 pairs to 50,000 pairs since the 1960s. The probable reasons for this decline are given as pesticides and habitat changes. In Portugal, Reis Jr. referred to large colonies in the south which now do not exist and the largest known colony in the country in the 1980s, at Castro Marim castle, was abandoned because of renovations to the building. The only Lesser Kestrels still breeding in the Algarve are on the western sea-cliffs. It is a summer migrant, wintering in Africa south of the Sahara.

Preferred habitat: The west coast of the Algarve, where there are ample sea-cliffs for nesting together with open heaths or cultivated land for hunting. It favours level or undulating terrain, but avoids forests and wetlands. It is very tolerant of human activity, where it is not persecuted, sometimes nesting in ruined outbuildings.

Food: Almost entirely insects, although it will take reptiles, small mammals, and birds. In Spain, one study showed that at least 85% of the number of food items taken were invertebrates (BWP 1980). It often hunts with others of the same species, flying low over the ground or chasing swarms high in the air. It will hover briefly, but far less than the Kestrel.

Breeding: Colonial or semi-colonial. Both sexes arrive at the breeding grounds in March, although the males arrive before the females. The male chooses the nest-site then advertises it by flying in front of the site with a conspicuous prey in his talons. When a female approaches, he gently chases her and leads her to the nest. The courtship display consists mainly of the male passing food to the female, talons to talons, and the pair wheeling together around the nest-site. The nest is a slight depression, with no material or lining, on a ledge or in a hole of a building or cliff. Firstly, the site is scraped clear of stones and roots by the male and then the female forms a hollow in which one clutch of 3-5 eggs is laid. Incubation takes 4 weeks and is mainly by the female at night, whilst the pair incubates equally during the day. The young are cared for and fed by both parents, and sometimes young unmated males help to provision the nest. Fledging takes 4 weeks, after which the young remain with the parents, migrating with them 6-8 weeks after fledging. The age of first breeding can be at 1 or 2 years old. The pair-bond is monogamous and of seasonal duration only.

Hints on recognition: This species is most easily confused with the Kestrel (for which, see that species). The sexes are dissimilar and the juvenile resembles the female. The male, when perched or in flight, can be distinguished by a light blue-grey head with no black moustache, a chestnut brown back with no black spots, and a light blue-grey wing-band. The female is almost identical to the female Kestrel, but when seen really well her pale claws are diagnostic. This species is usually seen in groups chasing flying insects, with buoyant agile flight, only briefly hovering.

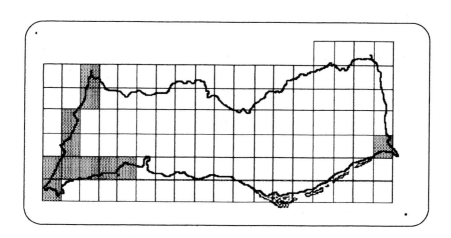

Hints on finding: A walk on the western sea-cliffs, from such starting points as Boca do Rio or Odeceixe (see Where to watch breeding birds, A), will usually produce good views of this species. However, the Kestrel also breeds on these cliffs and so care should be taken in identification.

Confirmation of breeding: See the Black Kite for a general explanation of the map.

Number of rectangles in which recorded: 11
Confirmed: 6

95

FALCO TINNUNCULUS

KESTREL

Portuguese name: Peneireiro-vulgar.

Distribution: The Kestrel is to be found in most of Europe, Africa, and Asia. In Europe, it breeds everywhere except for the Arctic coastlands and the Azores. It is well-distributed throughout Portugal (CEMPA).

Status in the Western Palearctic: Although there is no recent change in the range of this species, it has declined in many areas, probably owing to pesticides, changes in habitat, and a reduction in rodents. In Portugal, a major decline was detected during the course of the fieldwork for the national atlas from 1978 to 1984, although no specific cause was given. It is nowhere common in the Algarve, but the population is apparently stable. The Kestrel is resident in southern Europe.

Preferred habitat: This species is found in a wide range of habitats and altitudes, including sea-cliffs, woodland, cultivated ground, saltings and wetlands, and mountains. It avoids barren mountains, treeless terrain, and extensive forests, but is very tolerant of human activities where it is not persecuted, often nesting in towns.

Food: Mainly small mammals, although it will also take birds, lizards, and large invertebrates. Occasionally, it will take carrion or steal food from other species. It characteristically hunts by sustained hovering, descending onto its prey in a series of swoops and hovers. It can, however, take prey in direct flight or by snatching it from trees or bushes.

Breeding: Well before the start of the breeding season, during the winter, the male chooses a nesting area and advertises it by gliding slowly towards the prospective eyrie with his wings held upwards in a 'V'. The courtship display is performed by the pair and involves circling, chasing, and mock attacks by the male upon the female. Pair-bonding is strengthened by early copulation, often several weeks before the nest is started, and by mutual nibbling of toes and around the bill. In early March, the pair chooses the nest-site. This may be a hole in a tree, building or burrow, it may be a ledge on a cliff or bridge, or it may be on top of an old nest of another species. If the nest is in a hole or on a ledge, the female makes a shallow scrape which both sexes line with twigs, straw, and debris. The same nest may be used in successive years. One clutch of 3-6 eggs is laid. Incubation takes 4 weeks and is by the female only, although the male will occasionally sit for brief periods. The young are cared for and fed at first by the female alone, while the male hunts. When the chicks are well-grown, both parents hunt. Fledging takes 4 weeks and the young do not become independent before at least a further 4 weeks. The age of first breeding is one year old. The pair-bond is monogamous and can be of several years' duration.

Hints on recognition: This falcon can only be confused with the Lesser Kestrel (for which, see that species). The sexes are dissimilar but the juvenile resembles the female. The male, when perched or in flight, can be distinguished by a light blue-grey head with a pronounced black moustache, a chestnut brown back with numerous black spots, and no grey wing-band. The female is almost identical to the female Lesser Kestrel, but when seen really well her dark claws are diagnostic. This species is less agile in flight than the Lesser Kestrel, relying on prolonged hovering when hunting, and is rarely seen in a group.

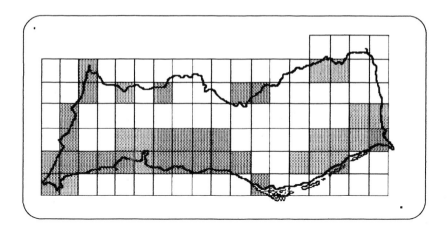

Hints on finding: A walk on the western sea-cliffs, from such starting points as Boca do Rio or Odeceixe (see Where to watch breeding birds, A), or along the cliffs between Albufeira and Portimão, will usually produce good views of this species. The Lesser Kestrel also breeds on the western cliffs, however, and so care should be taken in identification when in that area.

Confirmation of breeding: See the Black Kite for a general explanation of the map.

Number of rectangles in which recorded: 48
Confirmed: 28

97

FALCO PEREGRINUS

PEREGRINE

Portuguese name: Falcão-peregrino.

Distribution: The Peregrine breeds in most of Europe, northern and southern Asia (but not central), most of Africa except the deserts, Australia, North America, and the southern tip of South America. It is thinly distributed throughout Portugal (CEMPA).

Status in the Western Palearctic: This species suffered a catastrophic decline almost everywhere in the Western Palearctic, beginning in the 1950s. The principal cause was persistent organo-chloride pesticides, resulting in heavy adult mortality and very reduced reproductive success. There has been a slight recovery in some areas, following a total ban on these pesticides, but it is classified as endangered in most of its range has already become extinct in many places. The estimated breeding population of Portugal, as given by the national atlas, is in excess of 30 pairs, which is apparently more than were breeding earlier this century (Coverley). In the Algarve, where organo-chlorides were not widely used in the 1950s, the Peregrine is relatively common. It is resident, although migrants from further north overwinter in the Algarve.

Preferred habitat: Sea-cliffs, although it occasionally nests on inland cliffs. It requires extensive open terrain for hunting, including wetlands, but avoids very dry countryside, extensive forests, and heavily vegetated areas. It is tolerant of some human disturbance, where it is not persecuted.

Food: Mainly small birds, but it can take quite large ones such as geese and Grey Herons. It will also occasionally take small mammals, amphibians and lizards. The dramatic hunting technique of the Peregrine, called 'stooping', is renowned and much admired by falconers. The bird finds its prospective prey from circling flight or from a perch, it rises high above the prey, then dives (or stoops) with wings closed onto the prey. It is estimated that stoop speeds may be at least 240 km per hour, and possibly up to 410 km per hour (Brown 1976).

Breeding: The male chooses a nesting area during the winter months and advertises it by calling loudly, either from the ledge or from aerial figures-of-eight in front of the prospective eyrie. The courtship display involves elaborate flight-play, such as mock stoops by one bird upon its mate, chases, and locking talons in mid-air. Towards the end of February, a slight scrape or hollow is made by the female on a ledge or in the old nest of another species. One clutch of 3-4 eggs is laid. Incubation takes about one month and is by both sexes, although the female performs the greater share during the day and probably sits all night. The young are cared for and fed mainly by the female at first, the male provisioning the nest. When the chicks are well-grown, both parents hunt. Fledging takes 5-6 weeks and the young do not become independent for at least a further 2 months. The age of first breeding is 2 years old. The pair-bond is monogamous and lasts for life.

Hints on recognition: This falcon is up to one third larger than the Kestrel but has a shorter tail and relatively broader wings, giving it a stocky look and resembling a hawk with pointed wings. The adult is unmistakable in Portugal, being slate grey on the upper-parts with a distinctive black head and broad moustache. The underparts are whitish with pronounced black bands, contrasting with pure white throat and cheeks.

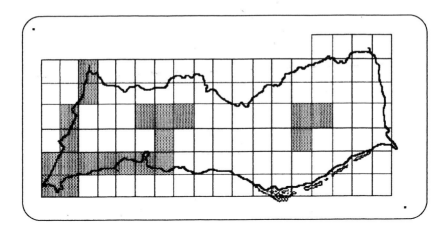

Hints on finding: A walk on the western sea-cliffs (see Where to watch breeding birds, A) will usually produce good views of this falcon hunting, without disturbing this endangered species.

Confirmation of breeding: Inland sightings have been obscured by shading an extra 3 rectangles in order to protect this species. The sea-cliff sightings, however, have been truly shown as they represent total coastal coverage in the west, thus hiding the whereabouts of individual eyries.

Number of rectangles in which recorded: 17
Confirmed breeding: 12

ALECTORIS RUFA

RED-LEGGED PARTRIDGE

Portuguese name: Perdiz-comum.

Distribution: The Red-legged Partridge now breeds in south-western Europe only. Its natural range included western Germany and Switzerland until the end of the last century, but it no longer breeds there. It has been introduced to several regions, reaching as far north as Britain (1673) and as far south as the Canaries, Madeira (before 1450), and the Azores. It is well-distributed throughout continental Portugal, although it is more common in the south than in the north (CEMPA).

Status in the Western Palearctic: There has been a decrease in its natural range, probably owing to climatic changes, and it has become extinct in Germany and Switzerland. In many other areas it has declined because of hunting pressures. Although under extreme pressure from modernisation of agriculture and coastal development, as well as hunting, numbers appear to be stable in the Algarve away from the coast. It is resident.

Preferred habitat: Hilly scrubland and crops, where it can hide. It favours areas which include low or open vegetation, where it can run from danger without having to fly. It avoids areas with an Atlantic climate, unbroken forests or wetlands, as well as the higher hill-tops. However, it is tolerant of human disturbance where it is protected and will use gardens, vineyards, etc.

Food: Mainly seeds, fruits, leaves, and roots, although it will also take insects. In one study in Portugal, it was found that only 3% of the food taken were insects - mainly ants, beetles, and grasshoppers (Pinheiro 1970). Roots and insects are dug from the ground with the beak, rather than with the feet.

Breeding: During the winter months, the male selects a nesting territory, which he defends with a characteristic song resembling the chuffing of a steam engine, delivered from the ground or from a perch in a tree. In March or April, the male makes one or more scrapes, lined with small pieces of vegetation, on the ground. In one of the nests, one clutch of 10-16 eggs is laid, which is incubated by the female. Often a second clutch is laid simultaneously in another of the nests, in which case this is incubated by the male. If only one brood is hatched the young are cared for by both parents, otherwise one parent cares for each brood. Incubation takes about three and a half weeks. The young are able to feed themselves immediately after birth and are able to fly a little at about 10 days. The chicks are fully-grown at 7-8 weeks old, but do not become independent until the following spring. The age of first breeding is one year. The pair-bond can be monogamous or bigamous, and may last for life.

Hints on recognition: The only species known to breed in the Algarve with which this may be confused is the introduced Partridge (for which, see that species), and then only when it is in flight. Other species of game-bird are frequently introduced (e.g. the very similar Rock Partridge *Alectoris graeca* in the Serra da Estrela, northern Portugal) and therefore care should be taken in identification. Both sexes are brown with: red beak and legs; white throat, brow and 'eyebrow'; black stripe through the eye and prominent black 'necklace'; grey breast, and prominent black, grey and chestnut bars on the flanks.

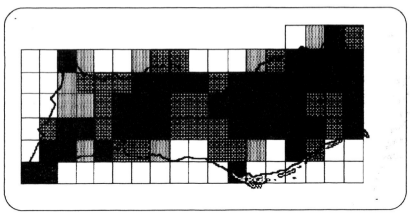

Hints on finding: This species is particularly numerous in the southern foothills of the western Serras. The singing male can be clearly heard at a distance, although he tends to run rather than fly from his vantage point when approached too directly. Stealth is required to obtain good views of him.

Confirmation of breeding: Abundance varies locally within suitable habitats, depending on the temporary banning or lifting of restrictions on hunting. The only squares showing a total absence are those which have no suitable cover (e.g. the extreme west) and those which are too disturbed by man (e.g. the touristic areas).

Number of rectangles in which recorded: 78
Possible breeding: 0
Probable breeding: 7
Confirmed breeding: 71

PERDIX PERDIX

PARTRIDGE

Portuguese name: Perdiz-charrela.

Distribution: The Partridge breeds in the temperate latitudes of Europe, Central Asia, and North America (where it was introduced). In the Iberian Peninsula, it was known only in northern Spain and north-eastern Portugal, although the national atlas found none. It is probably not a native of the Algarve, but an introduced game species, although it is possible that those birds found during the course of the fieldwork for this book could represent a population not hitherto known.

Status in the Western Palearctic: BWP (1980) states that there has been a steady decline in mean population levels throughout its range, ranging from 50% to 90%. The probable reason for this decline is the removal of cover to create larger units for intensive farming, especially as the preferred habitat of this species is also the type of ground most suited to arable farming. Coverley and BWP mention this species breeding in the north-east of Portugal, but none was found during the course of field-work for the national atlas. It is not known whether those birds breeding in the Algarve are native or introduced. It is resident.

Preferred habitat: Low continuous grass or herbage, not much higher than its head, with nearby scrub for concealment and nesting. It avoids rocky or steep terrain, coasts, wet or arid land, and uninterrupted forests. It is fairly tolerant of human disturbance.

Food: Mainly plant material, such as seeds and young leaves. Insects are also taken, especially for feeding the chicks. Most insects are picked from the ground with the bill, although ants nests are scratched with the feet. It feeds mainly at dawn and dusk.

Breeding: During the winter months, young birds form pairs - usually the male choosing the female. Often several pairings occur before the final mate is chosen. Older birds re-unite with the mate from the previous year. The mutual courtship display may involve the male standing with body stretched upwards, whilst the female rubs the markings on his flanks and breast with her bill, ending with both sexes rubbing necks and bills together, heads pointing upwards. By the end of March, the pair has chosen a nesting territory, which the male advertises with a distinctive song likened to a rusty gate screeching. In April, the female makes a shallow scrape on the ground in dense vegetation, lined with grass and leaves, in which she lays one clutch of 10-20 eggs. Incubation is by the female alone and takes about 3 1/2 weeks. The young are able to feed themselves upon hatching and are able to fly a little at about 15 days. Both parents care for the young. The chicks are fully grown at aboout 14 weeks old, but remain with the parents until the following breeding season. The pair-bond is monogamous and often lasts for life.

Hints on recognition: The only native species breeding in the Algarve with which this may be confused is the Red-legged Partridge (for which, see that species), and then only in flight. When standing, both sexes are dappled brown on the upperparts, with chestnut face and throat, grey breast, grey belly with a distinctive irregularly-shaped chestnut patch, and heavy chestnut bars on the flanks.

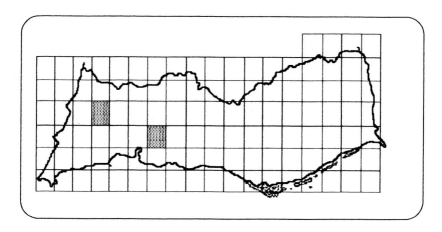

Hints on finding: Owing to the rarity of this species in the Algarve, no help is given in this section.

Confirmation of breeding: Breeding was confirmed in two completely separate areas of the western Algarve. It is probable that it exists elsewhere in the Algarve but has been under-recorded, owing to its similarity in flight to the Red-legged Partridge and to its skulking behaviour.

Number of rectangles in which recorded:	2
Possible breeding:	0
Probable breeding:	0
Confirmed breeding:	2

COTURNIX COTURNIX

QUAIL

Portuguese name: Codorniz.

Distribution: The Quail is to be found throughout the temperate latitudes of the Western Palearctic, including the Azores where it was introduced in the early 16th century, as well as southern and eastern Africa, and central Asia as far south as northern India. In Europe, it is mainly confined to the south and east. It is well-distributed throughout Portugal, although it is more common in the south than in the north (CEMPA).

Status in the Western Palearctic: Owing to natural fluctuations in populations and to the difficulty in proving breeding for this species, its status is uncertain. There would appear to be a general decrease in range and numbers, probably because of hunting pressures (especially on migration across exposed coastlines), habitat changes, and mechanized farming methods. Despite there being no documented evidence to indicate any decrease in the Algarve, it would appear from local knowledge that this species used to breed in most of the northern rectangles shown in the BBA until the 1970s. It is generally a summer migrant, wintering in Africa south of the Sahara, although some are resident in the Algarve.

Preferred habitat: Level or undulating grasslands or cereal-crops, with few or no trees and bushes. It avoids rocky terrain and extremes of dryness or wetness, as well as areas exposed to strong winds. It is tolerant of human activities where there is ample cover for it to hide.

Food: Mainly seeds and invertebrates, which it takes by scratching the ground with its beak and feet.

Breeding: The male arrives at the breeding area in early April, before the female, and advertises his presence with a far-carrying call of "whit, whit-whit", which is commonly rendered as "Wet my lips". The female arrives shortly afterwards and advertises her presence with a soft "bru-bru", forming a duet with the male. The courtship display of the male consists of circling the female with his neck stretched, throat and breast feathers ruffled, and wing nearest the female trailing on the ground, whilst sighing gently. The female forms a shallow scrape, thinly lined with whatever vegetation is locally available, on the ground in grass or crops. One clutch (occasionally two) of 8-13 eggs is laid in early May. Incubation takes 2 1/2 to 3 weeks and is by the female only. The young are nidifugous and self-feeding. The chicks are cared for by the female alone, who leads them from the nest within a few hours of hatching. They are able to flutter at 1 1/2 weeks and fly at 2 1/2 weeks. They remain as a family party for a further 4-7 weeks before becoming independent and breed for the first time at 1 year old. The pair-bond is variable and can be monogamous, bigamous, polygamous, or promiscuous. It probably lasts for one season only, even where the birds are resident.

Hints on recognition: This tiny game-bird, the same length as a Skylark, can rarely be seen well enough to identify from its plumage. It is plump with very short legs, coloured brown with streaks and spots to camouflage it perfectly in its natural habitat. The male has a black streak down the centre of its throat, joining with black moustaches to form a circle on each side of the throat. It readily hides in or runs through long grass or cereals and rarely flies.

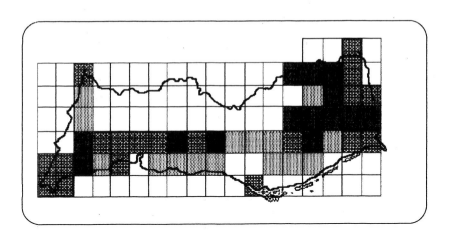

Hints on finding: This secretive little bird is very rarely seen as it prefers to run through cover than to fly and particularly favours cereal crops, which cannot be entered by the observer. However, in March and April, the distinctive call of the male advertises his whereabouts in the Serra de Calderão or in the southern foothills of the western Serras, e.g. the grasslands to the south of the road from Silves to Messines.

Confirmation of breeding: This species has undoubtably been under-recorded, owing to its breeding habits, and, for the same reason, it was difficult to prove breeding in many cases.

Number of rectangles in which recorded: 48
Possible breeding: 4
Probable breeding: 11
Confirmed breeding: 33

PHASIANUS COLCHICUS

PHEASANT

Portuguese name: Faisão.

Distribution: The Pheasant originated in southern USSR, and possibly Turkey and S.E. Europe. It was introduced in very early times to neighbouring parts of Europe, from there to the remainder of Europe, and later to North America, Hawaii, and Australasia. Several similar and related species of Pheasant from Asia have been cross-bred with the original, resulting in many variants.

Status in the Western Palearctic: The wild population in the USSR is probably extinct and is now very rare in Turkey. Elsewhere, the introduced populations are managed for hunting and fluctuate, depending on hunting pressures, the scale of releases, and the breeding successes of the various game-rearing estates. In all parts of its present range, there are feral populations which have at some time escaped from hunting estates and BWP shows a Portuguese population between Lisbon and Spain. It is resident.

Preferred habitat: Open fields and cultivation with ample cover for concealment and nesting. It favours areas with some woodland or coverts and it requires year-round access to water. It adapts readily to local human activities and will tolerate some disturbance.

Food: Seeds and fruit, roots, shoots, and invertebrates. It particularly favours cereals, berries and small nuts (including acorns). The invertebrates taken are mainly arthropods. It takes the food by scratching and digging in the ground with its beak. It will also take fruit or shoots from trees by climbing through the foliage.

Breeding: In early winter, both sexes join together to form flocks. Later, the males detach themselves from the flock and establish territories, which are advertised by loud crowing calls and wing-drumming from a vantage point or tree. The females form single-sex groups and wander through the territories of the males. The male, on seeing a female, struts around her, head down and wattles swollen, ear-tufts erect, tail spread, and the wing nearest the female touching the ground. Between March and early June, the female makes a shallow depression on the ground in dense vegetation, in which she lays one clutch of 8-15 eggs. She sometimes uses the nests of another Pheasant, however, regardless of other eggs already in the nest. Incubation is by the female alone and takes nearly 4 weeks. When the female begins incubating, the male often loses interest in her and the territory and wanders away, although he will sometimes rejoin her when the chicks have hatched. The young are self-feeding almost from birth and can fly a little and swim at about 12 days. The female cares for the young, with varying help from the male, until their independence at 10-11 weeks old. First breeding is at one year old. The pair-bond can be monogamous, especially where the ratio of males to females is approximately equal. Where shooting is heavy, the females may outnumber the males considerably, creating a surplus of females, and possibly encouraging harems and polygyny. It is of seasonal duration only.

Hints on recognition: Both sexes can easily be told from other game-birds by the extremely long tail (as much as double the body-length), which is very wide at the base, tapering to a long point. The female is a plain speckled brown, whereas the male is a rich reddish-brown. The male's head pattern is variable but is always iridescent bottle-green with bright red wattles.

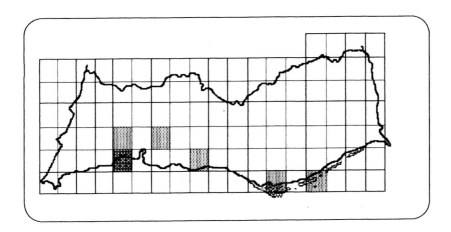

Hints on finding: Quiet coastal areas of suitable habitat are the most fruitful areas to search. The male's loud crowing, heard mostly in the spring, is similar to that of a domestic cock but is distinctive and far-carrying.

Confirmation of breeding: This species' foothold in the Algarve appears to be very tenuous and it is unlikely to spread. Its noisy behaviour and large size make it an easy prey for hunters and predators alike.

Number of rectangles in which recorded: 6
Possible breeding: 2
Probable breeding: 3
Confirmed breeding: 1

RALLUS AQUATICUS

WATER RAIL

Portuguese name: Frango d'água.

Distribution: The Water Rail breeds throughout the temperate latitudes of Europe (including Iceland) and Asia, as well as the coastal regions of North Africa. The range of this species in Portugal is little known because of the difficulty in gaining proof of breeding and the highly secretive nature of the bird, but it appears to be thinly distributed in all suitable habitats (CEMPA). Breeding was not proved in the Algarve by the national atlas.

Status in the Western Palearctic: The status of this species is obscured by the difficulty in assessing numbers of this secretive bird; however it would appear to be stable in areas where there has been no loss in habitat. It does not seem to be uncommon in the Algarve in suitable areas. Despite the loss of many of its traditional nesting habitats, such as marshland, it appears to be accepting new ones, such as private reservoirs and water-hazards on golf-courses. It is a summer visitor in much of its range but is a resident of western Europe.

Preferred habitat: Marshland with fresh water, open mud with nearby tall aquatic vegetation, and well-vegetated banks of rivers with year-round water. It favours marshland with trees and dry patches, rather than uniform swamps, and avoids precipitous valley-bottoms. It is tolerant of human disturbance and readily adapts to artificial water features.

Food: Almost anything, including invertebrates, fish, amphibians, small birds (including their eggs) and mammals, carrion, fruit, seeds, shoots and roots. It will take food from shallow water by wading or by swimming. It also actively hunts prey on land and will climb vegetation for berries or insects.

Breeding: The male chooses a territory during the late winter months and defends it aggressively. He advertises it with a variety of squeals, whistles and grunts, including what is called 'sharming', which starts as a grunting groan, rises to a crescendo of high-pitched trilling whistles like piglets squealing, then dies down to the original groan. The courtship display of the male consists of bowing to the female, wings raised to show his prominently marked flanks, and raising his tail to expose the white under tail-coverts. In March, the pair makes a substantial nest of dead leaves and plants, on the ground or in the water anchored to vegetation. The nest is hidden in dense vegetation, often with the surrounding plants pulled down to form a canopy. Two clutches of 6-11 eggs are laid. Incubation takes about 3 weeks and is by both parents, although the female does the larger share. The young are brooded and fed by both parents for the first few days after hatching. They then leave the nest and are self-feeding. Often the second clutch is laid soon after the hatching of the first clutch, in which case the male cares for the first brood whilst the female is incubating. Fledging takes 3-4 weeks and the young become independent at about 8 weeks old, although the parents often desert the chicks before this. The pair-bond is monogamous and of seasonal duration only.

Hints on recognition: This rail is 25-30% smaller than a Moorhen but approx. 15-30% larger than the Baillon's Crake. It has a very long red bill, bright red eyes, brown legs and upperparts, blue-grey underparts with prominent black and white bars on the flanks, and a conspicuous white undertail.

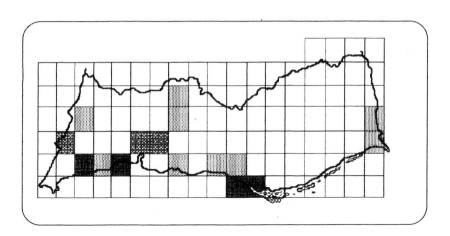

Hints on finding: This bird is extremely difficult to see, as it feeds on mud or in water within areas of dense vegetation and it rarely flies. To see this species, the observer requires luck or long hours spent hidden in a suitable area. However, it is very vocal and thus its presence can be quickly detected. It can frequently be heard at such reed-beds as those at Boca do Rio, Quinta do Lago, and Ludo (see Where to watch breeding birds, A and E).

Confirmation of breeding: Owing to the secretive habits of this species, confirmation of breeding and an accurate assessment of abundance were difficult to obtain.

Number of rectangles in which recorded: 16
Possible breeding: 2
Probable breeding: 6
Confirmed breeding: 8

PORZANA PUSILLA

BAILLON'S CRAKE

Portuguese name: Franga-d'água-pequena.

Distribution: The Baillon's Crake breeds in the middle latitudes of the Western Palearctic and Asia, as well as southern Africa, Australasia and the Celebes. In Europe, it is mainly to be found in the ex-USSR, breeding in only a few scattered localities elsewhere. The national atlas found this species in two localities only, both near Lisbon, but was unable to prove breeding.

Status in the Western Palearctic: Its status is imperfectly known, due to the difficulty in proving breeding or assessing the abundance of this highly secretive bird. It would appear, however, to have declined throughout the Western Palearctic, except in the Netherlands, since the last century. It has become extinct in many regions, probably because of destruction of habitat. Coverley mentions it breeding in northern Portugal, although none was found there by the national atlas. It is a summer migrant, wintering probably in Ethiopian Africa, although individuals have been heard in the Algarve during the winter months.

Preferred habitat: Freshwater marshland, wet fringes to reed-beds, and paddy-fields. It favours rushes, bulrushes, sedge, and short or sparse reed-beds, but avoids tall reedbeds and very dense cover.

Food: Mainly aquatic invertebrates, for which it searches whilst swimming or walking over floating vegetation or mud. It is a fairly strong swimmer and has been recorded diving for food. It will also take seeds and plants.

Breeding: Migrants return in March, when the male takes up a territory. He advertises it by making a creaking call, made mostly at night, which has been likened to a fingernail being drawn across a comb. Courtship includes the same call, given in a weak circling flight over the prospective nest-site. In April, the pair builds a nest of dead leaves and stems on the ground, in thick vegetation close to the water's edge or on a tussock in the water. Often the vegetation is pulled over the nest to form a canopy. One clutch (possibly two) of 6-8 eggs is laid. Incubation is by both sexes and takes nearly 3 weeks. The young are cared for and fed by both parents for the first few days, after which they are self-feeding. When there are two clutches, or when the hatch is not asynchronous, the male cares for the first brood whilst the female is incubating. The young fledge at about 5 weeks old and become independent shortly afterwards, although sometimes the brood disperses when the chicks are only half-grown. The age of first breeding is one year. The pair-bond is monogamous and of seasonal duration.

Hints on recognition: The only species with which this can be confused are the Little Crake *Porzana parva*, which has occurred in Portugal and which breeds in southern Spain, and the Water Rail (for which, see that species). It is a very small water-bird, like a plump Skylark. Both sexes are streaked brown on the upperparts and blue-grey on the underparts (the female Little Crake is all brown). The eyes are red, the beak yellow, and the legs yellow-brown (the Little Crake's legs are greenish). The flanks and undertail are barred light and dark grey (the Little Crake is barred cream and brown on the flanks and the undertail is plain light brown). The juvenile particularly resembles the female or juvenile Little Crake, but the leg-colouring is always brown.

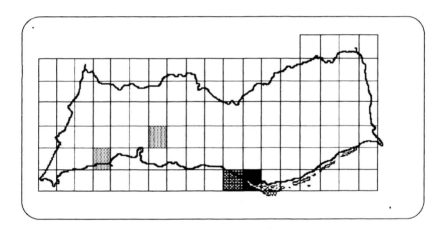

Hints on finding: This bird is extremely difficult to see, as it remains always in wetland vegetation and rarely flies. To see this species, scurrying across a path or a break in the cover, the observer requires luck or long hours spent hidden in a suitable area. Its loud call is the best indication of the presence of this species. It can be heard at such reed-beds as those at Boca do Rio and Ludo (see Where to watch breeding birds, A and E).

Confirmation of breeding: Breeding was proved in the Ludo area and Boca do Rio only, although it probably breeds also along the Arade. The nature of this species' habitat, together with its secretive behaviour, made it difficult to obtain a true picture of this species' abundance.

Number of rectangles in which recorded: 4
Possible breeding: 0
Probable breeding: 1
Confirmed breeding: 3

GALLINULA CHLOROPUS

MOORHEN

Portuguese name: Galinha-d'água.

Distribution: The Moorhen is to be found in most parts of the world except the far north and Australasia. It breeds in every country of Europe, except Iceland. It is well distributed throughout Portugal wherever there is suitable habitat (CEMPA).

Status in the Western Palearctic: There are considerable fluctuations in numbers in northern Europe, due to hard winters, but there is no evidence of any general decline and it has increased markedly in some areas. In Portugal, it is more common in the centre and south than in the north, primarily because there are fewer suitable breeding sites in the north (CEMPA). Despite drainage of coastal marshes in the Algarve and resultant decline in numbers, it is now successfully colonizing many of the hundreds of tiny, inland, private reservoirs and is increasing steadily. It is a migrant in some parts of its range, but is resident in western Europe.

Preferred habitat: Wet pasture or marshland with some open freshwater and cover available. It moves freely on dry land and climbs trees readily, in addition to swimming and diving well. It will accept any freshwater with cover for nesting, including mountain streams which mainly dry out in the summer months. It is very tolerant of human disturbance and often uses small farm reservoirs or water-hazards on golf-courses.

Food: Almost anything locally available, either plant or animal material, underwater or on the ground. While swimming, it obtains food by dipping its head under the water, by taking it from the surface, or by up-ending. On land, it pecks insects, seeds, and fruit from the ground or from plants. It will also steal food from other species, eat dead or very small fish, take birds' eggs, and eat rubbish such as vegetable peelings and scraps.

Breeding: The pair-bond is formed at the start of the nesting season, when the pair (or sometimes the male alone) establishes a breeding territory for nesting and feeding. It is proclaimed by the male's crowing and is strenuously defended by both sexes. During mutual courtship displays, the birds bow to one another to hide the shield (which provokes antagonism when exhibited). The nest of twigs and stems, lined with grass, is built in early March by the pair, the male bringing most of the material whilst the female completes the construction. It may be in emergent vegetation, attached to a bush overhanging the water, on a platform of branches in the water, or in a tree up to 8m above ground. One to three clutches of 5-9 eggs are laid from March to late July. Incubation takes 3 weeks and is by both parents. Although the young are nidifugous, they are fed and cared for by both parents and by siblings from earlier broods. They are self-feeding by 4 weeks but continue to be fed until about 6 weeks old. The young become independent at about 10 weeks old and breed for the first time at one year old. The pair-bond is monogamous and may be of seasonal duration only, but many bonds last for at least several years.

Hints on recognition: This species can only be confused with the Coot and the Purple Gallinule (for which, see those species). It is about the size of a Feral Pigeon, which is smaller than either the Coot or the Gallinule. It is mostly black, with a prominent red beak (yellow-tipped) and red shield, and is conspicuously white on the undertail. The legs are a bright yellow-green and, when it is seen clearly, a white stripe can be seen along the side.

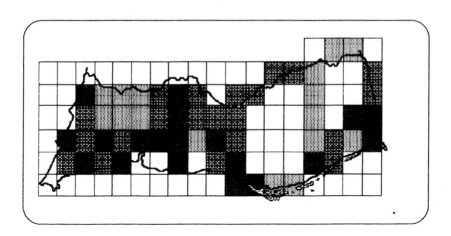

Hints on finding: Although this species can be seen in any freshwater environment, the most easily obtained views are from the hide at Quinta do Lago (see Where to watch breeding birds, E) and the surrounding golf-courses.

Confirmation of breeding:

Number of rectangles in which recorded: 55
Possible breeding: 0
Probable breeding: 13
Confirmed breeding: 42

PORPHYRIO PORPHYRIO

PURPLE GALLINULE

Portuguese name: Caimão-comum.

Distribution: The Purple Gallinule is mainly restricted to western and southern Africa, southern Asia (including the Indian sub-continent), and Australasia. In Europe, it is only to be found breeding in the Algarve, in one area of Spain, in Sardinia, and in one area in the ex-USSR. In North Africa, it breeds at one site in Morocco, one in Algeria and two in Tunisia.

Status in the Western Palearctic: There has been a marked decline in this species during this century, probably owing to destruction of habitat. It has become extinct in Italy, Greece, and Turkey, as well as most of Spain and Portugal. Coverley mentions that this species used to breed near Coimbra and in the Golegã marsh, but had already disappeared by the time "The Birds of Portugal" was written. In the Algarve, it is rigorously protected and has recently expanded from one breeding site to three, two of which are within the Ria Formosa. It is resident.

Preferred habitat: Lush wetlands with slow-moving or still shallow water, over-grown with reeds, sedge, or reedmace in warm climates. It avoids trees and bushes, although it can climb fairly well, and avoids flying or swimming over open areas of water. It is tolerant of human disturbance.

Food: All parts of aquatic and semi-aquatic plants, as well as insects, eggs, young birds, and various aquatic prey. The seeds of reeds are stripped off with its bill and the dry casing on some plants are removed by its comb-like toes. It will pull up rushes from the mud (often submerging its head and neck) to eat the soft tubers. It uses its bill to turn over stones for small invertebrates. Larger prey are held between its toes, lifted to the bill and pieces torn off.

Breeding: The male selects a breeding territory and advertises his presence by short flights, cackling loudly. In courtship, the male brings water-weeds in his bill to the female, bows to her, flaps his wings in the air, stretches and bows several times, then brings his wings forwards, quivering them and calling loudly. In March, a nest of dead waterplants is made by the pair, the male bringing most of the material whilst the female completes most of the construction. It is sited just above water level in emergent vegetation. One clutch of 3-6 eggs is laid. Incubation takes about 3 1/2 weeks and is by both parents, although the female does the larger share. The young are fed by both parents until about 2 weeks old when they become self-feeding, although the parents may continue to feed them for several weeks more. Sometimes the grown young from the previous year will help the parents. The young become independent at about 7 weeks old, although they do not finally fledge until about 9 weeks old. The age of first breeding is not known. The pair-bond is monogamous, but it is not known whether it is of seasonal duration or not.

Hints on recognition: When seen clearly, this species is unmistakable. It is large (almost twice the size of the Moorhen), predominately violet-blue (slightly greenish on the back) with striking white undertail, long red legs, and a massive wedge-shaped red bill and shield.

Hints on finding: The only known breeding sites are Ludo, Quinta do Lago, and Vilamoura (which site was being destroyed during the course of the fieldwork for the BBA). Good views may often be obtained of this species from the bridge by the farm at Ludo and from the hide at Quinta do Lago (see Where to watch breeding birds, E).

Confirmation of breeding: There are estimated to be 10-15 pairs breeding at Ludo (CEMPA) and a further 3-4 pairs at Quinta do Lago. At least 2 pairs bred successfully at Vilamoura before the destruction of the main reed-beds.

Number of rectangles in which recorded: 2
Possible breeding: 0
Probable breeding: 0
Confirmed breeding: 2

FULICA ATRA

COOT

Portuguese name: Galeirão-comum.

Distribution: The Coot breeds throughout the temperate latitudes of Europe and Asia, North Africa, the Indian sub-continent, and Australasia. It is to be found mostly in the centre and south of Portugal, apparently because of the lack of suitable habitat in the north rather than to a regional tendency in the species (CEMPA).

Status in the Western Palearctic: There have been marked fluctuations in numbers in part of this species' range, owing to hard winters. It would, however, appear to be increasing generally, primarily because of its adaptability to new environments. It would seem to be common in Portugal and the BBA found it everywhere in the Algarve where there was suitable habitat. In western Europe, it is mainly resident, although many individuals migrate or disperse.

Preferred habitat: Open freshwater, generally larger than that required by the Moorhen, with adequate emergent or floating vegetation for nesting and concealment. It particularly favours medium-sized ponds or reservoirs, with gently sloping banks devoid of trees or bushes, in open grassland. It is very tolerant of human activities where it is not persecuted and will readily use town ponds and water-hazards on golf-courses.

Food: Mainly plant material, including algae, but it will also occasionally take insects, molluscs, birds and their eggs, fish, small mammals, and amphibians. Aquatic food is pecked from the surface of the water whilst the bird is swimming or caught by the bird diving or up-ending. Plant material is broken off with the bill or grazed on dry land. It often becomes tame enough to be hand fed, when it readily accepts bread, etc.

Breeding: Pair-formation takes place whilst the birds are still in their winter flocks, before a territory is established, and is probably initiated by the female. She calls and sometimes carries plant material in her bill, the male follows her and she bows deeply, hiding her shield from him (the shield would otherwise provoke aggression). The nest is built by the pair, the male bringing most of the material whilst the female completes most of the construction. It is made from locally-available plants, often lined with finer materials, in shallow water amongst vegetation. One clutch of 6-10 eggs is laid in March. Incubation takes a little over 3 weeks and is by both parents. Before the time of hatching, the male makes one or more 'brooding platforms' for roosting and night-time brooding of the young. The young are cared for and fed by both parents, although the family is often split when the chicks are well-grown, with each parent caring exclusively for part of the brood. Fledging and independence occur at 8 or 9 weeks old, although the young become self-feeding at about one month old. The age of first breeding is 1 or 2 years old. The pair-bond is monogamous and may be of seasonal duration. However, the territory is often maintained throughout the year or pairs remain together within the winter flocks, in which cases the bond may last for several years at least.

Hints on recognition: This species is most easily confused with the Moorhen (for which, see that species). It is about 20% larger than the Moorhen, all black, including the undertail, with a prominent white beak and shield.

116

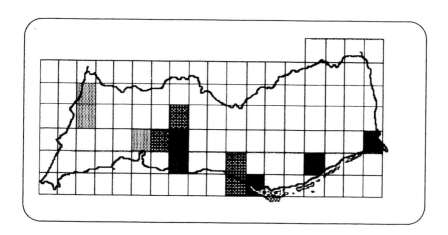

Hints on finding: The most easily obtained views of this species are from the bridge by the farm at Ludo or from the hide at Quinta do Lago (see Where to watch breeding birds, E).

Confirmation of breeding:

Number of rectangles in which recorded:	12
Possible breeding:	0
Probable breeding:	4
Confirmed breeding:	8

TETRAX TETRAX

LITTLE BUSTARD

Portuguese name: Sisão.

Distribution: The Little Bustard is restricted to the middle latitiudes of the Western Palearctic and adjacent Central Asia. In Europe, it is only found in France and the western Mediterranean, and the north-east Black Sea region. It is mainly confined to the southern half of Portugal (CEMPA).

Status in the Western Palearctic: In most of its range it has declined markedly during the last century, probably owing to habitat changes and hunting pressures (it is legal quarry). It has become extinct in most of Europe and North Africa, with only Spain maintaining reasonable numbers. Its status in Portugal is not known, but it would appear to be currently stable in the Algarve, although much reduced since the beginning of this century. It is resident.

Preferred habitat: Open grasslands, level or rolling, including grassy dunes and cereal crops. It particularly requires a clear uninterrupted view from the nesting area, with little or no intrusion of trees. It avoids wetlands and totally barren terrain. It is not tolerant of human disturbance.

Food: Mainly plants and invertebrates, although it will very occasionally take small vertebrates such as frogs and voles. It favours in particular young shoots and grasses, which it pecks off, as well as flowers and cereal grains. Studies in USSR and France showed 70-86% of the food taken was plant material. The young, however, are fed principally on insects, especially grasshoppers, during the first few days after hatching.

Breeding: The male arrives in March from his winter feeding areas and selects a nesting territory. In Portugal, 13-16 males were estimated to occupy 1 km^2 (Ferguson-Lees 1967). He chooses one or more display sites within the territory, from which he advertises his presence. He will snort loudly, leap into the air to show the wing markings, or stamp his feet in sharply accelerating rhythm. Late breeding males will sometimes perform this display communally whilst still flocking. The male develops a fleshy collar around the neck which accentuates the bold neck-pattern. The female arrives up to 4 weeks later and mates with virtually no courtship. She makes a shallow, unlined scrape on the ground in low vegetation and lays one clutch of 3-5 eggs in April. Incubation takes 3 weeks and is by the female alone. The young are cared for by the female only, although the male will often help to protect the brood. The chicks become self-feeding at about one week old, but remain with the female until well into their first winter. Fledging takes about 4 weeks but the chicks are not fully grown until 7-8 weeks old. The age of first breeding is 2 years old. The pair-bond may be monogamous or polygynous and is of seasonal duration only.

Hints on recognition: It can only be confused with the Great Bustard (for which, see that species). It is brown on the upperparts, speckled and spotted for ground camouflage, and whitish on the underparts. It is similar in body size to the Pheasant, but with a very long neck and long legs. The male in breeding plumage is unmistakable, having an inflated black collar around the whole neck with a conspicuous white 'V' on the throat and a white slash across the breast. The female resembles a female Turkey *Meleagris gallopavo*. In flight, both sexes show considerable white on the rear of the wing, with black trailing edge, tip, and patch near the carpal joint, and produce a whistling sound with their wings.

118

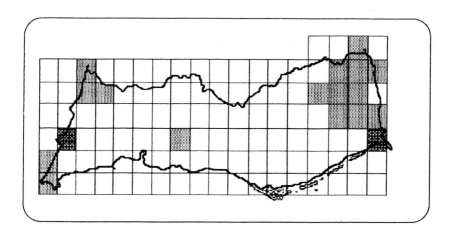

Hints on finding: The open grasslands and heaths of the extreme eastern and western areas of the Algarve hold the largest populations. To find this species requires luck. A walk across a suitable habitat between Castro Marim and Azinhal, with frequent scans from vantage points may produce a view of it. In the west, the grassy dunes inland from Carrapateira or Aljezur and the grasslands north of Vila do Bispo contain reasonable numbers of birds.

Confirmation of breeding:

Number of rectangles in which recorded: 18
Possible breeding: 1
Probable breeding: 9
Confirmed breeding: 8

OTIS TARDA

GREAT BUSTARD

Portuguese name: Abetarda-comum.

Distribution: The Great Bustard is to be found in scattered localities throughout the middle latitudes of Europe and Asia. It no longer breeds in most of Europe, having become extinct in a broad belt of countries from Scandanavia through Great Britain and France to Italy and Greece. The only site now occupied in North Africa is one in Morocco. In Portugal, it is mainly restricted to the Alentejo.

Status in the Western Palearctic: The range of this species increased during the 18th century, owing to forest clearances creating suitable habitat. It decreased rapidly during the 19th century, when the grasslands and meadows were replaced with arable land. It further shrank and became severely fragmented during this century following farming mechanization, use of pesticides, irrigation, planting of commercial trees, and increased hunting pressures. It is now classed as an endangered species and afforded protection in many countries, but it is still widely hunted. Its status in Portugal is not known. It is resident in Europe.

Preferred habitat: Very open undulating country, with unrestricted views over long distances. It avoids hills, forests or even scattered trees, wetlands (although in the Algarve it locally uses dried-up marshes), and areas with fences or ditches. It is not tolerant of human disturbance.

Food: Mainly plants and invertebrates. Vegetation is grazed or pecked, large insects are stalked and grabbed with the beak. Occasionally small mammals, amphibians, and reptiles are caught by rapid ground pursuit, and it will also take nestlings from the ground.

Breeding: Traditional display grounds are used by groups, or 'leks', of males. This display is extraordinarily elaborate, the males inflating their gular pouches (which extend from throat to breast) by a series of gulps into huge 'powder-puff' balloons. The whiskers become erect to cover the face, the wings stretch down and backwards with the carpal joints almost on the ground, and the tail twists over the back, so that a basically brown bird almost instantly becomes a round 'fluffy' ball of white. In this posture, the male stamps with his feet and slowly wheels around, causing the pouch to swing rhythmically from side to side. The female is attracted by this display, approaches a male and the two copulate. The male's only role is to attract and fertilize as many females as possible. One clutch of 2-3 eggs is laid in April, in a shallow, unlined scrape on the ground in low vegetation. Incubation takes 3-4 weeks. The young are nidifugous, fledging at about 5 weeks old and becoming independent during their first winter. Females first breed at 3-4 years old and males at 5-6 years. The pair-bond is polygynous and promiscuous and lasts only until fertilization of the female.

Hints on recognition: The only species with which this may be confused is the Little Bustard (for which, see that species). The male, which is upto 50% bigger than the female, is very large - the same size as the White Stork. It is stately in its gait, with head and tail held high, like a Turkey *Meleagris gallopavo*. Both sexes are chestnut, rippled with black, on the upperparts, whitish on the underparts, with grey on the face, throat, and upper half of the neck. The male has long white whiskers. In flight, both sexes show a white wing-bar (the male's being very broad) with black trailing edge, but the outer half of the wing is all grey.

M   F

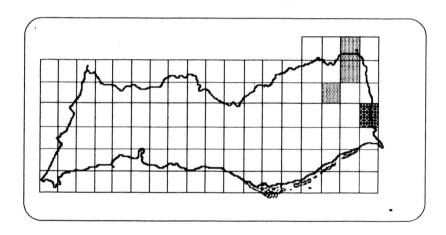

Hints on finding: See Where to watch birds, G. Individuals can often be found feeding on the dried-up marshes of this area or can be seen with a telescope on the grasslands from a good vantage point.

Confirmation of breeding:

Number of rectangles in which recorded:	4
Possible breeding:	0
Probable breeding:	3
Confirmed breeding:	1

HIMANTOPUS HIMANTOPUS

BLACK-WINGED STILT

Portuguese name: Perna-longa.

Distribution: The Black-winged Stilt breeds in scattered localities throughout Africa and southern Europe, and is well distributed in Central Asia, the Indian sub-continent, south-east Asia, Australasia, and most of America. It has sporadically attempted to breed in most European countries. It is primarily found in the southern half of Portugal, with only a few coastal sites in the northern half (CEMPA).

Status in the Western Palearctic: Numbers fluctuate markedly from year to year, depending on water levels, resulting in the temporary desertion of one region in favour of another outside of its normal range. There has apparently been some recent decrease in Eastern Europe, whereas it has increased and spread in Spain and Italy. It is far more common in the Algarve than in any other part of Portugal (CEMPA). It is mainly a summer visitor to Europe, wintering in central Africa just north of the Equator, although many individuals can be seen in the Algarve during the winter months.

Preferred habitat: Shallow, still water, either fresh or saline, with open banks or islands, e.g. salt-pans, paddy-fields, and shallow lagoons. It avoids cold areas, as well as excessively dried-up or flooded terrain. It will tolerate small areas of short vegetation but prefers unvegetated banks. It accepts routine human activities, such as workers clearing out salt-pans.

Food: Mainly invertebrates, particularly aquatic insects. It most commonly wades in the water, pecking the food from the surface or from submerged plants, although it will also swim. Flying insects are taken by pursuit and jumping upon them.

Breeding: Colonial or semi-colonial, often with Avocets, Kentish Plovers, and Little Terns. Individuals return to the breeding grounds in early March and pair-formation occurs shortly afterwards. The male advertises his presence by hovering, legs dangling, over one or more prospective nest-sites. There is no special courtship display, the female simply associating with a male more and more frequently until the male accepts her presence. Although this species breeds in a loose colony, a nest-site territory is established and strongly defended against rivals. Both sexes build the nest, which can be a simple scrape on dry ground, sometimes lined with shells or dry vegetation, or a substantial mound of mud and aquatic plants in shallow water. One clutch of 3-4 eggs is laid, between April and late June. Incubation takes 3 weeks or a little more and is by both parents. The young are self-feeding and can swim well from hatching. Both parents care for them, and other adults in the colony will help to protect any chick by direct attack on the intruder or by distraction displays (e.g. feigning a broken leg or wing). Fledging takes 4-5 weeks and the young become independent 2-4 weeks later. First breeding is not until at least 2 years old. The pair-bond is monogamous and of seasonal duration only.

Hints on recognition: This distinctive black and white wader is easily recognizable by its extremely long red legs. The female is pure white except for the black wings, whilst the male and immatures are blackish on the crowns and the back of the necks. The beak is long, black and thin. In flight, the all black wings, contrasting with the pure white body and long red legs, can be identified even when not seen clearly.

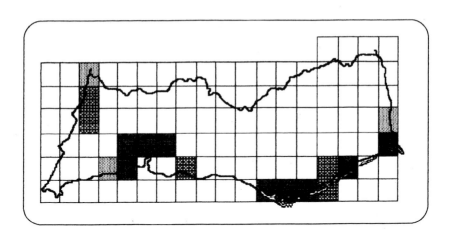

Hints on finding: The most easily observed individuals can be seen at Tavira, from the road leading to the ferry for Tavira Island. They can also be easily seen in the Castro Marim reserve and at Ludo (see Where to watch breeding birds, F and E), as well as from the sea-wall across the Alvor marshes (see Where to watch breeding birds, B).

Confirmation of breeding:

Number of rectangles in which recorded:	17
Possible breeding:	1
Probable breeding:	0
Confirmed breeding:	16

RECURVIROSTRA AVOSETTA

AVOCET

Portuguese name: Alfaiate.

Distribution: The Avocet breeds in the middle latitudes of Europe and Asia, and three sites on the north coast of Africa, and southern and eastern Africa. In Portugal, it breeds at only one site outside of the Algarve (CEMPA).

Status in the Western Palearctic: This species declined in many parts of Europe in the 19th century, but has since recovered and recolonised (possibly owing to climatic changes as well as to protection). Successful breeding in North Africa depends largely on annual rainfall. Some European birds winter in Africa, although most remain within Europe. It is resident in the Algarve, the population being augmented in winter by migrants from further north as Portugal is one of the principal wintering grounds.

Preferred habitat: Shallow, highly saline water with ridges or islands of dry ground for nesting, e.g. salt-pans. It avoids cold or rocky coasts, fast-flowing water, vegetation, woodland, and dry regions. It is tolerant of some routine human activities, such as workmen cleaning the salt-pans.

Food: Mainly marine invertebrates, crustaceans, and worms. The Avocet's upturned bill has specially evolved for sweeping back and forth to sift out prey from loose sediment or soft mud in less than 15cm of water.

In addition to using this 'scything' method of feeding, it will also visually locate and grab its prey in clear water or from the surface of mud. Occasionally, small fish and plant material are taken.

Breeding: Colonial, often with Black-winged Stilts, Kentish Plovers, and Little Terns. Pair-formation occurs during early spring and appears to involve no special courtship displays, the female simply associating with the male more and more until she overcomes his aggression. Both sexes make the nest, which can be either a scrape scantily lined with vegetation or shells, or a more substantial mound of mud and vegetation in the water. One clutch of 3-4 eggs is laid in late April or in May, with replacement clutches up until mid-July. Both parents share the incubation, which takes 3-4 weeks. The care of the young is by both parents, although the young are often left in 'crèches' under the care of a few adults while the parents feed elsewhere. The chicks are able to self-feed and swim well from hatching, but do not fledge until 5-6 weeks old. The young often remain dependent upon the parents for some time after fledging. Juveniles do not start to breed until 2 or even 3 years old. Often, young birds do not return to their breeding-grounds, thus they may be born in one country, winter in another country, then move on to a third country to breed. The pair-bond is monogamous and of seasonal duration only.

Hints on recognition: This strikingly patterned black and white wader, with its blue legs and uniquely upturned bill, is unmistakable. In flight, it appears to be mainly white with black wing-tips and cap, and four black streaks on the wing and back.

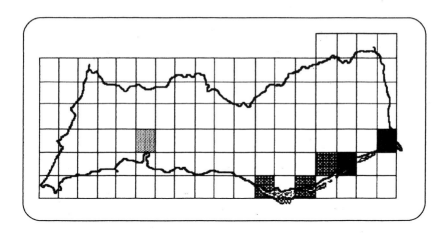

Hints on finding: This species can easily be seen at Tavira, from the road leading to the ferry for Tavira Island, and in the Castro Marim reserve (see Where to watch breeding birds, F and E).

Confirmation of breeding: The four rectangles with confirmed breeding include the single western one.

Number of rectangles in which recorded:	6
Possible breeding:	2
Probable breeding:	0
Confirmed breeding:	4

BURHINUS OEDICNEMUS

STONE CURLEW

Portuguese name: Alcaravão.

Distribution: The Stone Curlew is well-distributed in much of temperate Europe and North Africa, Central and S.W. Asia, the Indian sub-continent and S.E. Asia. In Portugal, it is confined to the southern half of the country and the north-eastern borders with Spain (CEMPA).

Status in the Western Palearctic: In most of its range it has declined markedly from the mid-19th century onwards, mainly because of loss of habitat from agriculture and afforestation. It has become extinct in its former breeding grounds in Holland and Germany and virtually extinct in many other areas. In Portugal, Coverley mentions that this species used to breed in several places where it no longer breeds. In the Algarve, it is steadily declining owing to the destruction of its habitat by urbanization, tourism, and intensive farming methods. It is resident in Portugal, although the population is augmented in winter by migrants from further north.

Preferred habitat: Very open dry ground with good all-round visibility, including heathland, grasslands, dried up salt-marshes, and sand-dunes. This species prefers to run rather than fly, so that the ground must be free of impediments and broken or heavily vegetated terrain is avoided. It favours the edges of wetlands or surface water, but dislikes wet terrain. Where it is not persecuted, it will tolerate limited human activity.

Food: Mainly invertebrates and small vertebrates, such as lizards and rodents, which are caught at night. Prey moving on the ground is seen or heard and approached by a quick run, followed by a stab with the bill. Flying prey, such as moths, are chased and caught by jumping. Birds' eggs are also sometimes taken.

Breeding: Most young birds breed as close as possible to the site where they were hatched, sometimes even using their natal nest-scrape. The nesting territory, which may be separate and at some distance from the feeding area, is established by the pair. During this period, several pairs will gather on a ridge or slope and display, performing leaps and charging one another, whilst calling loudly. In March or early April, both sexes help to make a fairly deep scrape, lined with any locally available material, including stones, shells, or rabbit droppings. The nest is sited on the ground, often in the open. One clutch of 2-3 eggs is laid in April. Incubation takes 3 1/2 weeks and is by both sexes. The young are nidifugous, but they are unable to walk properly until the second day and are fed by the parents at first. Both parents care for the young and will defend them by direct attack or by injury-feigning. Fledging takes 5-6 weeks and the young become independent shortly afterwards. Most young birds do not breed until 3 years old. The pair-bond is monogamous and probably for life.

Hints on recognition: This species resembles no other to be found in Europe. It is entirely speckled light brown, with a white throat and facial markings, and with white and dark-brown wing-bars. It stands distinctly upright on long yellow legs, with a bold yellow eye and black-tipped yellow bill. It rarely flies, but when seen in flight it shows a complicated and bold pattern of black and white on the wings.

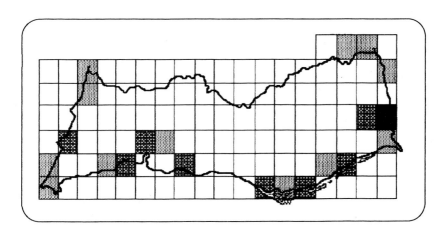

Hints on finding: The distinctive call of "Cur-Leee", resembling that of the Curlew *Numenius arquata*, is the best pointer to the presence of this species. This call is most frequently heard in March-April and in July, especially just after sunset. The Stone Curlew is most abundant in the sand-dunes near Carrapateira and Aljezur, on the dried-up marshes of Alvor and along the Arade, the coastal grasslands of the Ria Formosa and Castro Marim reserves, and the grass-lands of the north-east.

Confirmation of breeding: This species is probably under-recorded, owing to its tendancy to run rather than fly and to its ability to see intruders from a considerable distance.

Number of rectangles in which recorded: 21
Possible breeding: 0
Probable breeding: 6
Confirmed breeding: 15

GLAREOLA PRATINCOLA

COLLARED PRATINCOLE

Portuguese name: Perdiz-do-mar.

Distribution: The Collared Pratincole breeds in the middle latitudes of the Western Palearctic and western Asia, as well as in scattered localities throughout central and southern Africa. It is restricted to the southern half of the Portugal (CEMPA).

Status in the Western Palearctic: Its numbers have recently declined in S.E. Europe and have been reduced by 90% in Israel, possibly because of disturbance, changes in agricultural or pastoral methods, and pesticides. It has, however, expanded northwards in Spain and bred for the first time in France in 1941. The population in Portugal fluctuates markedly, thus obscuring its status (CEMPA), but it would appear to be stable in the Algarve. It is a summer visitor, wintering just south of the Sahara.

Preferred habitat: Dry islands or ridges in salt-marsh or salt-pans, or totally undisturbed grassland next to salt-marsh. It particularly favours flat terrain, without ditches, trees, or tall herbage, and avoids wet conditions. It is tolerant of grazing animals where there is sufficient protection for the eggs, such as hollows in dried-out mud. One colony in the Alentejo nests in a field of bulls bred for fighting, which provides exceptional protection from human disturbance.

Food: Mainly insects caught on the wing, especially beetles, grasshoppers, and crickets. Although this species is technically a 'wader', its feeding habits are similar to Swallows. It will, however, occasionally hunt on foot.

Breeding: Colonial. Pair-formation is thought to occur during the winter or on spring migration, before arriving at the breeding grounds. Soon after arrival, in April, the pair advertises its presence, flying in circles over the colony uttering a trilling and rippling song. Members of a pair greet each other with elaborate bows, tails high in the air. Bowing is also performed in communal displays, away from the nest-sites, during the incubating period. A shallow scrape with little or no lining is built by both sexes on the open ground or amongst scant vegetation. Often the nest is made in a small hollow, such as a hoof-print in dried-out mud. One clutch of 2-4 eggs is laid in early May. Incubation takes 2 1/2 weeks and is by both parents. Although the chicks are nidifugous, they do not leave the nest until about 2-3 days old and are fed by means of regurgitation by the parents until about 1 week old. Fledging takes about one month, during which time the chicks move about freely but do not stray far from the natal site. The young are fed by the parents for several weeks after fledging. Young birds probably breed for the first time at one year old. The pair-bond is monogamous and of seasonal duration.

Hints on recognition: It can only be confused with the Black-winged Pratincole *Glareola nordmanni*, which does not come to Portugal. It is about the size of a Blackbird, mainly warm brown with a white belly. The facial pattern is distinctive, having a white ring around the black eye, a yellow throat ringed with black, and a black hooked bill with a long red streak running downwards from the inner corner. This facial pattern, together with the bird's upright stance, gives the species a 'disdainful' and aggressive appearance. In flight, it shows chestnut undersides to the wings, a white rump, and a strongly-forked tail. When flying, it strongly resembles a large Swallow.

128

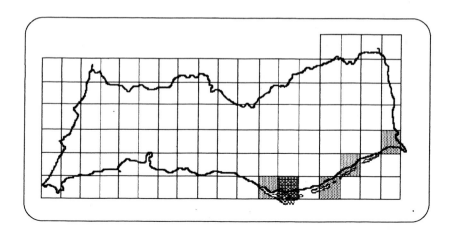

Hints on finding: The colony at the radio-station to the south-west of Olhão is most easily observed in May. Patience, however, is required to find a good viewpoint as individuals can fly in and out of the colony undetected on the opposite side of the enclosure to the observer. It should be noted that observers must on no account enter the fenced-area - not only because of disturbance to the birds but also because it is prohibited, the guards calling the police if intruders are seen.

Confirmation of breeding: It is particularly vulnerable to disturbance and nest-destruction by people and domestic flocks, so that nesting occurs where access is normally denied. Future nesting should be looked for elsewhere in the Ria Formosa.

Number of rectangles in which recorded: 5
Possible breeding: 1
Probable breeding: 1
Confirmed breeding: 3

CHARADRIUS DUBIUS

LITTLE RINGED PLOVER

Portuguese name:
Borrelho-pequeno-de-coleira.

Distribution: The Little Ringed Plover breeds in most parts of Europe, north-west Africa, Asia, and the Indian sub-continent.

Status in the Western Palearctic: This species has declined in much of central Europe, probably owing to climatic changes and habitat loss. There has been a marked increase, however, in north-west Europe. It is far more common in the south of Portugal than in the north, possibly owing to the larger extent of suitable habitat (CEMPA). There has been no recent change in its status in the Algarve. It is a summer migrant, wintering in the northern tropics of Africa, although a few over-winter.

Preferred habitat: Rivers, containing at least some shallow water in summer, with plentiful gravel or shingle. It particularly favours wide valleys, with few trees and no tall vegetation close to the river. It avoids saline habitats and marshes, except on migration, water-courses in narrow defiles with steep slopes, forests, and rocky terrain. It is tolerant of some human disturbance and readily uses streams through pasture where there is sufficient shingle inaccessible to domestic livestock.

Food: Small invertebrates, especially insects. Prey is taken from wet ground or from shallow water and is usually hunted visually. It will also occasionally eat vegetation, such as grass seeds.

Breeding: Pair-formation may occur before or after arrival at the breeding grounds in April. In the latter case, the male establishes a territory and advertises his presence by trilling song-flights, given along the length of the water-course claimed by him. He will approach all intruders aggressively, running towards them, head down, then suddenly raising himself vertically to show his breast and head pattern prominently. If the intruder is a female, she squats and hides her pattern (which is similar to the male's), preventing his aggression. When a female is accepted, the male makes one or more scrapes on the ground, to which he attempts to attract the female, this forming an important part of the courtship. The female chooses a scrape, which is some-times lined with small stones or vegetation. One or two clutches of 4 eggs are laid between mid-April and June. Incubation takes 3 1/2 weeks and is by both parents equally. The young are nidifugous and are self-feeding from the time of hatching. Both sexes care for the young, defending them by injury-feigning, although the female often leaves when the chicks are half-grown to lay a second clutch. Sometimes a third bird helps with the incubating and it is not known whether this may be the young or mate from a previous year. Fledging takes nearly one month and the young become independent 1-3 weeks later, although the first brood will often join the second brood. The age of first breeding is 2 years old. The pair-bond is monogamous and of seasonal duration.

Hints on recognition: Although this species can be confused with the Ringed Plover *Charadrius hiaticula* on migration, there are no similar species on its breeding grounds or habitat. It is light brown on the upperparts and white on the underparts, with flesh-coloured legs and an all-black beak. It has a broad continuous black collar, topped by a white collar and throat, and a black mask which divides in the front to form a white patch over the bill. When seen very clearly, a flesh-coloured ring around each eye can be observed. In flight, it shows no wing-bars.

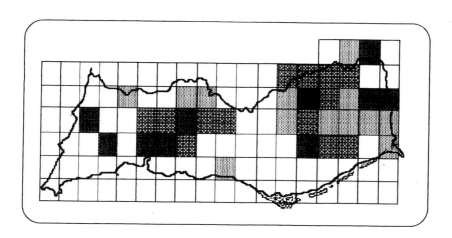

Hints on finding: This species can be found on stretches of shingle on such rivers as the Boi (running parallel to the west of the road going due south from Monchique), the Odelouca (see Where to watch breeding birds, D), the Odeleite, and the Foupana.

Confirmation of breeding:

Number of rectangles in which recorded: 36
Possible breeding: 0
Probable breeding: 9
Confirmed breeding: 27

131

CHARADRIUS ALEXANDRINUS

KENTISH PLOVER

Portuguese name:
Borrelho-de-coleira-interrompida.

Distribution: The Kentish Plover breeds in the temperate latitudes of Europe, Asia, northern Africa, and North America, and the western sea-board of S. America. It is found along the entire coastline of Portugal.

Status in the Western Palearctic: There appears to be an overall decline in this species in north-western and central Europe, probably owing to increased tourism and leisure activities. It has also declined along much of the southern coast of the Algarve, from the same causes. However, the protected Ria Formosa forms such a substantial portion of its habitat in the Algarve that there has been no significant decrease in the overall numbers. It is resident, although the local population is augmented in winter by migrants from further north.

Preferred habitat: Dry areas within, or very close to, a saline environment, e.g. salt-pans, sand-dunes and beaches. It particularly favours smooth sand with no vegetation and will often nest in the middle of sandy tracks or paths. It avoids rocky coastlines and freshwater environments. It is tolerant of some human disturbance.

Food: Mainly crustaceans, molluscs and worms, taken from the surface of the ground or by probing. It feeds in a typical Plover manner, making short but rapid runs, stopping suddenly to peck at the prey, abruptly tilting the whole body forwards. It will also stand on one foot and shake the other foot in water, soft sand or mud (called foot-trembling), which is thought to cause submerged prey to come to the surface.

Breeding: During the winter, the male chooses a nesting territory. He advertises his presence in song-flights, circling over the proposed nest-site, or by standing in an exposed position, his back and crown feathers erected whilst singing. At the approach of a female, the male runs to a selected spot and begins to make a scrape, all his movements being exaggerated and stylised. He continues making scrapes until a female is attracted and accepts the scrape for a nest. The scrape is made on the open ground, lined with small stones, flakes of dry mud, shells, or shreds of vegetation. One or two clutches of 2-3 eggs are laid between March and June. Incubation takes almost 4 weeks and is by both parents equally, although the female often sits during the day whilst the male sits mostly at night. The young are nidifugous. They are self-feeding and can swim well from the time of hatching. Both sexes care for the young, although one of the parents often leaves when the chicks are half-grown. Fledging takes about 5 weeks and the young become independent shortly after. The age of first breeding is 2 years old. The pair-bond is monogamous and may be of seasonal duration, although many pairs remain together for at least several seasons.

Hints on recognition: This species is similar to the Ringed Plover *C. hiaticula*, which does not breed in Portugal, and to the Little Ringed Plover (for which, see that species), which occupies a totally different habitat except on migration. It is light brown on the upperparts and pure white on the underparts, with black legs and beak. It has a blackish smudge on the side of the breast, adjoining the shoulder, and a black streak through the eye. The male has a chestnut cap, with a black patch on the crown above the eye. In flight, it shows a prominent white wing-bar.

F   M

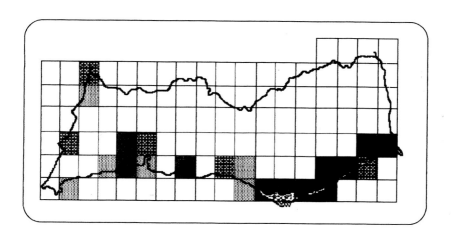

Hints on finding: This species can be seen on any of the sandy areas of the southern Algarve, such as the dunes at Alvor, the salt-marsh in front of Quinta do Lago, and the salt-pans at Ludo, Tavira or Castro Marim.

Confirmation of breeding:

Number of rectangles in which recorded:	22
Possible breeding:	0
Probable breeding:	1
Confirmed breeding:	21

ACTITIS HYPOLEUCOS

COMMON SANDPIPER

Portuguese name: Maçarico-das-rochas.

Distribution: The Common Sandpiper breeds throughout the middle and upper latitudes of Europe and Asia. It has bred in East Africa. It breeds commonly in N. and E. Europe, less commonly in the remainder of Europe. Breeding is evenly distributed throughout Portugal (CEMPA).

Status in the Western Palearctic: There has been a general decline in recent years in Great Britain and in central Europe, probably owing to changes in its preferred habitat caused by river modifications and increased pollution. Although BWP (1983) shows virtually no breeding records for this species in Portugal, the national Atlas and this book show that it is in fact quite common and breeds wherever the habitat is suitable. Despite the decrease elsewhere in its range, there is no evidence of this happening in the Algarve. Most European birds are migratory, wintering in central and southern Africa; it is thought, however, that the majority of birds breeding in the Algarve are resident.

Preferred habitat: Rivers and streams with shallow, flowing water, even in summer. Shingle with some low vegetation is necessary for nesting and rocks or tree-stumps are desirable for 'look-out posts'. It avoids water-courses flowing through dense forests as well as stagnant water, but will tolerate salt-water habitats such as salt-pans.

Food: This wader feeds by catching or by picking up insects. To catch an insect, it creeps up on its prey and snatches it from the ground or in flight. When searching for prey amongst stones or vegetation, it rarely probes as other waders do but locates the prey visually. Apart from the favoured diet of insects, it will also eat a wide range of other food, e.g. spiders, worms, small fish, frogs and tadpoles, and crustaceans.

Breeding: The male advertises his territory by singing and by slow flights low over the water, sometimes with the female. On the ground, there are numerous courtship displays but the most common is by one or both birds raising one or both wings towards the other bird, with tails fanned and depressed, often with one or both singing. In April, both sexes make several scrapes in the ground, from which the female will choose one, lining it with assorted debris or vegetable matter. The scrape may be made on flat or on sloping ground but it is almost always concealed within thick vegetation close to the water. One clutch of 3-4 eggs is laid in April or early May. Incubation is by both parents and takes about 3 weeks. Both parents care for and brood the young at first, but usually one of the adults leaves before the chicks fledge. The young are self-feeding from birth and can flutter short distances at about 2 weeks, but they do not fledge until almost a month old, at which age they become independent. Maturity is reached and breeding commences at 2 years old. The pair-bond is of seasonal duration only, but can last longer, and is generally monogamous.

Hints on recognition: This sandpiper walks with head and body held almost parallel to the ground and, whether walking or standing, it never seems to keep still, constantly bobbing its tail and head. When disturbed, it flies low with wings held stiffly in a downwards curve, calling a shrill piping "twee-wee-wee".

134

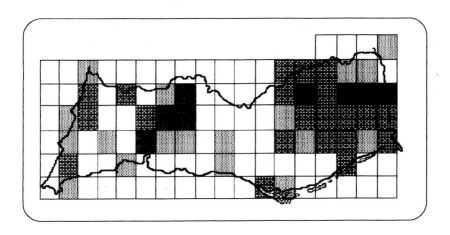

Hints on finding: Stretches of shallow water, shingle and patches of vegetation. The Odeleite, Odelouca, and Foupana Rivers (see Where to watch breeding birds, D and H) are particularly good and are easily reached by car. Care should be taken not to remain near an alarmed bird as the untended eggs and chicks of ground-nesting species are especially vulnerable.

Confirmation of breeding:

Number of rectangles in which recorded:	47
Possible breeding:	6
Probable breeding:	11
Confirmed breeding:	30

LARUS ARGENTATUS

HERRING GULL

Portuguese name: Gaivota-argêntea.

Distribution: The Herring Gull is to be found throughout the Northern Hemisphere. It is only known to breed in the southern half Portugal (CEMPA).

Status in the Western Palearctic: There has been a general extension of range and increase in numbers, probably owing to protection and to the increasing tendency of this species to scavenge on urban rubbish tips. Since the 1940s, the population in Portugal has grown dramatically, possibly because of an increase in fishing activities (CEMPA). For example, the Berlengas colony consisted of 300 pairs in 1939 whereas there were estimated to be 5000 pairs in 1983 (Teixeira 1984). It is resident, although most individuals disperse away from their colonies after breeding and the local population is augmented during the winter months by migrants from further north.

Preferred habitat: Sea-cliffs and sea-stacks. Although this is the only known breeding habitat in the Algarve, it is possible that some may be breeding on inaccessible parts of saltings, as has been found to be the case elsewhere in Portugal.

Food: Anything edible.
As a predator, this species will take prey such as fish from water - by flying close to the surface and dipping momentarily to snatch prey, by flying higher over the water and diving for prey, by catching prey whilst swimming, or by diving for prey whilst swimming. On land, it will actively hunt young birds, small mammals, molluscs and crabs, amphibians, insects, etc. In the air, it will pursue and take insects, birds, and bats with great agility. It frequently drops molluscs deliberately to crack the shell.
As a scavenger, it has become adapted to modern man, utilising rubbish tips extensively. It also follows the plough and scavenges offal or rejected fish thrown from fishing boats.
As a pirate, it robs other birds, including its own species.

Breeding: Colonial or semi-colonial. In March, or earlier, pairs return to their traditional colonies and the male takes up a nesting territory. He advertises his presence by first calling loudly with his head bent low almost to his breast, then raising his head high whilst still calling. When a female is attracted and accepted, the pair perform a mutual display in which they stand close together, facing the same way with bills downwards, jerking their heads and making choking sounds. In April, the pair constructs a mound of vegetation, lined with finer material, on a cliff-ledge or sea-stack. One clutch of 2-4 eggs is laid. Incubation takes one month and is by both sexes. The chicks are able to leave the nest at 2-3 days old but do not stray far, as they can be eaten by neighbouring adults. The young are cared for and fed by both parents. Fledging takes 5-6 weeks and the young become independent shortly afterwards. Juveniles do not breed until at least 3 years old, and often not until 7 years old. The pair-bond is monogamous and lasts for life.

Hints on recognition: This species is the only gull breeding in the region. Gulls may be distinguished from terns by their heavier build and flight, tending to soar, glide and swim frequently. It is pure white with pale grey wings tipped black. The beak is yellow with a prominent red patch on the lower mandible. The Iberian race *L.a.michahellis* has yellow legs, whereas *L.a.argenteus* of north-west Europe has pink legs.

JUVENILE

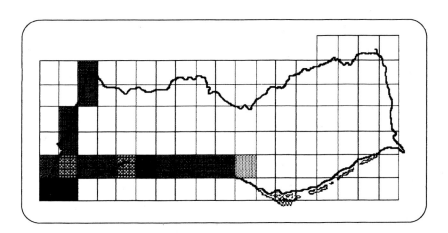

Hints on finding: Small colonies can easily be viewed on, for example, the stack just north of Cape St.Vincent lighthouse, the Ponte da Piedade south of Lagos, and at Ferragudo east of Portimão. Many individuals nest along all the sea-cliffs, and hundreds of non-breeding birds can be seen loafing on beaches, estuaries, and salt-pans - especially in the Ria Formosa and Castro Marim reserves.

Confirmation of breeding: Large numbers of non-breeders use the south coast of the Algarve for loafing and roosting. These have been ignored unless breeding could reasonably be suspected.

Number of rectangles in which recorded: 17
Possible breeding: 1
Probable breeding: 1
Confirmed breeding: 15

STERNA ALBIFRONS

LITTLE TERN

Portuguese name: Andorinha-do-mar-anã.

Distribution: The Little Tern breeds in the temperate and equitorial zones of the Northern Hemisphere, as well as S.E. Asia and Australia. In Portugal, the main breeding area is the Ria Formosa (CEMPA).

Status in the Western Palearctic: The population of Europe has declined markedly in recent years, mainly because of human disturbance on sandy beaches and dunes during the summer months, the breeding season. Other factors contributing to its decline are habitat changes and pollution. It has suffered in the Algarve from tourism and coastal urbanisation, destroying its habitat and disturbing its nesting during the breeding season. There was estimated to be about 200 pairs breeding in the Ria Formosa in 1983 (Araújo & Pina, 1984), since when it has probably declined. It is a summer visitor, wintering in western and southern Africa.

Preferred habitat: Sandy beaches and dunes, salt-pans, and sandy patches on salt-marshes, within easy reach of suitable feeding grounds. It particularly favours linear strips of bare sand or sandy soil, entirely clear of vegetation, e.g. salt-pans, along beaches, around lagoons and pools in saltings, and on small sandy islands.

Food: Small fish and invertebrates. It most commonly hunts by flying backwards and forwards over water, head directed downwards, hovering, then diving onto prey. It will also take insects from the surface of the water by skimming in flight and will actively pursue flying insects.

Breeding: Solitary or loosely colonial. Soon after arrival at the breeding grounds in May, the male tries to attract a female by carrying a small fish, calling loudly and flying towards the roosting area. When a female follows, he glides downwards, spiralling with his wings in a 'V' shape. The female glides after him and both settle in the roosting area. The male struts around her and gives her the fish. Further courtship feeding cements the pair-bond and is a prerequisite for copulation and for change-overs during early incubation. A shallow scrape is made by the female, sometimes aided by the male, and lined with small stones, shells, or dry vegetation. This is often made in May, when she sits in it and defends it, although laying does not usually start until June. One clutch of 1-4 eggs is laid. Incubation takes about 3 weeks and is at first by the female alone, later by both sexes equally. The young are able to leave the nest after a few days, often making their own scrapes. Both parents feed and care for the young during fledging, which takes almost 3 weeks, and continue to feed them until migration, although sometimes the young are divided between the parents. The young rarely breed until 3 years old, when they return to the natal area but not to the actual nest-site. The pair-bond is monogamous and of seasonal duration only.

Hints on recognition: Terns can be distinguished from gulls by their light build and flight, slightly forked tails, and their tendency to hunt with their bills pointing downwards and to fly up immediately after diving. The Little Tern is the only adult tern likely to be seen in Portugal with a white forehead and yellow bill tipped black. The upper wings are light grey with black along the entire outer edge, the cap is glossy black with a streak through the eye, and the body is pure white.

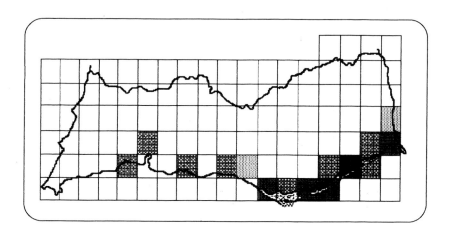

Hints on finding: This species can be observed, without disturbance to the birds, from the sea-wall across the Alvor marshes, from the road to the Tavira Island ferry (see Where to watch breeding birds, E), and from the hide at Quinta do Lago.

Confirmation of breeding:

Number of rectangles in which recorded:	15
Possible breeding:	1
Probable breeding:	3
Confirmed breeding:	11

139

COLUMBA LIVIA

ROCK DOVE

Portuguese name: Pombo-das rochas.

Distribution: The Rock Dove/Feral Pigeon is to be found in almost all temperate regions of the world. The present world-distribution of the Rock Dove is not exactly known because the wild population has interbred with feral pigeons and has been deliberately ignored by many surveys and atlases. This book, seeking to show the distribution of all birds breeding in the Algarve, includes for this species all pigeons and doves which look like Rock Doves and behave like Rock Doves, although there may not be any pure-blood Rock Doves left in Europe. Feral Pigeons are dealt with separately in Appendix I.

Status in the Western Palearctic: There is little written on the status of wild populations, owing to the presence of feral populations (see above Distribution). In the Algarve, there has probably been no recent change in its status, because of its breeding on inaccessible sea-cliffs. It is resident and sedentary.

Preferred habitat: Sea-cliffs and sea-stacks. One colony only was found on remote inland cliffs overlooking a river.

Food: Mainly seeds, especially cereals and weeds. It will occasionally take green leaves or buds, or even invertebrates. It feeds on the ground, in small flocks, by walking and pecking, and appears to have great difficulty in taking food from, for example, bushes. Pigeons and doves are the only birds to produce 'milk' for their young. It is made in the crop and contains proteins, fat, amylase, saccharases, rennet, and various vitamins. Chicks are fed initially on this crop-milk only.

Breeding: Loosely colonial or semi-colonial, usually a maximum of 6 pairs. The male establishes a nest-site and perch, which he advertises by short flights, including loud wing-claps and finishing with a 'parachute-style' descent with his wings held in a 'V'. When a female is attracted, the male circles her on foot, bowing and cooing, feathers ruffled and neck swollen. Courtship includes allopreening, as well as symbolic feeding whereby the female inserts her bill in that of the male and both make regurgitating movements. Sometimes the pair-bond is formed before the nest-site is chosen, in which case the pair searches for the site. A loose nest of roots and leaves is made, mainly by the female, in a deep hole or crevice of a cliff. Several clutches of 2 eggs are laid between March and July, although this species commonly breeds throughout the year. Incubation takes 2 1/2 weeks and is by both sexes. The young are cared for and fed by both parents, although, where another clutch has been laid, the male will often tend the first brood whilst the female is incubating. Fledging usually takes about 5 weeks, but it can be as little as 3 1/2 weeks, after which the young soon become independent. The age of first breeding is one year old. The pair-bond is monogamous and may last for life or be of seasonal duration only.

Hints on recognition: This dove is similar to the Woodpigeon and Stock Dove (for which, see those species). In its true wild plumage (rather than the various feral plumages), it is entirely medium grey, with a prominent white rump, two black wing-bars, and a black tip to the tail. In flight, the under-side of the wings appears whitish. When it is observed very closely, a glossy green and purple wash can be seen on the neck.

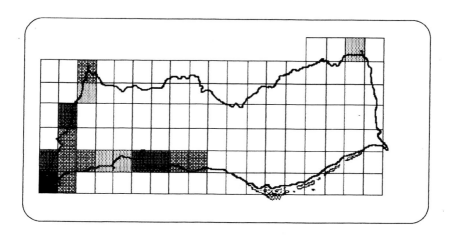

Hints on finding: A walk along the clifftops anywhere west of Albufeira should quickly produce a sight of this species. Those breeding on the Cape St. Vincent are the least likely to have crossed with feral birds.

Confirmation of breeding:

Number of rectangles in which recorded: 16
Possible breeding: 0
Probable breeding: 1
Confirmed breeding: 15

COLUMBA OENAS

STOCK DOVE

Portuguese name: Pombo-bravo.

Distribution: The Stock Dove breeds throughout temperate Europe, adjacent regions of central and S.W. Asia, and in Morocco. In Portugal, the national atlas found it breeding only in the extreme north, although there were a few sightings in the eastern Alentejo.

Status in the Western Palearctic: There has been a marked expansion in the range of this species in parts of western Europe during this century, counteracted by declines in many northern and eastern areas, probably linked to changes in agricultural practices. It was scarce in Portugal in Coverley's time, although it was apparently not uncommon just south of the Tagus, where it no longer breeds. It was not recorded in the Algarve by the national atlas. It is resident in western Europe, although migrants from further north winter in Iberia.

Preferred habitat: Open, rolling country-side with some mature broadleaved trees. It particularly favours parklands, where the well-grown trees have hollows or holes for nesting, close to water and to cereal crops or fields with plentiful seeds. It avoids rocky terrain, mountains, forests, wetlands, and coastal habitats, but is tolerant of human disturbance where it is not persecuted.

Food: Mainly plant material such as seeds, green leaves/buds, flowers, and berries. It will occasionally take invertebrates, e.g. slugs and snails, larvae, aquatic molluscs, etc. It usually takes food from the ground by walking and pecking, although it is capable of feeding in trees or bushes.

Breeding: The male establishes a territory during the winter months and advertises it by means of a distinctive song, an accelerating and rising series of "ooo-uh" notes, and by display flights similar to the Rock Dove (for which, see that species). When a female is attracted, the male approaches her with iridescent neck feathers ruffled and the cervical air-sac inflated. He bows to her several times, repeatedly fanning his tail and softly droning, before repeating the display flight. Further courtship includes aerial pursuits, courtship feeding, and allopreening of the head and neck. The male or the pair together searches for the nest-site, but the female makes the final choice. The nesthole is situated in a tree, on a cliff, or in a ruin and is used for several years. Both sexes line the hole with a few scraps of grass and leaves, or no lining at all. Several clutches of 2 eggs are laid, the first in early March. Incubation takes 2 1/2 weeks and is by both parents, although the female incubates mainly at night. The young are cared for by both sexes and are brooded for at least the first week after hatching. They are fed by both parents, initially on crop-milk (see Rock Dove for explanation). Fledging takes 3-4 weeks and the young become independent shortly afterwards. The age of first breeding is probably one year old and most young birds return to the natal area to breed. The pair-bond is monogamous and is thought to last for life, owing to strong fidelity to the nest-site.

Hints on recognition: This dove is similar to the Woodpigeon and Rock Dove (for which, see those species). It is entirely medium grey, with two abbreviated black wing-bars (little more than patches), a black tip to the tail, and no white on the rump. In flight, the under-sides of the wings appear dark. When it is observed closely, a glossy green wash on the neck and a rufous tinge to the breast can be seen.

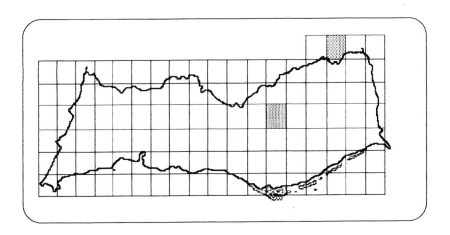

Hints on finding: As only two pairs, in entirely separate rectangles, were found, no help can be given in this section.

Confirmation of breeding:

Number of rectangles in which recorded:	2
Possible breeding:	0
Probable breeding:	1
Confirmed breeding:	1

COLUMBA PALUMBUS

WOODPIGEON

Portuguese name: Pombo-torcaz.

Distribution: The Woodpigeon breeds in most of Europe, including Iceland and the Azores, and in North Africa, Central Asia, and S.W.Asia. It is well distributed through-out Portugal (CEMPA).

Status in the Western Palearctic: There has been a marked expansion northwards and westwards of its range during this century, although it has become extinct in Madeira. In Coverley's time, this species would appear to have been mainly a migrant through Portugal (he mentions nesting in some of the northern mountains only, but huge clouds of migrants over Monchique), whereas the reverse is true today. The national atlas proved breeding at only one site in the Algarve and states that this species is more common in the north than in the south. In view of the density of nesting birds found by the BBA, this overview needs to be revised. It is resident in western Europe, with migrants from further north passing through Iberia..

Preferred habitat: Open woodland, includ-ing eucalyptus plantations. It particularly favours woodland edges by heaths and natu-ral meadows, but is tolerant of areas with few trees where there is sufficient available food (it will fly up to 15km to forage). It avoids wetlands and treeless terrain, but is otherwise adaptable to changing habitats. It is tolerant of some human disturbance where it is not persecuted.

Food: Plant material, including seeds, berries, leaves, flowers, and roots. It will occasionally take invertebrates such as earthworms, beetles, larvae, small insects, and slugs and snails. It mainly takes food on the ground, by walking and pecking. This species is also arboreal and agile, however, being able to clamber amongst small branches and even hang upside down.

Breeding: The male, or the pair together, returns to the breeding area in February and establishes a nesting territory. He advertises his presence by singing "coo-COOO-coo coo-coo" and by aerial displays similar to the Rock Dove (for which, see that species). When a female is attracted, the male's neck inflates to show the white and green, then he bows to her repeatedly, calling softly, and often leaps abruptly up and down in front of her. Further courtship includes feeding her and allopreening. He shows her the potential nest-site, whilst giving a special 'nest-call' and twitching his wings. The pair makes a nest of twigs in the branches or in the fork of a tree/bush. Two clutches of 1-2 eggs are laid. Incubation takes 2 1/2 weeks and is by both sexes, although the female takes about three-quarters of the share. The young are fed entirely on crop-milk (see Rock Dove for explanation) and brooded by both parents for the first week after hatching. Both sexes continue to feed and care for the chicks until they fledge at about one month old, and the young remain dependent for a further week. The age of first breeding is one year old. The pair-bond is monogamous and may be of seasonal duration or last for at least several seasons.

Hints on recognition: This species is similar to the Rock Dove and Stock Dove (for which, see those species). It is entirely medium grey, with a prominent white patch on the sides of the neck and across each wing. In flight, the under-side of the tail appears to be banded dark-light-dark. When it is observed closely, a glossy green patch to the rear of the white on the neck and a pinkish-brown tinge to the breast can be seen.

144

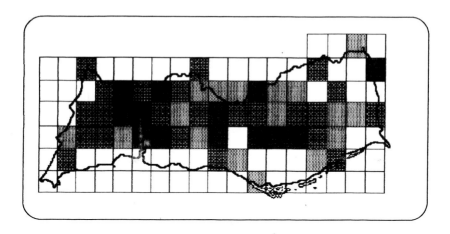

Hints on finding: The foothills of the Serra de Monchique and the Serra de Caldeirão contain the highest densities for this species. Throughout the spring and early summer, it can be quickly located by its song and wing-clapping display flight.

Confirmation of breeding: Numbers vary markedly from year to year in different rectangles, so that relative abundance was difficult to assess.

Number of rectangles in which recorded: 53
Possible breeding: 2
Probable breeding: 14
Confirmed breeding: 37

STREPTOPELIA TURTUR

TURTLE DOVE

Portuguese name: Rôla-comum.

Distribution: The Turtle Dove breeds throughout Europe, except the extreme north, and in most of northern Africa, Central Asia, and S.W. Asia. It is well distributed in Portugal (CEMPA).

Status in the Western Palearctic: The range of this species slightly increased in the north-west in the early part of this century, but has since decreased in most European countries. In Portugal, it is more common in the north, the southern population having decreased in recent years because of excessive hunting pressures (CEMPA). According to reports from the local inhabitants and hunters, the Turtle Dove used to be very common almost everywhere in the Algarve but is now relatively uncommon in places. It is a summer visitor, wintering in Africa to the north of the Equator and just to the south of its breeding range.

Preferred habitat: Mixed farmland with woods, copses, and scrub which includes some trees. It particularly favours warm sheltered lowlands with trees, easy access to water, and close to crops or fields with weeds. It avoids mountains, extensive forests and wetlands. It is tolerant of some human disturbance, where it is not persecuted, but will not nest close to habitations.

Food: Seeds and fruits, especially of weeds and cereals, which are taken mainly from the ground. It will occasionally take animal matter, such as earthworm cocoons, snails, and small insects.

Breeding: The pair-bond may be formed before arrival at the breeding grounds, or the males may arrive slightly earlier than the females. The male establishes a breeding territory and prospective nest-site during April. He advertises his presence by aerial display flights, consisting of steep climbs with wing-clapping, then a gliding spiral descent with wings and tail spread. He will also sing "turrr-turrr" (from which it gets its name) from a concealed perch. When a female is attracted, he erects his feathers to form a black and white ruff on each side of his neck and then performs a series of rapid bows, bowing so low that his belly touches the branch on which he is sitting. Courtship includes mutual display flights and chases through the trees, calling with a smacking sound like the sudden drawing of a cork from a bottle. When the female has chosen the nest-site, the male gathers small twigs, roots, grass, etc., from which the female constructs a flimsy nest in a tree or bush. Two, or sometimes three, clutches of 2 eggs are laid. Incubation takes about 2 weeks and is by both parents, although the female carries out the greater share. The young are cared for and fed by both sexes. They are brooded by the parents for the first week and thereafter by the female at night until they fledge. Fledging takes about 3 weeks, although the chicks are capable of short flights at 2 weeks old. They become independent shortly after fledging. The age of first breeding is one year old. The pair-bond is monogamous and of seasonal duration only, although it may last for more than one season because of site fidelity.

Hints on recognition: When seen clearly, this species is unmistakable. Both sexes have a blue-grey head and nape, with a black and white panel on the side of the neck, a pink-mauve breast, and orange-brown wings, spotted black. In flight, the bird shows dark undersides to the wings and an almost black fan-shaped tail prominently edged with white.

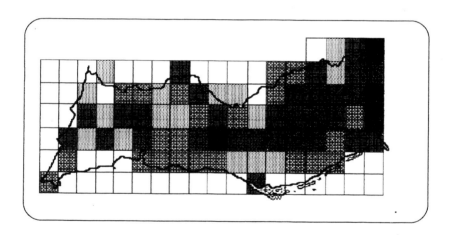

Hints on finding: This species can most commonly be found in open orchards and sequeiros, away from the coast and the tops of mountain. The display flight of the male, showing the tail pattern, can be seen from a distance, and the diagnostic song will further pin-point the presence of this dove.

Confirmation of breeding:

Number of rectangles in which recorded: 72
Possible breeding: 0
Probable breeding: 18
Confirmed breeding: 54

CLAMATOR GLANDARIUS

GREAT SPOTTED CUCKOO

Portuguese name: Cuco-rabilongo.

Distribution: The Great Spotted Cuckoo breeds around the Mediterranean Basin and in most of Africa. It is to be found in scattered localities throughout Portugal, but is uncommon everywhere (CEMPA).

Status in the Western Palearctic: Since the middle of this century, it has spread in France, Italy, and northern Spain, but no longer breeds in northern Africa. It would appear to have been scarce in Coverley's time. The European population is mostly migratory, wintering partly in northern Africa and partly south of the Sahara in central Africa. Some birds, however, remain all year in the southern Iberian Peninsula.

Preferred habitat: Mixed terrain with scrub, open areas, and mature oak-woods or pines. It avoids mountains, forests, wetlands, and dunes. It will use sequeiros, cultivated land, and grasslands, including golf-courses and gardens.

Food: Almost exclusively hairy caterpillars, especially the larvae of the processionary moth. The cuckoo strips the hairs from the caterpillars with its mandibles before eating . It will also take dragonflies, ants, beetles, crickets, grasshoppers, and occasionally lizards. Even the chicks, raised by foster-parents, will eat only insects, rejecting vertebrates and seeds that may be brought to them. It searches for its prey by hopping along the ground, tail raised and frequently making long bounds, although it will also hunt in bushes and trees.

Breeding: Parasitic, mainly on the Magpie *Pica pica*, but other corvids (crow family) are sometimes used, such as the Azure-winged Magpie. The lack of its favoured host in the Algarve could explain its scarcity in the region. In February or March, the male establishes a territory which he advertises by flying steeply upwards, in silence, from a tree-top and then gliding downwards, with tail fanned, uttering a rasping accelerating "keeow-keeeow". When a female is attracted, he courts her by allopreening. He also feeds her immediately before mating, when the male mounts the female with a caterpillar in his beak. Each bird holds one end of the caterpillar throughout copulation, the female being allowed to eat it only when he has finished. The female searches for suitable host-nests with incomplete clutches and lays one egg per nest, usually removing one of the host's eggs and damaging the remaining eggs. If necessary, the male will distract the host's attention whilst the female slips into the nest to lay. 18 eggs are laid, in 3 equal series with 5-8 days between them. Neither sex plays any part in the incubation of the eggs, which takes about 2 weeks, or in the care of the young. Fledging takes 2 1/2 to 3 weeks. The young cuckoo does not eject the eggs or young of the host species, but kills the chicks by smothering them or out-competing them for food. The young remain dependent on the host parents for at least 2 weeks after fledging and breed for the first time at one year old. The adults return to the wintering grounds soon after completing laying, well before the young migrate. The pair-bond is monogamous and probably of seasonal duration only.

Hints on recognition: There is no similar species to be found in Europe. It has dark upperparts, heavily spotted with white, and beige-cream underparts, including the undersides of the wings. It has a long blue-grey crest, which is readily erected, and a long fan-shaped tail edged with white.

148

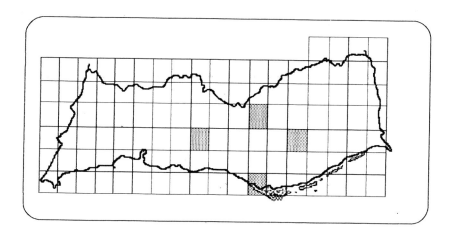

Hints on finding: The only known breeding site in the Algarve is the Ludo to Quinta do Lago area. The male's chattering and gobbling song or the female's bubbling "gi-gi-gi-gi" are an indication of this species' presence.

Confirmation of breeding: The difficulty in detecting this species and proving breeding has possibly led to under-recording.

Number of rectangles in which recorded:	4
Possible breeding:	1
Probable breeding:	2
Confirmed breeding:	1

CUCULUS CANORUS

CUCKOO

Portuguese name: Cuco-canoro.

Distribution: The Cuckoo breeds throughout Europe, except Iceland and the Azores, as well as in North Africa and the middle and upper latitudes of Asia. It is to be found throughout Portugal (CEMPA).

Status in the Western Palearctic: There have been recent decreases in the northwest of its range, for reasons imperfectly understood, but possibly linked to fluctuations in the host species. There appears to be no change in its status in Portugal during this century. It is a summer visitor, wintering in southern Africa.

Preferred habitat: It is to be found in almost all habitats, including wetlands and dunes, but not extensive forests, bare mountains, or urbanizations. It particularly favours areas with a mixed habitat of scrub, open terrain, and scattered trees, and is tolerant of limited human disturbance.

Food: Insects, especially caterpillars (including hairy and poisonous ones) and beetles. It perches motionless on a vantage point, such as a branch or overhead wires, then pounces on its prey beneath. It will search on foot for small prey, or will peck insects from the foliage or bark of trees. Occasionally, spiders, centipedes, earthworms, slugs and snails, amphibians, and birds' eggs or nestlings are taken.

Breeding: Parasitic on over 100 species world-wide. Birds return from their wintering grounds in March, when the male establishes and advertises a territory with the traditional song of "Cuc-koo", from which the species gets its name. In addition, the female holds a laying territory, which she advertises with a bubbling call. Either sex may be attracted to the call of the other one and may initiate the courtship display. This consists of head-bobbing and bowing whilst rotating slowly with wings and tail fanned. All males will court and copulate with all females within an area and neither sex takes any part in the incubation of the eggs or in the care of the young. The female finds the host species' nests by watching from a hidden perch or by observing which part of the host's territory is most defended, then searching. She chooses an incomplete clutch, removing at least one of the host's eggs and replacing it with one of her own. If there are numerous nests in the area, she will often damage those that she cannot use immediately so that she can use rebuilt nests later. Each female is capable of laying 25 eggs. Incubation takes about 12 days. The newly-hatched cuckoo ejects all other eggs or chicks from the nest, or smothers the host's chicks as soon as possible, the young cuckoo being much larger than the host species' young. Fledging takes 2 1/2 to 3 weeks and the young become independent 2-6 weeks later. The age of first breeding may be one year old, but is usually two. The pair-bond is promiscuous and lasts only for copulation.

Hints on recogniton: When seen perched, the Cuckoo is unmistakable. It is entirely grey on the upperparts, with a long fan-shaped tail spotted with white. The throat is light grey, the breast and belly white strongly barred with black, and the female has a wide deep-rufous breast-band. The female also has a rufous morph: entirely rufous-brown on the upperparts, heavily spotted and barred with black, entirely white on the underparts with a slight chestnut breast-band, strongly barred with black. In flight, it shows a long tail and long pointed wings, which sometimes causes confusion with falcons when observed only briefly.

BROWN PHASE   F   GREY PHASE

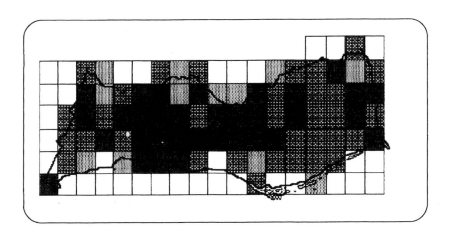

Hints on finding: This species is not easy to see; but the distinctive call of the male will pin-point its presence. The map clearly shows that it is more common in the middle of the Algarve than at the extremities.

Confirmation of breeding: The lack of nest-building or parental care made it difficult to prove breeding in most cases. It may be assumed, however, to breed in those rectangles where it is fairly common.

Number of rectangles in which recorded: 78
Possible breeding: 1
Probable breeding: 73
Confirmed breeding: 4

TYTO ALBA

BARN OWL

Portuguese name: Coruja-das-torres.

Distribution: The Barn Owl is to be found in most parts of the world, except Central Asia and some areas in the extreme north. In Europe, it is absent from the north-east and from the Azores. It is well-distributed throughout Portugal, but is most common in the centre of the country (CEMPA).

Status in the Western Palearctic: There has been a general decline in the European population, mainly as a result of pesticides, loss of nest-sites, and human persecution. There would appear to be no recent change in its status in Portugal, apart from a withdrawal from coastal urbanizations, and it is still to be found in most of its traditional sites in the Algarve. It is resident.

Preferred habitat: It particularly favours open farmland or grasslands, close to human settlement where there are ruins or churches for nesting and roosting. Buildings, whether used for nesting or roosting, must have a large enclosed area free of disturbance and with several entrances and exits. It will also use forests where there are sufficient hollow trees. It is not tolerant of human disturbance at the nest.

Food: Mainly small mammals, especially mice and voles but including bats. In a study in south-west Spain (Herrera 1974), it was found that three-quarters of the prey taken were mice and voles. It will also take small birds, especially from flocks going in to roost, as well as reptiles, amphibians, freshwater fish, and large insects. It is essentially nocturnal or crepuscular, being able to locate its prey by sound even in total darkness. It hunts by searching flight and by hovering, diving onto the prey and catching it with its feet. Indigestible matter is regurgitated in the form of large pellets, which often accumulate thickly below a favoured roost-site.

Breeding: The male establishes a territory and selects a potential nest-hole, advertising his presence by flying backwards and forwards over the territory, screeching. When a female is attracted, the male may hover in front of her, legs dangling. Courtship includes pursuit flights, mutual allopreening, and feeding of the female by the male. The pair-bond is formed during the winter months, at least one month before laying. The male shows the female the potential nest-site/sites, which may be in a building or in a tree, by flying in and out of it/them, purring quietly. The female sits in the nest-site for some time before laying, so that pellets accumulate, from which she makes a bed for the eggs. In March or April, the first clutch of 4-7 eggs is laid. Incubation lasts nearly 5 weeks and is by the female alone. Both parents care for and feed the young. Fledging takes about 7-8 weeks, the young becoming independent 3-5 weeks later. When there is a second clutch, it is laid about 100 days after the start of the first clutch. The age of first breeding is one year old. The pair-bond is monogamous (occasionally bigamous) and probably lasts for life.

Hints on recognition: The heart-shaped 'face' and pale colouring of this owl are diagnostic. The upperparts are yellowish-brown, spotted and streaked with light grey, and the underparts are pure white. In flight, seen in the dark by artificial light, this species appears to be all white. Although the nominate race *Tyto alba alba* breeds throughout western Europe, the Iberian population is lightly spotted grey on the underparts, resembling the North African race *T. a. Taerlangeri*.

152

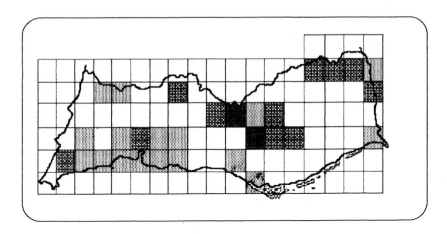

Hints on finding: A search by torchlight at night around the neighbourhood of a country village, especially where there is a traditional type of church with an open steeple or tower, can be fruitful.

Confirmation of breeding: As with other nocturnal species, coverage may not be complete and often confirmation of breeding was difficult to obtain.

Number of rectangles in which recorded: 30
Possible breeding: 0
Probable breeding: 10
Confirmed breeding: 20

OTUS SCOPS

SCOPS OWL

Portuguese name: Mocho-d'orelhas.

Distribution: The Scops Owl breeds in southern and eastern Europe, northern Africa, and Central and S.W. Asia. Although it is to be found in all parts of Portugal, it is more common in the north-east than elsewhere (CEMPA).

Status in the Western Palearctic: There has been a marked contraction in the northern part of its range, mainly due to changes in habitat and to fewer large insects. This species would appear to have been common in Portugal in Coverley's time, whereas today it is primarily a passage migrant through the Algarve, with a few overwintering. It was not shown to breed in the Algarve in the national atlas. The main wintering area of the various European populations is not known, but is thought to be in the northern Afrotropics.

Preferred habitat: Open oakwoods, although during passage it can be found in most habitats, including gardens. The single proved breeding which occurred during the course of the BBA was in a small area of mature oaks near an isolated farm. It is tolerant of some human disturbance, but does not use buildings for nesting or roosting.

Food: Large insects and other invertebrates, caught at night. In a study in southern Spain, it was found that invertebrates comprised more than 94% by number of the prey taken (Herrera and Hiraldo 1976). It will also take small birds, reptiles, amphibians, and mammals. It hunts mainly from a perch, swooping down to catch the prey with its feet, although moths are often caught in aerial pursuit and small prey is sought on the ground on foot. Indigestible matter is regurgitated in the form of large pellets.

Breeding: Migratory individuals return to the breeding grounds in March, when the male establishes a nesting territory. He advertises his presence by means of a monotonously repeated 'tyoo'. The longest nonstop session of calls recorded is 900 calls in 40 min (BWP, 1985). Unpaired females may also call, to attract males. During courtship, the female answers the male with her own call, forming a duet with his. The male shows her several prospective nest-holes, in buildings or old trees. He sits in the entrance to the hole, with his rear protruding for several minutes, before entering, scratching the floor and calling. The female chooses a hole and lays one clutch of 4-5 eggs in April in the bare cavity. Incubation is by the female alone and takes 3 1/2 weeks. During this period, and whilst the chicks are very small, the female summons the male to bring food by sticking her head out of the nest-hole and calling him. Both parents care for and feed the young, although the male provisions the nest at first while the female broods. Fledging takes 3-4 weeks and the young become independent 1-2 weeks later. The age of first breeding is not known but is probabaly one year old. The pair-bond is monogamous and is renewed annually where the birds are migratory. It is not known whether resident pairs remain together outside of the breeding season or not.

Hints on recognition: This tiny owl can easily be confused with the common Little Owl (for which, see that species). The Scops Owl, however, has small but distinct 'ear-tufts' and wide whitish 'eye-brows', giving it a rather frowning aspect, and its plumage is perfectly camouflaged as the trunk of a tree. The Little Owl, on the hand, is simply streaked and spotted and has no 'ear-tufts'.

154

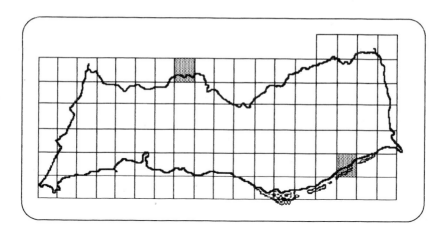

Hints on finding: This species was found breeding in one rectangle only and therefore no help can be given in this section. The sound of its call is no indication of its breeding as migrants frequently sing on their passage through the Algarve. In addition, its call closely resembles the common Midwife Toad.

Confirmation of breeding: As with other nocturnal species and for reasons given in Hints on finding, coverage may not be complete. Confirmed breeding was for one pair in the northern rectangle.

Number of rectangles in which recorded:	2
Possible breeding:	1
Probable breeding:	0
Confirmed breeding:	1

BUBO BUBO

EAGLE OWL

Portuguese name: Bufo-real.

Distribution: The Eagle Owl breeds in most of Europe, Asia and northern Africa. It is sparsely distributed, but not uncommon, throughout Portugal (CEMPA).

Status in the Western Palearctic: It is decreasing in much of its range, as a result of human persecution and poisonous seed-dressings, and has become extinct in many parts of Europe. It has recovered recently in some areas, following re-introductions and protection. In Portugal, it would appear to have declined markedly since Coverley's time. In the Algarve, the population is stable in the north but is decreasing rapidly in the south because of widespread urbanization. It is resident.

Preferred habitat: Open or sparsely wooded country, with steep rocky slopes. The presence of suitable ledges and/or trees for nesting and roosting is important. It avoids dense forests. It is tolerant of some human disturbance within its hunting range, where it is not persecuted, but will not tolerate disturbance near the nest, readily abandoning eggs and even young.

Food: Mainly mammals and birds, but it will also take eggs, reptiles, amphibians, fish, and occasionally invertebrates. The list of recorded prey is very long, but some of the more unusual mammals include young badgers and roe deer, lambs, calves, and wild boar. In studies carried out in southern France (Blondel and Badan 1976) and central Spain (Perez Mellado 1980), the greatest proportion of prey proved to be rabbits and hares. Although it usually waits on an open perch and swoops onto passing prey, it is said to search for roosting birds and kill them in their sleep (Glutz and Bauer 1980). It will also take the whole contents of the nests of such species as the Buzzard and the Grey Heron, including the incubating or brooding adults.

Breeding: The male selects a territory during the autumn months and advertises it with a far-carrying (up to 4km) call of "BOOO-hu" from a high tree-top or ridge. When a female is attracted, she duets with him, calling with a higher-pitched version of his call. In December, the male shows the female suitable nest-sites, in holes amongst rocks or on rocky ledges, entering the holes and scraping, whilst calling excitedly. The female chooses a site and lays one clutch of 2-4 eggs in early January. Established pairs use the same 1-2 nest-sites for several years. Incubation takes 5 weeks and is by the female alone, the male provisioning the nest until the chicks are about one month old. The young are cared for by both parents and fledge at about 8 weeks old, although they often walk out of the nest at 4 weeks old. They become independent after a further 12-16 weeks, but stay within the parents' territory until September or October. The age of first breeding is 2-3 years old. The pair-bond is monogamous and lasts for life.

Hints on recogniton: This huge owl, with a wing-span of up to 188cm, can only be confused with the Long-eared Owl (see Appendix I) if not seen well. When seen perched, the long 'ear-tufts' are particularly noticeable, although the smaller Long-eared Owl also has 'ear-tufts'. The latter, however, has a heart-shaped face when the 'ears' are lowered and is very heavily streaked over the entire underparts, whereas the Eagle Owl has a raptor-like face and is streaked on the breast only. In flight, the Eagle Owl is dark on the under-wing, whereas the Long-eared Owl is pale.

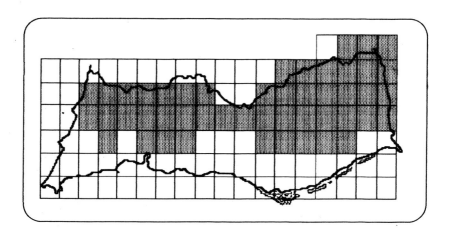

Hints on finding: A visit to the mountains an hour before dawn in November or December will usually enable the observer to hear this species call. The local people will readily confirm its whereabouts if asked for "boofoo".

Confirmation of breeding: As with other nocturnal species, coverage may not be complete and confirmation of breeding was difficult to obtain. It was, however, found in all likely habitats. See Black Kite for a general explanation of the map.

Number of rectangles in which recorded: 48
Confirmed breeding: 20

ATHENE NOCTUA

LITTLE OWL

Portuguese name: Mocho-galego.

Distribution: The Little Owl is to be found in almost all temperate latitudes of Europe, northern Africa, and Asia. It was introduced into Britain in the late 19th century and into New Zealand. It is well distributed throughout Portugal, although it is more common in the southern half of the country than in the north (CEMPA).

Status in the Western Palearctic: It has decreased recently in much of Europe, as a result of pesticides and loss of habitat, including loss of suitable nest-sites. The population would appear to be stable in the Algarve, however, outside of heavily-urbanized areas.

Preferred habitat: Open, dry country with plentiful old trees and stone-walls, such as the sequeiros found over much of the southern half of the Algarve. It avoids woods, wetlands, cereal crops, dunes, treeless terrain, and mountain-tops. It is tolerant of considerable human disturbance, where it is not persecuted.

Food: Small mammals and birds, reptiles, amphibians, and large invertebrates. It mainly catches its prey from a perch, but it will also search on foot for invertebrates on the ground. Although it will hunt during the night, as other owls do, it frequently hunts during the daytime, including at noon in the middle of summer.

Breeding: The male establishes a territory during the winter months and advertises his presence, during the day as well as the night, by loud shrieks, sometimes rapidly repeated in a crescendo. When a female is attracted, he shows her several potential nest-holes, in old trees or amongst stones, from which she chooses one. During the winter, she cleans out the nest-hole and spends most of the daytime sitting in it. This hole may be re-used in subsequent years if it is successful. The pair-bond is strenghthened by frequent allopreening and copulations throughout the year, regardless of breeding. The male and female may also duet, the male calling a questioning "hoo" and the female answering with a higher, softer "hoo". In April, one clutch of 2-4 eggs is laid. Incubation is by the female alone, the male provisioning her, and takes 4 weeks. The young are brooded and fed by the female, whilst the male catches and brings the food to her. Fledging takes 5 weeks, although the chicks are able to walk about at 3 weeks old and sometimes leave the nest at that age. The young can fly well by 5 weeks old but do not become independent for a further 3 weeks. Siblings will frequently eat one another, so that often only one or two chicks survive to fledge. The age of first breeding is one year old. The pair-bond is monogamous and usually for life, although the male and female will often occupy separate parts of their territory after the young have become independent until the renewal of breeding activities.

Hints on recognition: The only species with which this small owl can be confused is the Scops Owl (for which, see that species), which rarely breeds in the Algarve. It is medium-brown spotted with white on the upperparts, white with brown streaks on the underparts. It has a rounded head and silhouette. The flight is undulating or gliding and the wings appear broad and rounded.

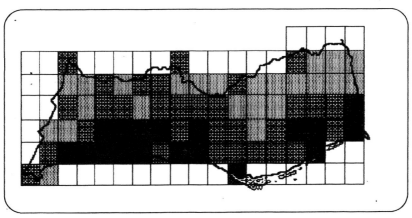

Hints on finding: This species can commonly be seen and heard almost anywhere in the lowland sequeiros. It frequently perches on overhead wires, especially in the western Algarve where there are few trees.

Confirmation of breeding: Owing to this species' diurnal habits and preference for lowland orchards, breeding confirmation was higher and coverage better than with the other owls. Coverage inland may not be complete, however, especially along the northern borders in areas with difficult access.

Number of rectangles in which recorded: 73
Possible breeding: 1
Probable breeding: 11
Confirmed breeding: 61

STRIX ALUCO

TAWNY OWL

Portuguese name: Coruja-do-mato.

Distribution: The Tawny Owl is to be found in most of Europe, except the extreme north, as well as south-west and central Asia through to south-east Asia. It is well-distributed throughout Portugal, although it is more common in the central part of the country than elsewhere (CEMPA).

Status in the Western Palearctic: Although this species declined during the 19th century in some areas, owing to persecution, it has since recovered through protection and has spread northwards. Its status in Portugal does not appear to have changed since Coverley's time, when it was mostly to be found in the centre of the country. It is resident.

Preferred habitat: Mature oakwoods. It particularly favours parklands, where there are plentiful old trees with holes for nesting and and where there is easy access to water. It avoids unbroken forests, treeless terrain, and wetlands. It is tolerant of some human disturbance where it is not persecuted.

Food: Mainly rodents, including young rabbits, but it also takes other mammals, amphibians, birds, and invertebrates. Although it will occasionally hunt in the daytime, it is normally nocturnal. It primarily hunts from a perch, swooping or gliding onto prey which is located by sound. It will also hunt, however, by flying in a zig-zag pattern over open ground and it occasionally hovers. In addition, it sometimes takes bats in flight, chicks from nests, and will wade in water for fish. Indigestible items are regurgitated in the form of pellets.

Breeding: The male selects a territory during the autumn months and advertises his presence with loud hoots: the familiar drawn-out and wavering "hoooooo". The territory serves for all activities and, once established, is maintained for life by the pair. When a female is attracted, she will call "too-wit", which is answered by his "twoo". This duet is popularly, but erroneously, ascribed to one bird. The pair-bond is further strenghthened by courtship feeding and allopreening. The pair, together or independently, inspect prospective nest-holes during the winter, although the female makes the final selection. This hole may be used in successive years or in rotation with one or two other holes. She cleans out the hole and makes a slight scrape, in which she lays one clutch of 2-4 eggs in late February or early March. Incubation is by the female alone and takes one month. The chicks are brooded and fed by the female only, whilst the male provisions the nest. The young fledge when they are 5 weeks old, although they usually leave the nest at 4 weeks old, and remain dependent on the parents for a further 3 months. The age of first breeding is 1-2 years old and the young breed as close as possible to the natal site. The pair-bond is monogamous and lasts for life.

Hints on recognition: This owl is approximately twice the size of the Little Owl and appears to be brown all over, heavily streaked. When seen clearly, the two separate discs of pale feathers round the eyes are diagnostic. Two morphs occur in roughly equal proportions: a dark grey and a rufous.

160

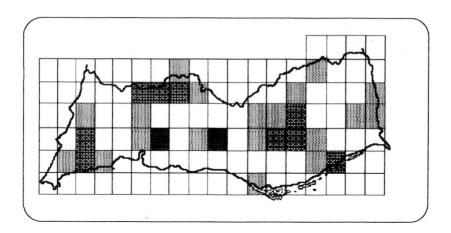

Hints on finding: The presence of this species can be quickly ascertained by the distinctive hoot, mainly heard at night in October-November and February-March. It is difficult to see, however, as it remains motionless and perfectly camouflaged when approached in daylight.

Confirmation of breeding: As with other nocturnal species, coverage may not be complete and confirmation of breeding was not always possible to obtain.

Number of rectangles in which recorded:	30
Possible breeding:	2
Probable breeding:	10
Confirmed breeding:	18

161

CAPRIMULGUS EUROPAEUS

NIGHTJAR

Portuguese name: Noitibó da Europa.

Distribution: Except for the extreme north, the Nightjar is widely distributed in Europe, north-west Africa, the Middle East and Central Asia.

Status in the Western Palearctic: It has decreased markedly throughout its entire range during most of this century and, although the exact cause for this decline is not yet known, loss of habitat is possibly a major factor. Coverley considered this species as being fairly common in Portugal but it is now generally regarded as a scarce breeder (CEMPA). There was no confirmed breeding shown anywhere in the national atlas nor indeed any presence at all in the Algarve. BWP (1985) also shows it as being absent from the region. The species is a summer visitor to Europe, generally arriving during late April or early May and departing again August to October for its wintering grounds in the central and southern latitudes of Africa.

Preferred habitat: Open, dry heathland with scattered trees, or woodland margins and clearings. It favours low hills but avoids mountains, the littoral, forests, tall grass or crops, reedbeds, and areas of human disturbance, although it may occur in these habitats on migration.

Food: Insects, especially moths and beetles, caught mainly at night. Prey may be taken in sustained hunting flight or may also be caught by short flights from a low perch or from the ground.

Breeding: Males arrive on the breeding grounds first, followed by the females a week or two later. The male claims a territory by singing from an elevated perch and often sings throughout the night, although most activity is at dusk and dawn. When the female arrives, the male follows her in slow courtship flight, gliding with wings raised and tail depressed, interspersed with wing-claps. The male probably chooses the nest-site and makes a slight scrape on the ground, in which the female lays 2 eggs. Incubation is mainly by the female and takes 2 1/2 to 3 weeks. The young are cared for and fed by both parents, with the female brooding them for the first 2 weeks, but they are able to walk away from the nest soon after hatching. Fledging takes about 2 1/2 weeks and the young remain dependent on the adults for a further 2 1/2 weeks. It is thought that a second clutch is often laid when the young of the first brood are almost fledged. When this happens, the male cares for the first brood whilst the females lays the second clutch. The pair-bond is monogamous and of seasonal duration only, although fidelity to the nest-site may result in the re-formation of the bond in subsequent years.

Hints on recognition: The Nightjar is a medium-sized, long-winged bird, perfectly camouflaged to resemble the ground on which it spends most of the day during the breeding season. When flushed, it flies up just in front of the intruder, showing large white patches on the tail (and wings in the case of the male). This species closely resembles the much larger Red-necked Nightjar (for which, see that species), which also breeds in the Algarve. Both species are nocturnal and there is no clear habitat separation between the two. If both sexes are seen together, the presence of large white spots on the wings and tail of one but not the other will usually distinguish this species, however the only sure way is to hear the churring song of the male.

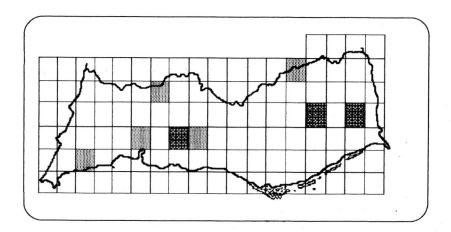

Hints on finding: As this species is so scarce in the Algarve, the best method of locating it is to listen at night for the male's churring song in any suitable habitat. Although this song might be mistaken for that of an insect, it is distinctive and diagnostic once learned.

Confirmation of breeding: This species' nocturnal habits, together with its close resemblance to the common Red-necked Nightjar, mean that coverage was almost certainly incomplete. All records for the BBA were for single years only.

Number of rectangles in which recorded: 8
Possible breeding: 1
Probable breeding: 6
Confirmed breeding: 1

CAPRIMULGUS RUFICOLLIS

RED-NECKED NIGHTJAR

Portuguese name:
Noitibó-de-nuca-vermelha
(Pássero-morcego).

Distribution: The Red-necked Nightjar breeds in the Iberian Peninsula and North Africa only. It occurs in most of Portugal, except the north-east, but is most common in the Alentejo and the Algarve (CEMPA).

Status in the Western Palearctic: According to Coverley, the Nightjar was more common than this species in Portugal in his time, whereas the reverse would be true today. This could reflect either an increase in the population or that Coverley took most of his observations from the north-east. Apart from a retreat away from the areas of urbanization on the south coast, there appears to be no change in its status in the Algarve. It is a summer visitor, wintering in West Africa.

Preferred habitat: Gentle slopes with sparse vegetation and some trees, including eucalyptus plantations with numerous clearings and tracks. It particularly favours rolling terrain, with no sharp changes in altitude, which has a mixture of open ground, scrub, and trees. It avoids the tops of mountains, unbroken forests, treeless grasslands, wetlands, and sand-dunes (although it will use these on migration). It is tolerant of limited human disturbance.

Food: Large insects, especially moths, which are caught mainly in flight at twilight and at night. It takes prey, which it feels coming in contact with its rictal bristles and highly sensitive palate lining, and stores it in a cavity in the mouth for digesting later. It will also search for prey, such as beetles or grasshoppers, on the ground.

Breeding: Soon after arrival in early May, the male selects a territory. He advertises his presence by his distinctive song, variously rendered as "Ka-KEK" or "Ta-TOK", repeated continuously and rapidly for several minutes at a time during the night. It is this song which gives the species the Algarvian names of Cacaque and Cavaca. When a female is attracted, he pursues her in aerial courtship, frequently clapping his wings loudly. The female makes a shallow scrape on the ground, in the open or among scant vegetation. There is no lining to the nest and, frequently, the two eggs are laid in a natural hollow or depression. Incubation is mainly by the female and takes 2 1/2 weeks. The young are fed and cared for by both parents, although the male alone will often care for them when the female begins incubating the second clutch, if the young are almost fledged. Fledging takes 2 1/2 weeks, although the chicks can walk away from the nest soon after hatching, sometimes walking up to 50m per day. The parents search for the chicks by hovering on returning from hunting. The young are independent at 4-5 weeks old and probably breed for the first time at one year old. The pair-bond is monogamous and of seasonal duration only.

Hints on recognition: It is a medium-sized, long-winged bird, camouflaged perfectly to resemble the ground on which it spends most of the day. When flushed, it flies up just in front of the intruder, showing large white patches on the tail and wings. This species closely resembles the much smaller Nightjar (for which, see that species). Both species are nocturnal and there is no clear habitat separation between the two. If two birds are seen together, the presence of large white spots on the wings and tail of both may indicate this species, but they could be two males. The only sure way is to hear the diagnostic song of the male.

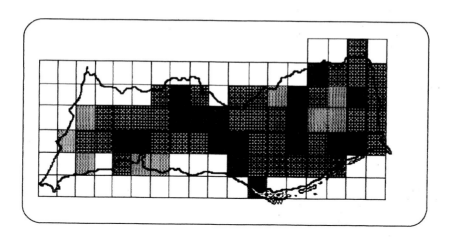

Hints on finding: The location of its distinctive song, given mainly just after dusk or shortly before dawn, is the easiest way of finding this species. Observation of the area in June, if it is not obscured by trees, will often produce glimpses of the bird hovering or hawking in the late evening. A drive along suitable tracks after dark will usually catch it in the headlights.

Confirmation of breeding: As with other nocturnal species, coverage may not be complete and confirmation of breeding was not always possible to obtain.

Number of rectangles in which recorded: 60
Possible breeding: 0
Probable breeding: 15
Confirmed breeding: 45

APUS APUS

SWIFT

Portuguese name: Andorinhão-preto.

Distribution: The Swift breeds throughout Europe, except the extreme north, along the north-west coast of Africa, and in much of Asia. It is well-distributed and fairly common throughout Portugal (CEMPA).

Status in the Western Palearctic: It is thought to have increased during the last century, owing to the species adapting well to human urbanizations and using buildings for nesting. The population in the Algarve would appear to be stable or slightly increasing. It is a summer visitor, wintering mainly in Zaire and Tanzania south to Zimbabwe and Mozambique. Flocks of 100 birds or more are regularly seen in the Algarve during the winter, when they hawk for insects ahead of a front and are blown northwards.

Preferred habitat: Sea-cliffs and towns. Providing that there are ample nest-sites and plentiful flying prey, the surrounding countryside over which it hawks for insects is irrelevant. All activities, excepting incubation but including sleeping, are carried out on the wing.

Food: Almost entirely flying insects and airborne spiders, which are taken exclusively in flight. This species frequently hawks insects blown upwards before a front, when it may hunt as high as 1km above ground-level. Normally, however, it flies relatively low where there is the greatest density of prey to be found. In a study in Gibraltar, (Finlayson 1979), it was estimated that some 18 million insects were taken by breeding Swifts every day.

Breeding: Colonial. Both sexes arrive at the breeding colony in late March or early April. The male selects a nest-site in a hole, crevice, or ledge in a cliff or building. Warehouses or railway-stations with open roofs, churches with towers, and castle-walls are particularly favoured. Unmated females prospect suitable holes, looking for one which contains an unmated male. When such a male is found, she enters tentatively, showing her white throat as an appeasement gesture and inviting allopreening. The pair will defend the area immediately around the nest-site, but they do not hold any other territory. The nest-site is re-used every year by the pair and even retained if one partner dies and a new mate is found. Both sexes collect grass, leaves, and feathers from the air and make a shallow nest, cemented with saliva. One clutch of 2-3 eggs is laid. Incubation is by both parents and takes about 3 weeks. The chicks are cared for and fed by both parents. Fledging takes about 6 weeks and the young become independent immediately. The age of first successful breeding is probably 4 years old, although juveniles frequently pair and build nests at one year old. Young birds rarely, if ever, return to the natal site to breed. The pairbond is monogamous and usually lasts for life, although it is not maintained during the winter months.

Hints on recognition: Swifts are frequently thought of together with swallows and martins, even though they are not even slightly related. Swifts have extremely long scythe-shaped wings, are all black except for a small pale patch on the throat, and fly very fast with little flapping of the wings. The only species with which the Swift can be properly confused is the Pallid Swift (for which, see that species). Early in the season, when only adults are flying, these two species can be separated in good light by the Swift appearing to be jet black, whereas the Pallid Swift appears to be dark brown.

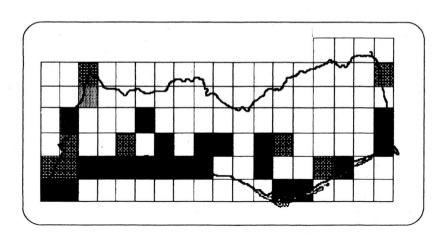

Hints on finding: This species can commonly be seen wheeling and screaming over such cities and towns as Lagos, Portimão, Silves, Faro, Olhão, Tavira, and Vila Real de Stº António, as well as many others.

Confirmation of breeding: The Swift feeds well away from the breeding area and so only probable and confirmed breeding are shown.

Number of rectangles in which recorded: 30
Probable breeding: 0
Confirmed breeding: 30

APUS PALLIDUS

PALLID SWIFT

Portuguese name: Andorinhão-pálido.

Distribution: The Pallid Swift is to be found in southern Europe, extending into S.W. Asia and the Middle East, as well as being sparsely distributed in most of the northern half of Africa. In the Western Palearctic, it is mainly confined to the Mediterranean Basin. It breeds throughout the southern two-thirds of Portugal, but is most common on the Algarve coast (CEMPA).

Status in the Western Palearctic: This species is nowhere common, but is thought to be increasing in France. Its actual status anywhere in its range is not known precisely, because of its similarity to the common Swift. It would appear to have been rare in Coverley's time, although its apparent absence could be through difficulties in identification. The population in the Algarve is, however, probably increasing. It is a summer visitor, wintering in central Africa.

Preferred habitat: Sea-cliffs. It occasionally nests in trees, including palm-trees, and in buildings. As with the Swift, providing that there are ample nest-sites and plentiful flying prey, the surrounding countryside over which it hawks for insects is irrelevant. All activities, other than incubation, are carried out on the wing and so the terrain is unimportant. It is less tolerant of human disturbance than the Swift and rarely nests in towns.

Food: Mainly flying insects, taken exclusively on the wing. It is said to fly lower than the Swift and to take a wider range of prey, including flying ants, beetles, dragonflies, spiders, etc.

Breeding: Colonial, often with the Swift or Alpine Swift. Birds return from their winter quarters in April and establish possession of nest-sites. The way in which nest-sites are found or pairs formed is not known, but it is probably the same as for the Swift. It would appear that the air-space above the colony is defended against birds from other colonies, the birds being able to recognize individual members of their own colony. The pair gathers grass and feathers from the air and forms a shallow nest, cemented with saliva, in a hole or crevice. Two clutches of 2-3 eggs are laid. Incubation is by both sexes equally and takes about 3 weeks. The chicks are cared for and fed by both parents. Fledging takes nearly 7 weeks and the young become independent immediately afterwards. The age of first breeding is not recorded, but is thought to be the same as for the Swift. The pair-bond is monogamous and probably lasts for life, owing to the fidelity of both sexes to the nest-site.

Hints on recognition: It is very similar to the Swift (for which, see that species). See also that species for separation of swifts from swallows and martins. Early in the season, when only adults are flying, it can be seen in good light that the Pallid Swift is dark brown whereas the Swift is blackish. Later in the season, however, when brownish juvenile Swifts are flying, identification becomes more difficult. Both have pale throats and forked tails. When both species are seen together clearly, it may be observed that the Pallid Swift has a broader and flatter head and a slightly shorter, more roundly forked tail. Sometimes, its flight may appear slower, with heavier wing-beats, and may include more planing.

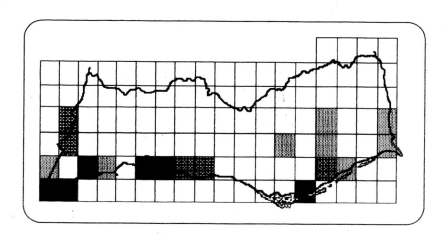

Hints on finding: A walk along the sea-cliffs of the Cape St. Vincent Peninsula or along the cliffs between Albufeira and Portimão will generally provide good views of this bird.

Confirmation of breeding: This species feeds well away from the breeding area and so only probable and confirmed breeding are shown. Confusion with the similar Swift has probably resulted in some under-recording.

Number of rectangles in which recorded: 19
Probable breeding: 2
Confirmed breeding: 17

APUS MELBA

ALPINE SWIFT

Portuguese name: Andorinhão-real.

Distribution: The Alpine Swift breeds around the Mediterranean Basin, reaching as far north as Germany and extending through south-west and central Asia as far as Sri Lanka, as well as at scattered sites throughout eastern and southern Africa. In Portugal, it is to be found mainly in the north-east and south-west, the biggest colonies being on the Douro and the second biggest in the Algarve (CEMPA).

Status in the Western Palearctic: It has recently increased its range to the north, including the first proved breeding in Germany in 1955 (Glutz and Bauer 1980), probably owing to this species' adaptation to nesting in buildings. There would, however, appear to be no change in its status in Portugal since Coverley's time. It is a summer visitor to Europe, wintering in eastern and southern Africa in the same areas as African residents. Flocks of 100 birds of more, however, have been seen in midwinter in the Algarve, flying in front of a depression.

Preferred habitat: Sea-cliffs for nesting, although it will also use buildings. As with other swifts, providing that there are ample nest-sites and plentiful flying prey, the surrounding countryside over which it hawks for insects is irrelevant. The area over which it hunts, however, is greater than with other swifts and birds have been estimated to cover 600-1000km daily.

Food: Mainly flying insects and airborne spiders, caught exclusively in flight. It may sometimes feed at night on moths attracted to lights. Indigestible items are ejected as pellets.

Breeding: Colonial, often with Swifts and Pallid Swifts. In April, the males return to the nest-sites, in holes or on ledges, which they established when they were one year old. The females arrive shortly afterwards and rejoin their mates of the previous year. The pair-bond is renewed with mutual allopreening and billing. Soon after arrival, the pair begins to form a shallow nest of straw and feathers, which are gathered in flight and then cemented together with saliva. One clutch of 2-4 eggs is laid. Incubation is by both sexes equally and takes about 3 weeks. The young are cared for and fed by both parents and become independent from the time of fledging. Fledging takes about 7 weeks, although the young move about outside of the nest from about one month old onwards. The age of first breeding is at 2-3 years old and is rarely at the natal site. Although one year olds usually pair and establish a nest-site, they rarely breed successfully. The pair-bond is monogamous and often for life, perhaps because of a strong fidelity to the nest-site. It is not thought that the pair stays together during the winter months.

Hints on recognition: This swift is easily distinguished from other swifts. It is large, about 20% bigger than the Swift, and is strongly marked dark-brown (appearing almost black) and white. The upperparts, as well as the undersides of the wings and tail, are entirely dark brown, whereas the underside of the body is white with a brown collar. The call is totally different from the screeching of other swifts, being a high-pitched trill "titititititit" rising to a crescendo.

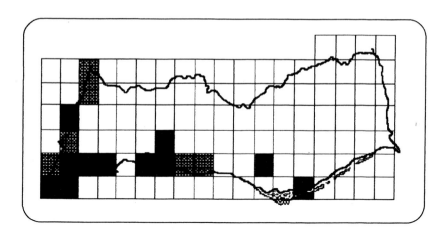

Hints on finding: A walk on the cliff-tops of the west coast or between Albufeira and Portimão will almost always produce good views of this species.

Confirmation of breeding: This species feeds well away from the breeding area (see under Preferred habitat) and so only probable and confirmed breeding are shown.

Number of rectangles in which recorded: 17
Probable breeding: 2
Confirmed breeding: 15

ALCEDO ATTHIS

KINGFISHER

Portuguese name: Guarda-rios-comum.

Distribution: The Kingfisher is to be found in most of temperate Europe, Asia, and northern Africa, as well as S.E. Asia as far south as Indonesia. It is well distributed throughout Portugal (CEMPA).

Status in the Western Palearctic: There has been a general decrease in numbers in many countries recently, because of water pollution, persecution, and the destruction of river-banks during river 'improvement'. Although it is still fairly common in the Algarve, here too it has decreased, particularly in the over-developed areas of the coast and in the Monchique area (see Chapter 2 Page 23). It is resident.

Preferred habitat: Rivers, marshes with pools, drainage ditches, etc. It particularly favours still or slow-moving, year-round freshwater, with banks for nesting. It will tolerate brackish or salt water, however, and commonly nests in the banks of salt-pans and salt-marshes. It will also nest in pine-woods, marshy grassland, lowland horticulture, and by dried-up rivers, with no water present, but where there is sufficient prey other than fish. It is tolerant of some human disturbance.

Food: Small freshwater fish, aquatic insects, and amphibians. Where there is no water, it will take small reptiles and large insects, and on the coast it readily takes crustaceans, especially small crabs. The favoured hunting technique is to perch, motionless, over a pool, then to dive into the water, snatching the prey and returning to the perch with it. It can be observed on a windy day, body moving with the perch but the head perfectly still. It will also hover, especially where there are no perches or when in pursuit of flying insects.

Breeding: In December or January, the male establishes and vigorously defends both a nesting territory and a separate feeding territory. He sings freely, when advertising his presence and when a female is attracted. The pair-bond is strengthened by courtship feeding and by aerial chases. In late January or early Februay, the male, helped by the female, digs a tunnel in a steep bank or clears out the tunnel from the previous year. At the end of the tunnel, a chamber is made in which 2, 3 or sometimes 4 clutches of 6-7 eggs are laid on the bare earth. The same tunnel may be used for all clutches, or new ones may be made during the breeding season. Incubation of the first two clutches is by both parents, but the third and fourth clutches may be incubated by one parent whilst the other cares for the previous brood. Incubation takes almost 3 weeks and fledging takes 3 1/2 to 4 weeks. The young are cared for and fed by both parents, or by one parent alone, and become independent within a few days of fledging. The age of first breeding is one year old, although juveniles from an early brood have been known to breed in their first year. The pair-bond is usually monogamous, but the male is sometimes polygamous. The male holds his territory all the year and the female may hold an adjacent or overlapping territory, in which case the pair-bond is often renewed each year. Otherwise, it is of seasonal duration only.

Hints on recognition: This brilliantly coloured little bird is vivid blue-green above, orange-chestnut below, with a white throat and patch on each side of the neck. The male's bill is almost all black, whereas the lower mandible of the female is mostly reddish. It cannot be confused with any other species.

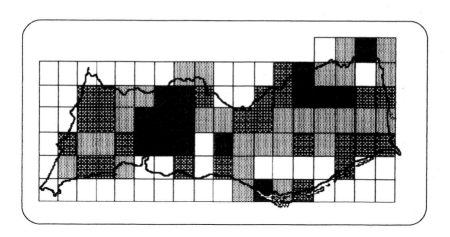

Hints on finding: A walk along the banks of suitable rivers, such as the Arade, Odelouca, and Boi, or by drainage ditches such as at Penina or Ludo, will usually produce good views of this species. It can also be readily seen from the hides at Quinta do Lago and Quinta da Marinha (see Where to watch breeding birds, E).

Confirmation of breeding:

Number of rectangles in which recorded:	68
Possible breeding:	3
Probable breeding:	13
Confirmed breeding:	52

MEROPS APIASTER

BEE-EATER

Portuguese name: Abelharuco-comum.

Distribution: The Bee-eater breeds in southern Europe, Asia Minor, south-west and central Asia, as well as the northern and southern extremities of Africa. It is confined to the north-east and to the southern two-thirds of Portugal (CEMPA).

Status in the Western Palearctic: It is subject to marked fluctuations in breeding range and periodically breeds outside of its normal limits. It has reached, and at least attempted to breed, as far north as Great Britain, Sweden, and Finland. There would appear to be no general change in its status in Portugal since Coverley's time. It has declined in much of the Algarve lowlands, however, as a result of the destruction, directly or indirectly, of its nest-sites.

Preferred habitat: The habitat in which it is found is determined by nesting requirements, i.e. warm, open terrain, with some trees or wires for perching and soft or sandy banks for nesting. It frequently uses river-banks, but its habit of using sand-pits or banks where sand is being extracted for urbanizations is contributing to its decline on the south coast.

Food: As its name would suggest, it commonly takes bees and wasps, which it rubs or bangs until the sting or venom is discharged. It will also take almost any other insect, e.g. dragonflies, butterflies, ants, etc. It hunts from a perch, such as a branch or overhead wires. Alternately gliding on stiff wings and flapping its wings rapidly, it twists and turns for up to several hundred metres in pursuit of prey, before returning to the same perch (or nearby). Occasionally, it will hunt by low searching flights or by hovering. It ejects indigestible items in the form of pellets.

Breeding: Individuals arrive at the breeding area in March, when most pair-bonds are formed. A week or so later, the pairs move to their traditional colony and continue with courtship. The male will alight next to, or close to, the female, sidling along till he touches her, often with food for her. He jerks rhythmically upwards, throat feathers ruffled, calling, sometimes opening one or both wings. It is said that the male starts the excavation of the nest-hole and selects the site, but often several holes are started and the female makes the final selection. The nest-tunnels are made in sloping or vertical banks, or sometimes into flat ground, and have an enlarged chamber at the inner end, which is not lined. Both sexes excavate equally. One clutch of 6-7 eggs is laid in April. Incubation takes nearly 3 weeks and is by both parents, the female sitting overnight. The young are fed and cared for by both parents, often helped by unmated birds. Fledging takes 3-4 weeks and the young probably become independent shortly afterwards, although they continue to use the nest-hole for roosting and may remain with the parents until at least migration. The age of first breeding is probably 1-2 years old. The pair-bond is monogamous and may last for life, although the relationship between the sexes is not known outside of the breeding season.

Hints on recognition: The Bee-eater has the most exotic colouring of all the Algarve's birds. The upperparts are a kaleidoscope of blues, greens, browns, and yellows; the underparts are turquoise with a bright yellow throat. In flight, the wings are held as rigid triangles and the long wedge-shaped tail, with two long protruding feathers, make a distinctive silhouette.

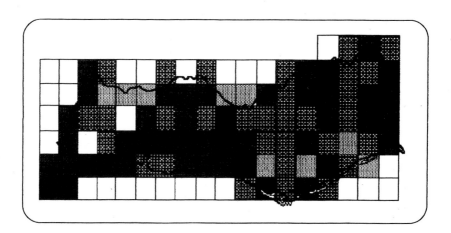

Hints on finding: Most rivers, as well as many sandy banks in the lowlands, contain colonies. Exceptional views can be had of this species from the hide at Quinta da Marinha (see Where to watch breeding birds, E).

Confirmation of breeding:

Number of rectangles in which recorded:	85
Possible breeding:	2
Probable breeding:	4
Confirmed breeding:	79

175

UPUPA EPOPS

HOOPOE

Portuguese name: Poupa.

Distribution: The Hoopoe is to be found throughout southern Europe and Asia, reaching almost to latitude 60⁰N, and in most of Africa. In Europe, it has sporadically bred in such countries as Great Britain, Denmark, and Sweden. It is well distributed throughout Portugal, but is least common in the north-west (CEMPA).

Status in the Western Palearctic: This species has decreased markedly in Scandanavia this century, probably owing to climatic changes, aggravated by habitat destruction and by pesticides. There would appear to be no change in its status in Portugal, except in areas of intense urbanization. It is a summer visitor to most of Europe, wintering with resident populations in Africa. Many birds overwinter in the Algarve, however, and probably the local population is resident and dispersive.

Preferred habitat: Dry, fairly open terrain, with numerous old trees or walls for nesting. It particularly favours well-established sequeiros. It avoids forests, wetlands, tall cereal crops, and mountains, but will tolerate sand-dunes where there are sufficient nest-sites. It is tolerant of human intrusion where it is not persecuted, often using mature gardens.

Food: Mainly invertebrates, especially large insects and their larvae or pupae, but it will also take reptiles and amphibians. It mainly forages on the ground, by walking about jabbing and probing with its long bill. Prey is located by sight or by random probing in the ground, dung heaps, rubbish, carrion, etc., where insects may congregate. Individuals may feed up to 2km from the nest-site.

Breeding: Many birds pair up during the autumn months, when moulting is complete, whereas others form pairs in February. The male selects a territory and begins to make his well-known "poop-poop" song from an elevated perch, whilst bowing his beak rhymically to his breast, neck feathers ruffled. When a female is attracted, there are vigorous sexual chases, often joined by other birds, with the male calling loudly and raising his crest up and down. The male searches for suitable nest-sites in trees or walls and shows them to the female by walking round and round the outside, then going in and out of them calling excitedly. The pair chooses which nest-hole will be used for the first clutch and cleans out any old debris which may be inside, including projections of wood on the interior walls. Sometimes the nest is lined with grass, leaves, pine-needles or moss, but sometimes it is left bare. Pairs which are formed in the autumn often lay the first clutch of 7-8 eggs in December and frequently have 4 broods (CEMPA). Pairs formed in the spring, lay the first clutch in March and have 2-3 broods. Incubation takes 2 or more weeks and is by the female alone. The young are cared for and fed by the female only, the food being brought by the male, who will rarely enter the hole. The male feeds the chicks through the entrance hole if another clutch is laid before they fledge. Fledging takes about 4 weeks, after which the young continue to be fed by the parents or the male for some time. The pair-bond is monogamous and of seasonal duration only.

Hints on recognition: The Hoopoe is a striking bird, pinky-brown with black-and-white striped wings and black-tipped erectile crest. It flaps its broad, rounded wings heavily in flight, when the pattern is particularly pronounced.

Hints on finding: The far-carrying call of "poop-poop" in a suitable habitat is a clear indication of the presence of this species. If the song is followed quietly to its source, the bird can almost always be seen well, as it is not a shy species. One should not look into its nest, however, as both adult and chick can aim foul-smelling liquid faeces with remarkable accuracy at an intruder.

Confirmation of breeding:

Number of rectangles in which recorded:	73
Possible breeding:	2
Probable breeding:	15
Confirmed breeding:	56

JYNX TORQUILLA

WRYNECK

Portuguese Name: Torcicolo.

Distribution: The Wryneck breeds in most of Europe, the middle latitudes of Asia, Algeria, and northern Tunisia. In the Iberian Peninsula, it is mainly restricted to the north of Spain and to the northern border of Portugal (CEMPA). The national atlas proved breeding in the central Algarve and the BBA shows it fairly well-distributed in the same area and north to the Alentejo border.

Status in the Western Palearctic: This species has declined markedly in much of its range and has become extinct in many areas. Although climatic changes, followed by habitat changes and pesticides, are thought to be the reason, the complete story is still not known. It would appear from the accounts of Reis Jr. and Coverley, that the Wryneck was not uncommon earlier this century, although the national atlas shows it as sparsely distributed in Portugal. In the Algarve, numbers appear to be stable, at least over the past two decades. It is a summer visitor, wintering in central Africa, although many overwinter in the Algarve.

Preferred habitat: Very open, mature oak-woods, such as parklands. It is also to be found in mature sequeiros and stands of trees by rivers. It avoids dense woodland and terrain with tall herbage, including cereal crops. It is shy and does not tolerate much human disturbance.

Food: Insects, especially ants and their larvae. Ants are taken from nests, either by digging them out with its bill or by breaking up the nest. It pecks at the easily available ants and larvae and then uses its long glutinous tongue to reach the more inaccessible prey. In addition to insects, it will occasionally take spiders, woodlice, frog tadpoles, and birds' eggs.

Breeding: The majority of birds return to the breeding grounds in March or April, when both sexes search for potential nest-holes. Both sexes call vigorously, which serves to attract a mate and to advertise the possession of a nest-site. The two birds approach one another, calling excitedly, until the female indicates submission. Both birds may continue advertising separate holes, but the female usually makes the final choice. Unlike other woodpeckers, Wrynecks do not make their own nest-holes but use existing ones in trees, walls, or banks. Both sexes clear out any debris inside, including the nests of other species which may already be using the hole, but do not add any lining. One or two clutches of 7-10 eggs are laid, the second clutch often being laid in the same nest whilst the first clutch orbrood is still there. Alternatively, a different hole may be used for the second clutch. Incubation takes nearlt two weeks and is by both sexes, although the female carries out the greater share. The chicks are cared for and fed by both parents and fledging takes about 3 weeks. The young become independent 1-2 weeks afterwards and breed for the first time at one year old. The pair-bond is monogamous and of seasonal duration only, although there is strong site-fidelity.

Hints on recognition: The Wryneck is only slightly smaller than a Song Thrush, which it closely resembles when seen briefly in flight. The plumage on its upperparts is perfectly camouflaged as a tree-trunk, whilst the throat and breast are warm brown finely barred with dark brown, the belly whitish spotted with brown. The distinctive manner in which it can twist its head over its back, or stretch it forwards with the bill pointing upwards, gives it its name.

178

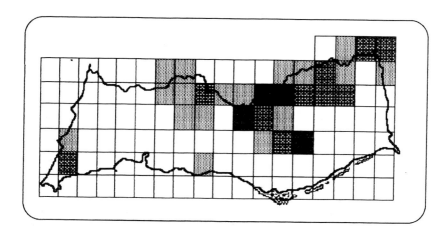

Hints on finding: This species is particularly common in the oakwoods around Ameixal, although its cryptic plumage makes it difficult to see. Its loud "ee-ee-ee-ee-ee", resembling a Kestrel, can be clearly heard during the period immediately preceding laying and is the best indicator of its presence.

Confirmation of breeding:

Number of rectangles in which recorded:	31
Possible breeding:	1
Probable breeding:	16
Confirmed breeding:	14

179

PICUS VIRIDIS

GREEN WOODPECKER

Portuguese name: Peto-verde.

Distribution: The Green Woodpecker is confined to Europe and the Middle East. It is absent from northern Europe, being unable to withstand cold winters. It is also absent from many parts of the Mediterranean coastline, especially from the islands, possibly because of the lack of suitable mature broadleaved woodland. It is more common in the northern and western-central regions of Portugal than in the remainder of the country, where it is mainly absent except for the Algarve (CEMPA).

Status in the Western Palearctic: It is fairly common throughout its breeding range, although there has been some decline in Italy. Despite its intolerance of cold weather, it has expanded its range northwards this century, numbers fluctuating with hard winters. In the Algarve, as well as in the rest of Portugal, there appears to be no change in its status since Coverley's time. It is resident and sedentary.

Preferred habitat: Parkland with mature oaks or scattered copses of mature broadleaf trees. It also favours scrub, where there are sufficient oaks present to provide nest holes, and sequeiros away from habitation. It avoids unbroken forest, although it will use broadleaf trees along the side of tracks or on the fringes of eucalyptus plantations. The foothills are preferred to either the mountain tops or the coastal belt.

Food: This species feeds almost entirely on adult and pupal ants. Its tongue, extending to more than 10cm long, is coated with a sticky secretion from the salival glands, enabling the bird to probe otherwise inaccessible tunnels and chambers of ant-hills. It feeds mostly on the ground, but it will sometimes search for ants on the trunks of trees or take other insects from rotten wood, etc.

Breeding: The pair-bond is formed during the winter, when both the male and the female can be heard repeatedly advertising their territories with a loud yaffle, sounding like laughter. Initially, each sex advertises its own hole and defends it against the other one, then each tries to attract the other one to its own hole for nesting. By February the nest-site is chosen. If neither existing hole is chosen, a new hole is excavated by the pair, although the male does most of the work. The hole has an entrance of 6cm dia. and is made in very soft wood, such as a dead and rotting tree. The same hole or tree is often used in successive years, but not necessarily by the same pair. One clutch of 5-7 eggs is laid in March. Incubation is by both sexes equally and takes about 2 1/2 weeks. The young are cared for and fed by both parents and fledging takes 3 1/2 to 4 weeks. They become independent 3-7 weeks afterwards and breed the following year. The pair-bond is monogamous and of seasonal duration only, but is often loosely maintained and renewed the following season owing to site-fidelity.

Hints on recognition: If seen feeding, this large greenish woodpecker is unmistakable in the Algarve. It hops freely on the ground, often well away from trees, rising in front of the observer with a loud "kyack". It rarely 'drums', as other woodpeckers do, but yaffles. Its flight, like all woodpeckers, is undulating, alternating gliding, its wings closed, with strong flapping. In the race *P.v.sharpei*, found in the Iberian Peninsula, the male shows a pronouced red moustachial streak, both sexes have little or no black on the cheeks, and the call is thinner and higher-pitched than that of other races.

M   F

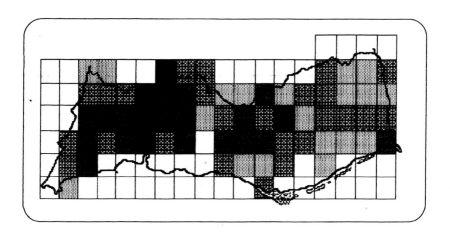

Hints on finding: When this species is feeding, it is often difficult to detect. If, however, the observer goes to any suitable habitat in the hills on a sunny day, especially in the early spring, the loud laughter-like 'yaffle' call is unmistakable.

Confirmation of breeding :

Number of rectangles in which recorded:	66
Possible breeding:	0
Probable breeding:	18
Confirmed breeding:	48

181

DENDROCOPOS MAJOR

GREAT SPOTTED WOODPECKER

Portuguese name:
Pica-pau-malhado-grande.

Distribution: The Great Spotted Woodpecker breeds in the middle latitudes of Europe and Asia, as far south as Hainan on the eastern sea-board of Asia, and in northern Africa, including the Canaries. It is well distributed throughout Portugal, although it is more common in the centre and the south than in the north (CEMPA).

Status in the Western Palearctic: During the 19th century there was a considerable decrease in Great Britain, followed by a recovery. It is common and stable in most of Europe, with some northward expansion this century. There would appear to be no recent change in its status in Portugal. It is resident.

Preferred habitat: Mature woodlands. It can be found in sequeiros and in more open country or scrub, where there are sufficient suitable trees for nesting. It is also common in farmland or even open grasslands, where it can use telephone poles for nesting and drumming. It avoids extensive or unbroken eucalyptus plantations, as well as treeless terrain. It is tolerant of limited human disturbance.

Food: Mainly insects. It rarely feeds on the ground, but actively searches for prey on trees by tearing off the bark with its bill. On dead or decaying trees, it can chisel holes up to 10cm deep for wood-boring beetles. Prey is caught with its tongue, which can extend 40mm, and impaling it on the harpoon-like tip or catching it with the sticky coating. During the breeding season it also takes a large number of birds' eggs and nestlings.

Breeding: Both sexes select and defend individual territories during the winter months. In January, they advertise their own roosting holes as a prospective nest-site by drumming on nearby trees or telephone poles. The pair-bond is formed slowly, after several weeks of pursuit-flights and aggressive encounters. When the pair has accepted one another, each shows the prospective nest-hole to the mate, but probably the female makes the final choice. In March, both sexes complete the excavation of the nest-hole, if necessary, so that it has an entrance diameter of 5-6cm and a chamber with an internal diameter of 11-12cm. The hole is made in a soft or rotten tree, or in a telephone pole, and may be used in subsequent years. One clutch of 4-7 eggs is laid. Incubation takes about 1 1/2 weeks and is by both sexes, although the male carries out the greater share. The young are cared for and fed by both parents, fledging taking about 3 weeks. The young are fed by both sexes for at least a further week, although frequently the brood is split between the parents and occasionally the female leaves before the chicks are fledged. The age of first breeding is probably one year old! The pair-bond is monogamous and of seasonal duration only, although it is often renewed the following year owing to site-fidelity.

Hints on recognition: It is about the same size as a Song Thrush, but appears larger owing to its greater bulk. It is conspicuously patterned black and white on the upperparts, and totally white on the underparts except for brilliant crimson on the under tail coverts. The Iberian race *D.m. hispanus*, is creamy-buff, rather than white, on the underparts. The male has a small red patch on the nape. It has a strongly undulating flight, showing a prominent white patch on the upperside of each wing, with spots on the trailing edge only (see also the Lesser Spotted Woodpecker).

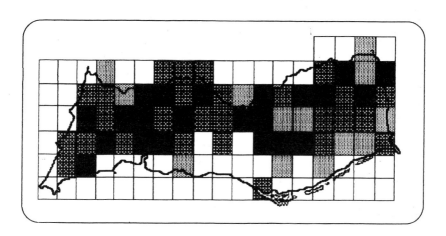

Hints on finding: It is most common in the foothills of the Serras, where its drumming or loud "chick" can be heard in suitable habitats. An inspection of telephone poles will quickly reveal its presence in an area, either from the existence of nest-holes or from the torn and broken condition of the top of the poles.

Confirmation of breeding:

Number of rectangles in which recorded: 62
Possible breeding: 0
Probable breeding: 8
Confirmed breeding: 54

DENDROCOPOS MINOR

LESSER SPOTTED WOODPECKER

Portuguese name:
Pica-pau-malhado-pequeno.

Distribution: The Lesser Spotted Wood-pecker breeds in the middle and northern latitudes of Europe, the middle latitudes of Asia, Algeria, and Tunisia. It is largely absent from the Iberian Peninsula, but was proved breeding at scattered localities in southern Portugal by the national atlas.

Status in the Western Palearctic: With the exception of Finland, where it is declining rapidly, there appears to be no change in its general status. In Portugal, Coverley mentioned that this species had been reported in the extreme north, on the Minho, but it was not found there by the national atlas. Its status in the Algarve is not known, but the BBA found it to be more common than hitherto supposed. It is resident.

Preferred habitat: Open or parkland-type oakwoods. It will also use copses and con-tinuous lines of broadleaved trees. It avoids treeless terrain or areas where it would have to make exposed flights. It is tolerant of some human disturbance and is occasionally to be found in gardens.

Food: Almost entirely insects. It rarely feeds on the ground, preferring to search for insects on the surface of trees. It is capable of removing small pieces of bark or rotten wood to find beetle larvae, but not to the extent of the Great Spotted Woodpecker. Occasionally it will eat fruit or take flying prey in aerial pursuit.

Breeding: Both sexes select and defend individual territories during the winter, drumming frequently, and established pairs maintain adjoining territories. From December onwards, the male will also call frequently and loudly. As with other wood-peckers, pair-formation is preceded by considerable aggression and chasing. The antagonistic drumming eventually becomes a duet and one bird will approach the other in a fluttering butterfly-like flight. Once the bond is formed, the pair excavates a new hole in a tree, often in a rotten side branch, the entrance having a diameter of 3 to 3.5cm and the chamber having an internal diameter of 10-12cm. The nest-hole is not normally re-used in subsequent years. One clutch of 4-6 eggs is laid in the bare hole in April. Incubation takes 1 1/2 weeks and is by both parents, the male incubating at night, or by the male alone. The chicks are cared for and fed by both parents, although often only the male feeds them. Fledging takes 2 1/2 to 3 weeks. The young remain with the parents for some time after fledging and often the brood is split between the parents. The age of first breeding is probably one year old. The pair-bond is monogamous and often lasts for more than one season, possibly owing to strong site-fidelity.

Hints on recognition: It is very small, being the same size as a Greenfinch. The upper-parts are boldly marked black and white, the underparts light buff with dark streaks. The male has a bright crimson cap, whereas the female has a white one. In flight, white spots cover almost all the upper sides of the wings and appear to form rows or horizontal stripes across the two wings. The drumming is higher-pitched and more rapid than that of the Greater Spotted Woodpecker. In addition, it readily calls, resembling a softer version of the calls of the Kestrel or the Wryneck. Iberian birds have deeper buff-brown foreheads and underparts than most other populations.

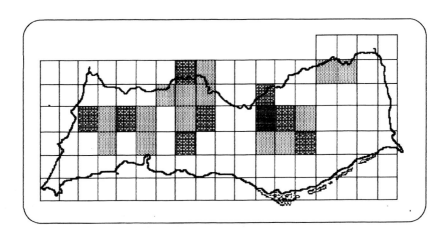

Hints on finding: The oakwoods to the south of Foia and around Cachopo or Barranco do Velho are the easiest to work. This tiny woodpecker is very difficult to see, however, as it remains amongst the smaller branches of mature trees, rather than on the trunk. The drumming combined with calling, heard mostly in the early spring, is the quickest way of pinpointing this species.

Confirmation of breeding: This quiet, tiny bird is easily overlooked in the canopy of mature oaks, resulting in probable under-recording of the species.

Number of rectangles in which recorded: 23
Possible breeding: 1
Probable breeding: 9
Confirmed breeding: 13

CALANDRELLA BRACHYDACTYLA

SHORT-TOED LARK

Portuguese name: Calhandrinha-comum.

Distribution: The Short-toed Lark breeds in southern Europe, south-western Asia, the middle latitudes of Asia, except the eastern sea-board, and northern Africa. It is well-distributed throughout the southern half of Portugal and along the north-eastern borders with Spain (CEMPA).

Status in the Western Palearctic: Although it has decreased in France, other populations would appear to be stable. Despite increased disturbance and loss of habitat on the south coast of the Algarve, there is no evidence of any general decrease in numbers. It is a summer visitor, wintering in central Africa.

Preferred habitat: Short dry grass, e.g. dunes, sandy coastal areas, and the parched grasslands of the north-east. It avoids forests and other arboreal habitats, but will tolerate sparse garigue and salt-marshes, where there are sufficient dry open areas. It is tolerant of considerable human disturbance.

Food: Insects and seeds. It will peck food from the ground or from low plants and will dig with its bill. Occasionally it will hover. It is said to drink saline water when necessary and that it is capable of surviving for months without any water at all.

Breeding: Semi-colonial. Birds return to the breeding grounds in February or March, when the female is said to select the territory, although the male advertises and defends it. The male gives an elaborate song-flight over the nesting area, which he mainly performs early or late in the day. He ascends steeply, giving the first part of the song, then continues climbing to 30-50m giving the main part of the song, whereupon he briefly hangs motionless in the sky or meanders erratically before fluttering down almost to the ground and starting again from the beginning. The female chooses a nest-site on the ground, partly sheltered by a tuft of vegetation, and forms a shallow depression lined with grass and leaves, which is then lined with feathers, wool and thistle-down. Two clutches of 3-5 eggs are laid. Incubation takes almost 2 weeks and is by the female alone. Fledging also takes almost 2 weeks, although the chicks leave the nest when about 10 days old. The young are brooded by the female alone but both parents defend and feed them. The first brood becomes independent shortly after fledging but the second brood remains with the parents for several weeks. The age of first breeding is one year old. The pair-bond is monogamous and of seasonal duration only.

Hints on recognition: All the larks and pipits are superficially similar, but the Short-toed Lark particularly resembles the Lesser Short-toed Lark (for which, see that species). Early in the season, when there are only adults to be found, it is relatively easy to separate the species when seen clearly. The Short-toed Lark is a warm brown on the upperparts, heavily streaked with black, and the underparts appear almost white. It has a chestnut cap, a white supercilium, and a blackish streak through the eye. Particularly noticeable is a black patch on the side of the neck just above the shoulder.

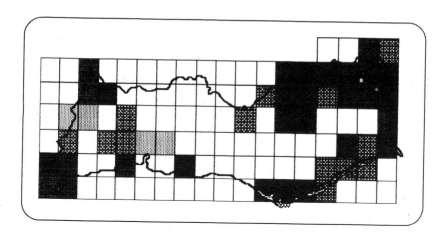

Hints on finding: Together with the Crested Lark, this is the most common lark to be found behind the sand-dunes of the south coast. It is relatively approachable and clear views can often be obtained if it is followed with binoculars to an open area. The sea-wall at Alvor is particularly advantageous.

Confirmation of breeding:

Number of rectangles in which recorded:	46
Possible breeding:	0
Probable breeding:	6
Confirmed breeding:	40

CALANDRELLA RUFESCENS

LESSER SHORT-TOED LARK

Portuguese name:
Calhandrinha-das-marismas.

Distribution: The Lesser Short-toed Lark is to be found in the Iberian Peninsula, northern Africa (including the Canaries), south-west Asia, and the middle latitudes of Asia. In Portugal, it is not known to have bred outside of the Algarve (CEMPA).

Status in the Western Palearctic: There is apparently no information on changes in status anywhere in its range. Coverley mentions this species having been recorded several times in the Algarve but did not know whether it bred or not. The national atlas shows it present in only one place in Portugal, in the south-west Algarve, whereas the BBA found it in most suitable habitats. It is resident.

Preferred habitat: Short, dry grass or extremely sparse heath with short grass. Unlike its congener the Short-toed Lark (for which, see that species), it is not normally associated with sand-dunes or sandy grass, nor with garigue, and it requires access to water. It avoids all well-vegetated terrain and is not tolerant of human disturbance.

Food: Mainly invertebrates, but also seeds including cereal grains. It pecks food from the ground or from low plants and will dig with its bill. It will also leap from the ground in pursuit of flying insects.

Breeding: It often breeds in association with the Short-toed Lark. In February, the male begins to sing strongly over the prospective nesting area. The song-flight pattern is similar to that of the Short-toed Lark, but the main song is more continuous and includes imitations of other species. The female answers him from the ground, upon which he lands near her and moves round her with 'light dancing steps' (BWP, 1988). In March, the female makes a shallow scrape on the ground in the shelter of a tussock. She lines the scrape with vegetation, then with an inner lining of fine material. One to two clutches of 3-4 eggs are laid. Incubation takes 12 days and is mainly by the female, although the male occasionally helps. Fledging takes 2 to 2 1/2 weeks, but the chicks leave the nest when about 9 days old, remaining near the nest at first then gradually moving further away. The young are cared for and fed by both parents, although the female carries out most of the brooding. The young become independent a few weeks after fledging and probably breed for the first time at one year old. The pair-bond is monogamous and may be of seasonal duration only.

Hints on recognition: Whereas the initial impression of the Short-toed Lark is rufous above and all white below, the Lesser Short-toed Lark appears to be dark to medium brown above and cream heavily streaked with brown below. It is nearer to a small pipit in build and colouring than to other Algarvian larks. Later in the breeding season, however, the streaked brown-coloured juvenile Short-toed Larks can cause confusion.

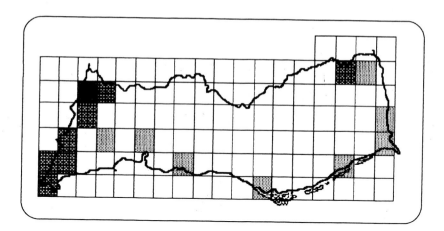

Hints on finding: It is most common on the flat grasslands inland from the west coast and is easiest to recognize early in the season when only adults are present. In the winter, small flocks can be found relatively easily on the inland salt-marshes and meadows along the Arade.

Confirmation of breeding: The similarity of this species to juvenile Short-toed Larks and the difficulty of getting good views for identification have led to confusion in the two species and probable under-recording of this less common species.

Number of rectangles in which recorded: 16
Possible breeding: 0
Probable breeding: 4
Confirmed breeding: 12

GALERIDA CRISTATA

CRESTED LARK

Portuguese name: Cotovia-de-poupa.

Distribution: The Crested Lark breeds in most of temperate Europe and Asia, and in the northern half of Africa. In Portugal, it is far more common in the southern half of the country than in the north (CEMPA).

Status in the Western Palearctic: It has declined this century in the north and east of Europe and has become extinct in Norway. It was apparently common in the north of Portugal in Coverley's time, but was scarce during the fieldwork for the national atlas. There appears to be no decrease in the Algarve, except in areas of high urbanization. It is resident.

Preferred habitat: Coastal grasslands, sand-dunes, salinas, and dry parts of saltings. Scrub, woods, tall vegetation, and mountains are avoided. It is tolerant of human disturbance and sometimes uses tilled land close to farms. It is often found in association with the Short-toed Lark on the south coast.

Food: Plant material, such as seeds and leaves, and invertebrates, especially beetles. Most food is taken from the ground, or from just below the surface by digging with its bill. It also pecks food from low plants and will take flying insects in aerial-pursuit. The chicks are fed almost entirely on insects, especially caterpillars and grasshoppers.

Breeding: During the winter months the male establishes a nesting territory, which he advertises by singing vigorously. The song may be given in flight, when he ascends up to 70m in the air and hovers into the wind, or it may be given from the ground or a low perch. In the morning, he often commences singing well before dawn. When a female is attracted, he lands near her, his crest erect, his feathers ruffled, and his tail fanned and raised vertically. He hops around her buoyantly as though dancing, then spreads his wings, fluttering them rapidly. Later, the male may show the female suitable nest-sites within his territory. In March, the female makes a shallow depression on the ground, in the open or in the shelter of a bush or tussock. She lines it with grass and often makes a dome to give it shade from the sun. Two to three clutches of 3-5 eggs are laid, a new nest for each clutch. Incubation takes almost 2 weeks and is by the female alone, although the male may protect the eggs while she is feeding. The young are cared for and fed by both parents, the female brooding them for the first week. Fledging takes at least 2 weeks, although the chicks leave the nest when about 9 days old. They are unable to fly well until 3 weeks old and frequently remain for several weeks more with the parents, or with the male alone if the female is incubating a second brood. The age of first breeding is one year old. The pair-bond is monogamous and probably lasts for more than the breeding season, owing to site-fidelity.

Hints on recognition: This lark is a bulky bird of non-descript streaked brown plumage and is very similar to the Thekla Lark (for which, see that species). Although these two larks may be found together on the Cape St. Vincent Peninsula, usually they occupy totally separate habitats. The call of "tee-teetee" from the Crested is thin- ner and higher-pitched, the bill is longer, the crest shorter, and the plumage paler with no rufous on the rump. In flight, the wings appear to be very broad and rounded, the undersides of which are a warm buff. The Iberian race *G.c.pallida* is paler than other European races.

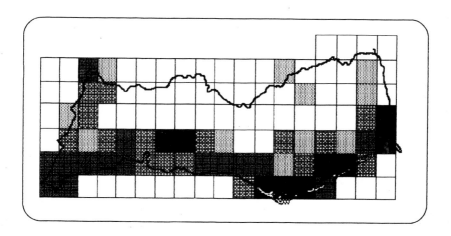

Hints on finding: This is the most common large lark on the salt-pans of Ludo, Tavira, and Castro Marim, and on the sandy grasses of Alvor and Quinta do Lago.

Confirmation of breeding: Confusion with the Thekla Lark may have led to under-recording in non-typical habitats.

Number of rectangles in which recorded: 51
Possible breeding: 0
Probable breeding: 10
Confirmed breeding: 41

GALERIDA THEKLAE

THEKLA LARK

Portuguese name: Cotovia-montesina.

Distribution: The Thekla Lark is to be found mainly in the Iberian Peninsula and North Africa, with small populations in southern France and eastern Africa. In Portugal, it is confined to the eastern borders with Spain and to the Algarve (CEMPA).

Status in the Western Palearctic: There is no information on the general status of this species. The population in the Algarve would appear to be stable, at least over the last two decades. It is resident and sedentary.

Preferred habitat: Very sparse, open scrub or heath. It particularly favours the rolling garigue and grasslands of the north-eastern Algarve, where it is often in association with the Short-toed Lark. It will tolerate dense scrub where there are plentiful bare patches of ground, but avoids mountain-tops and coastal habitats, except on the Cape St. Vincent Peninsula. Although not shy, it is not tolerant of human disturbance near the nest.

Food: Invertebrates and seeds. Most food is pecked from the ground, although it will leap into the air after flying insects and turn over stones with its bill in search of prey. The young are fed entirely on invertebrates.

Breeding: During the winter months, the male establishes a breeding territory, which he advertises by song from January onwards. He will ascend rapidly high into the air, singing and circling until a considerable height is reached, then drops silently to the ground.

He will also sing from a vantage point on the ground or from a low bush. If a female approaches, he pursues her, twittering excitedly. If she is attracted, he lands near her, raising his tail vertically and singing quietly. He circles her, alternately bobbing and 'curtseying', then spreads his wings, fluttering them rapidly. In February, the female makes a shallow depression lined with grass on the ground, in the open or in the shelter of a tussock or bush. Occasionally, she will make a complete platform-type nest low in a bush. Two clutches of 3-4 eggs are laid and a new nest is made for each clutch. Incubation takes almost 2 weeks and is by the female alone, although the male may protect the eggs while she is feeding. The young are cared for and fed by both parents, the female brooding them for the first week. Fledging is at about 15 days old. Although the chicks leave the nest when about 9 days old, they are unable to fly well until 3 weeks old, after which the family remain together for some weeks. The male will often care for the first brood whilst the female is incubating the second clutch. The age of first breeding is one year old. The pair-bond is monogamous and appears to last for several seasons or possibly for life, the pair remaining on territory throughout the year.

Hints on recognition: This lark is a bulky bird of non-descript streaked brown plumage and is very similar to the Crested Lark (for which, see that species). Although these two larks may be found together on the Cape St. Vincent Peninsula, they usually occupy totally separate habitats. Where they occur together, the song is heard to be more melodious and warbling with a lower pitch than that of the Crested. The bill is shorter, the crest longer, and the plumage noticeably darker with prominent rufous colouring on the rump. In flight, the wings appear to be very broad and rounded, the undersides of which are grey.

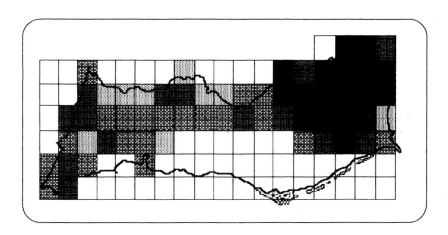

Hints on finding: This species is very numerous in the north-eastern Algarve and can be easily found anywhere along the Martim Longo to Alcoutim road, where the Crested Lark is absent.

Confirmation of breeding: Confusion with the Crested Lark may have led to under-recording in non-typical habitats.

Number of rectangles in which recorded: 61
Possible breeding: 1
Probable breeding: 8
Confirmed breeding: 52

LULLULA ARBOREA

WOODLARK

Portuguese name: Cotovia-pequena.

Distribution: The Woodlark is confined to the lower latitudes of Europe, to North Africa, and to south-west Asia. It is well-distributed throughout Portugal and is the most common lark (CEMPA).

Status in the Western Palearctic: Although numbers have decreased in much of its range, possibly as a result of climatic and habitat changes, there is no evidence of any general decrease in Portugal. There would appear to be a recent decline, however, in the western Algarve, probably because of increased eucalyptus afforestation and destruction of ground-cover. It is resident.

Preferred habitat: Parkland oak-woods, very open mature woodland (including sequeiros), and sparse scrub with scattered mature trees. As with other larks, it requires open or bare areas of ground on which to run but it also requires trees, from which to sing, and some undergrowth. Where the terrain is otherwise suitable but where there are no trees, it uses posts, walls, and overhead wires as song-posts. Unbroken woodland, bare ground, and coastal habitats are avoided. It is not shy, but is intolerant of human disturbance near the nest-site.

Food: Invertebrates and seeds. Food is taken by pecking on the surface of the ground or from low plants. The chicks are fed almost entirely on invertebrates.

Breeding: During the winter months, the male establishes a territory and, from January onwards, advertises his possession by song, mainly in the early morning. He spirals upwards in fluttering flight from the top of a tree, to a height of between 50m and 100m above ground, singing, then descends silently, often to the same tree. The song may also be given from the tree-top or from some other vantage-point. If a female approaches, the male pursues her vigorously, then lands by her with crest erect. If she is attracted, they will both perform mutual courtship, whereby they bob and curtsey, tails raised and spread, wings quivering, and breast feathers ruffled. Once paired, the female will also sing. In March, both sexes make several deep depressions in the ground, in the shelter of tussocks or plants. The female lines one with vegetation and then makes an inner lining of fine grass and hair. Two or three clutches of 3-5 eggs are laid, a new nest being made for each clutch. Incubation takes about 2 weeks and is by the female alone, the male escorting and guarding her. Fledging takes almost 2 weeks, but the young can leave the nest at 8 days old if they are disturbed. The young are cared for and fed by both parents, or by the male alone if the female has started incubating the next clutch. All broods stay as a family with the parents until the autumn. The age of first breeding is one year old. The pair-bond is monogamous and may be renewed each year, owing to site-fidelity, although the pair probably does not stay together outside of the breeding season.

Hints on recognition: The Woodlark is slimmer and has a smaller crest than the crested larks *Galeridae*, resembling more closely the Skylark (for which, see that species). It has a strong facial pattern, especially the prominent white supercillium extending to the nape and sometimes joining across the back of the head. When the crest is raised slightly, the back of the head has a distinctive square appearance. Also note the small white-black-white patch on the edge of the wing, near the shoulder, which is also visible in flight.

194

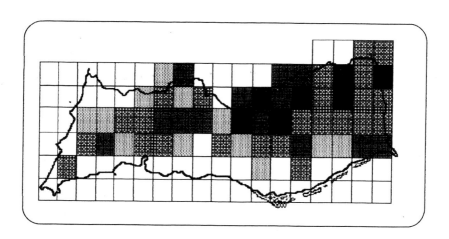

Hints on finding: In early spring, the distinctive song will pin point the presence of this species. It is a beautifully melodious song, gradually descending in pitch and sounding remarkably melancholy. If the song is followed to its source, the bird will often appear as a tiny speck in the sky or at the top of the tallest tree.

Confirmation of breeding:

Number of rectangles in which recorded:	56
Possible breeding:	0
Probable breeding:	12
Confirmed breeding:	44

ALAUDA ARVENSIS

SKYLARK

Portuguese name: Laverca.

Distribution: The Skylark breeds in all temperate latitudes of Europe and Asia, and in North Africa. It was introduced from Great Britain into Australia and New Zealand in the mid-1800s. It is confined mainly to the north and to the south-western coast of Portugal (CEMPA), although the BBA also found it in the north-east of the Algarve.

Status in the Western Palearctic: Although it has decreased slightly in some parts of its range, there would appear to be no general decline. From Coverley's account, there has apparently been some recent increase in northern Portugal, although there is no evidence of any change in the Algarve. It is mainly resident, with the local population augmented by passage and winter migrants.

Preferred habitat: Sparse grassland with few or no trees. It particularly favours the open grasslands of the west coast and the north-eastern Algarve, as well as the exposed tops of Foia. It avoids human presence and all types of woodland.

Food: Invertebrates and seeds, including cereal grains. It will also eat leaves and fallen fruit. Almost all food is taken by pecking at the surface of the ground or from low plants, although it will occasionally dig with its bill or take flying insects in aerial pursuit. It rarely drinks, but has been recorded drinking sea-water.

Breeding: During the winter months, the male establishes a territory and advertises his presence by song, which is usually given in flight or, occasionally, from the ground or a perch. In song-flight, he ascends steeply into the wind, then continues upwards, spiralling and singing vigorously. Then he hovers, continuing to singing, and finally glides downwards still singing. The main period for song starts in January, continuing through the spring, and it is often heard well before dawn. If a female is attracted, the male lands near her and displays. He leaps into the air in front of her and bows, his neck feathers erect like a ruff and his wings quivering. The female approaches him and they may flutter around together, or he may chase her, until she is fully accepted. In March, the female makes a shallow depression on the ground, usually in the open but sometimes by a tuft of grass. She lines the depression with grass, then makes an inner lining of very fine grass. Two or three clutches of 3-5 eggs are laid. Incubation takes 11 days and is by the female alone. The young are cared for and fed by both parents and they usually leave the nest completely when 8-10 days old, although they can walk if necessary at 6 days old. Fledging takes 18-20 days and the young become independent 5-7 days later. The age of first breeding is one year old. The pair-bond is monogamous and of seasonal duration only, but it may be renewed in subsequent years owing to site-fidelity.

Hints on recognition: In general colouring, it is closer to a pipit than a lark. It is streaked brown on the upperparts and white on the underparts, streaked with brown on the breast. The crest is small. The song-flight pattern is distinctive, more sustained than that of other larks, and more likely to ascend out of view. The race from southern Portugal *A.a.sierrae* is generally much darker than the migrant races which pass through the region.

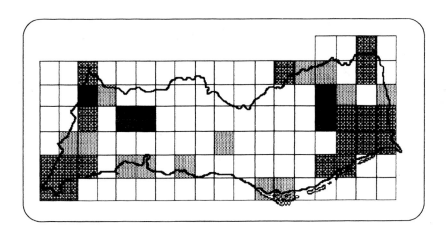

Hints on finding: This lark can easily be found on the top of Foia, where it is locally common. It is also not uncommon on the Cape St. Vincent Peninsula, but is more difficult to find amongst the other species of larks breeding there.

Confirmation of breeding:

Number of rectangles in which recorded:	36
Possible breeding:	1
Probable breeding:	10
Confirmed breeding:	25

RIPARIA RIPARIA

SAND MARTIN

Portuguese name: Andorinha-das-barreiras.

Distribution: The Sand Martin breeds in all the temperate latitudes of the Northern Hemisphere, except North Africa where it only breeds in Egypt. It has a restricted and localised distribution in Portugal, with numbers greatly affected by drought conditions in the Sahel during migration.

Status in the Western Palearctic: It has decreased in many parts of Europe, possibly caused by habitat destruction, and it would appear to be far less common in Portugal today than it was in Coverley's time. The only known colony in the Algarve, at Vilamoura, was destroyed in 1992 and it is not yet known whether it will become established elsewhere or become extinct in the region. It is a summer visitor, wintering in central and southern Africa.

Preferred habitat: Soft sandy banks, suitable for nest-tunnels, e.g. river banks, or sand-pits and other cliffs excavated by man. It avoids dense woodland, mountains, deserts, narrow valleys, and urbanized areas, but is mainly independent of terrain for feeding.

Food: Small airborne invertebrates, caught almost exclusively in flight and sometimes a kilometre or more from the nest-site. It will also take prey from the surface of water, frequently by hovering.

Breeding: Colonial. Older males return to the nesting colonies in March and take possession of an existing hole; young males return 2-3 weeks later and dig a shallow hole. Birds return as close as possible to the natal site. Each male will sit at the entrance to his hole and sing, with plumage ruffled and closed wings vibrating. The females hover in front of the holes, 'inspecting' the site and the resident male, until one is chosen. Several holes may be entered before one is finally selected and the female is accepted by the male. Once the pair is formed, they excavate a tunnel approx. 65cm long with a chamber 4-6cm in diameter at the end, in which a nest of vegetation and feathers is made. Two clutches of 4-6 eggs are laid, although the second clutch is often in a different hole and with a different mate. Incubation takes about 2 weeks and is by both sexes in equal shares during the daytime and mostly by the female at night. The chicks are cared for and fed by both parents. Fledging takes about 3 weeks and the young become independent about one week later. The age of first breeding is one year old. The pair-bond is basically monogamous, although males will often try to copulate with other females. It is of seasonal duration only.

Hints on recognition: It is similar in size and shape to the House Martin (for which, see that species), although it has only a slight fork to the tail. It is plain brown on the upperparts and white, with a contrasting brown collar, on the underparts. It is most likely to be confused with the Crag Martin (for which, see that species), which has the same general colouring but which is light brown on the entire underparts.

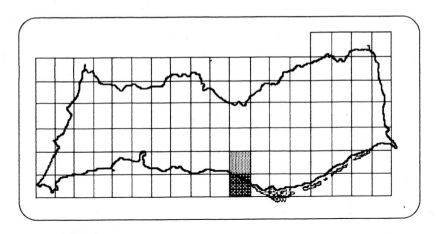

Hints on finding: It is generally faithful to its natal area and so, although the colony at Vilamoura was destroyed, birds should be looked for in the area between that site and Loulé (where they have occasionally been seen).

Confirmation of breeding: Breeding was found at only one site, which has subsequently been removed. It is not known whether this species will continue to breed in the Algarve or not.

Number of rectangles in which recorded:	2
Possible breeding:	1
Probable breeding:	0
Confirmed breeding:	1

PTYONOPROGNE RUPESTRIS

CRAG MARTIN

Portuguese name: Andorinha-das-rochas.

Distribution: The Crag Martin breeds in southern Europe, the middle latitudes of Asia, south-west Asia, and northern Africa. It is confined mainly to the north and east of Portugal (CEMPA).

Status in the Western Palearctic: It has expanded its range in some parts of eastern Europe, but has declined in France and become almost extinct in Germany. Although it is most common in the northern half of Portugal, it has increased in the south in the second half of this century (CEMPA) and was increasing in the Algarve during the course of the BBA. It is resident but dispersive, and the local population is considerably augmented by visitors from further north during the winter.

Preferred habitat: Cliffs and modern bridges for nesting. In the Algarve, it has particularly colonized the new bridges which have been built in the north-east of the region. As an aerial feeder, it is mainly independent of the terrain over which it hunts, although it generally prefers rocky hills and coasts to woodlands and lowland agriculture. It is dependent on access to water.

Food: Small airborne insects, caught almost exclusively in flight and usually within 2km of the nesting colony. It has been recorded taking insects from the surface of water in Portugal (BWP 1988).

Breeding: Colonial. Individuals return to the nesting colony in March, with 5-6 pairs per colony. Although there is considerable aerial chasing and noisy calling on arrival at the colony, many pairs have already been formed during the winter. Nests from previous years are often re-used, but it is not known whether or not by the same birds. The nest-site is a crevice or shallow hole, usually under an overhang, on a cliff or a modern bridge. Although this species commonly roosts on buildings during the winter in the Algarve, it has not yet been reported nesting on them. In early April, the pair builds a half-cup of mud, lined with feathers and vegetation. Two clutches of 3-5 eggs are laid. Incubation takes 2 weeks or more and is mainly by the female, although the male will help for short periods. The chicks are cared for and fed by both parents, being brooded by them for the first week or so after hatching. Fledging takes 3 1/2 to 4 weeks and the young become independent about 2 weeks afterwards. The age of first breeding is probably one year old. The pair-bond is thought to be monogamous and of seasonal duration only, but there is no evidence for this.

Hints on recognition: This species is similar in size and shape to the House Martin (for which, see that species), although it has no fork to the tail. It is plain medium-brown on the upperparts and plain light-brown on the underparts. It most closely resembles the scarce Sand Martin (for which, see that species), but lacks the white underparts with contrasting brown collar. When seen clearly in flight from below, a row of white spots can be observed along the trailing edge of the tail.

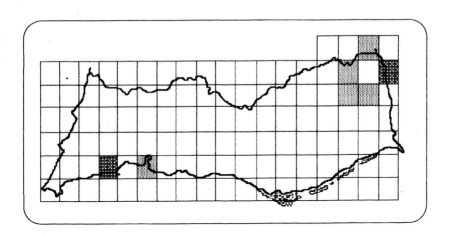

Hints on finding: This species is rapidly colonizing the north-eastern Algarve, using new road bridges. The new side-roads which have been made to small villages are all worth investigation. The two colonies on the cliffs at Praia do Vau (west of Portimão) and Praia da Luz (west of Lagos) are easy of access, but may not survive tourism.

Confirmation of breeding: As the programme for opening up the interior includes more new bridges, further colonies should be expected.

Number of rectangles in which recorded: 7
Possible breeding: 0
Probable breeding: 0
Confirmed breeding: 7

HIRUNDO RUSTICA

SWALLOW

Portuguese name: Andorinha-das-chaminés

Distribution: The Swallow breeds throughout the Northern Hemisphere, except the extreme northern tundra and the southern deserts. It is common in all regions of Portugal (CEMPA).

Status in the Western Palearctic: It has declined recently in some parts of Europe, possibly because of habitat changes and pesticides, but numbers would appear to be stable in Portugal. It is a summer visitor, wintering in central and southern Africa, although a few overwinter in the Algarve.

Preferred habitat: Farmland with plentiful outhouses for nesting. It particularly favours pastures and crops, with open buildings such as barns and sheds and with easy access to water. It avoids woodlands, steep gorges, dense urbanizations, and arid conditions such as sand-dunes.

Food: Small airborne insects, taken almost exclusively in flight from close to the surface of water or the ground. Most prey is taken in aerial-pursuit, but it will also take insects directly from water, by hovering or dipping, and directly from the ground, by hovering or foraging on foot.

Breeding: Most birds return to their natal area in February or March, although some individuals may nest several kilometres distant. The males arrive first, followed shortly by the females, although they sometimes arrive already paired. The male establishes a territory, which serves for courtship, nesting, and some feeding. He typically sings from flight, circling over the building, or from an exposed perch, to warn off rivals and to attract a mate. When a female approaches, he swoops down towards the prospective nest-site and attempts to entice her to stay, by calling and by pursuing her. If she remains, he guards her jealously, whilst other males try to chase her into their territories. He often begins to build a nest, or to refurbish an old one. Once a female has accepted the site, however, she does most of the building. The nest is made from mud-pellets, mixed with plant material and the bird's own saliva, and is sited on a narrow ledge or beam against a wall in a building. It is lined with feathers, which both sexes collect. Two to three clutches of 4-5 eggs are laid, usually the same nest being used for a complete season. Incubation takes a little more than 2 weeks and is mainly by the female. The chicks are cared for and fed by both parents. Fledging takes about 3 weeks and the young become independent a few weeks afterwards, although the last brood may stay with the parents at least until migration. The age of first breeding is 1 year old for females and 1-2 years old for males. The pair-bond is mainly monogamous, although polygyny may occur and often birds of either sex will mate with neighbouring birds. The bond is of seasonal duration only, but may be renewed in subsequent years owing to site-fidelity.

Hints on recognition: When seen well, the Swallow can only be confused with the Red-rumped Swallow (for which, see that species). It is glossy blue-black on the upperparts with two long tail-streamers, making the tail longer than the body. The underside of the body is white with a red throat and a blue-black collar, the underside of the tail is dark and edged with white spots.

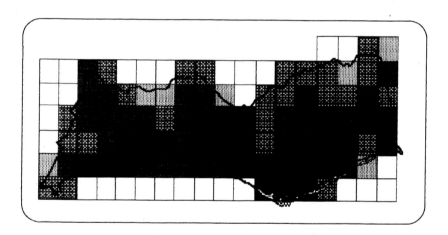

Hints on finding: This species can be found in the vicinity of almost any lowland farm with outbuildings, often sitting on overhead wires.

Confirmation of breeding:

Number of rectangles in which recorded: 84
Possible breeding: 1
Probable breeding: 0
Confirmed breeding: 83

HIRUNDO DAURICA

RED-RUMPED SWALLOW

Portuguese name: Andorinha-daurica.

Distribution: The Red-rumped Swallow breeds in the Mediterranean Basin, especially in the extreme south-eastern and south-western regions, as well as in southern Asia and at many scattered sites throughout Africa. It is well-distributed in Portugal, but is more common in the south than in the north (CEMPA).

Status in the Western Palearctic: It is spreading northwards in Europe, breeding for the first time in France in 1963, and has increased recently in northern Portugal (Santos Júnior, J.R. dos, 1960). It is a summer visitor to Europe, probably wintering in the northern Afrotropics.

Preferred habitat: Bridges and culverts, for nesting, over or near water. It will occasionally use buildings and ruins, but it generally prefers to be away from human settlements. It feeds over pasture and open sparse scrub and, as it rarely flies more than 50m from its nest, it particularly favours quiet rural areas.

Food: Airborne invertebrates, which are taken in aerial-pursuit. Where there are concentrations of prey, such as emerging winged ants, it will also feed on the ground or from vegetation.

Breeding: Solitary or in small colonies. Birds return to the breeding grounds in March, the older birds before the younger ones, either singly or more often already in pairs. The male sings from display-flight near the prospective nest-site, circling the female. He frequently includes distinctive actions, such as suddenly throwing his head and tail up in the air or making 'parachute' dives. The pair chooses the nest-site. In April, they make a nest of mud pellets, mixed with grass and lined with fine grass, wool, and feathers. Often an old nest is re-used or refurbished. The nest is shaped like a bowl, with a tunnel-shaped entrance approx. 10cm long (nests with two tunnels have been recorded), which is attached to the underside of the ceiling of the chosen site. Two or three clutches of 2-5 eggs are laid, the same nest being used for all broods. Incubation takes 2 weeks and is by both sexes equally. Fledging takes 3 to 4 weeks. The young are cared for and fed by both parents and become independent about one week after fledging, although they often continue to roost in the nest for several weeks. They breed for the first time at one year old. The pair-bond is monogamous and of seasonal duration only, but may be renewed in subsequent years owing to site-fidelity.

Hints on recognition: This species resembles the Swallow (for which, see that species) in size, shape, and general colouring. It is blue-black on the upperparts, with a light chestnut collar across the nape and a prominent pale-rufous rump. The underside is entirely pale rufous, except for the tail and under-tail coverts which are plain black. The flight of the Red-rumped Swallow is slower and includes more gliding than the Swallow.

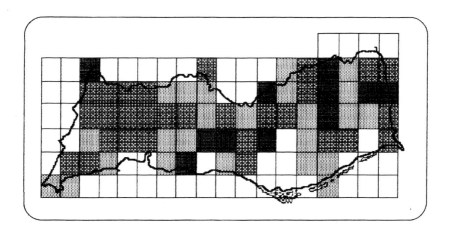

Hints on finding: The underside of inland bridges, away from human disturbance, should be searched for the distinctive bottle-shaped nest. When one is found, the observer can watch from a hidden vantage point for the return of the adults. Care should be taken that the birds cannot see the observer, otherwise they may not return to the nest. See also Where to watch breeding birds H.

Confirmation of breeding:

Number of rectangles in which recorded:	64
Possible breeding:	2
Probable breeding:	5
Confirmed breeding:	57

DELICHON URBICA

HOUSE MARTIN

Portuguese name: Andorinha-dos-beirais.

Distribution: The House Martin breeds in most of Europe, the northern and middle latitudes of Asia, and the coastal regions of northern Africa. It has bred irregularly in South Africa and Iceland, and bred for the first time in Israel in the 1970s. It is well distributed throughout Portugal and was found in every 'square' by the national atlas, with no apparent preference for north or south.

Status in the Western Palearctic: It has recently declined in some areas yet increased in others. In Portugal, Coverley mentions that it was absent from some parts of the north, whereas it is to be found everywhere today, perhaps indicating an increase in its range. It is a summer visitor to Europe, wintering in the Afrotropics.

Preferred habitat: Medium-sized towns and cities for nesting, although isolated buildings, bridges, and sea-cliffs are also used. It is less dependent on the surrounding habitat than the swallows and the other martins, as it tends to feed in a higher airspace. It is very tolerant of human disturbance.

Food: Flying insects, which are taken almost entirely in aerial-pursuit, and other airborne invertebrates. It will, however, perch to take advantage of concentrations of insects on the ground, on walls or rocks, and on plants.

Breeding: Colonial. Individuals return to the traditional nesting-area in January, older birds arriving before 1-year-olds, and are often already paired. Most birds are faithful to the natal colony or its near vicinity. The male inspects several sites or old nests before choosing one, which he then defends and advertises by song. When a female is attracted, to the site and the male, he will attempt to entice her to remain, by calling and by chasing her back to the site if she leaves. Once he is accepted by her, the male starts to build a nest or to refurbish an old one. Both sexes complete the nest, which is a half-cup made of mud pellets, lined with feathers, in the angle between a vertical surface and an overhang. The most common site is the eaves of a building, although high bridges and the western sea-cliffs are also used. Two or three broods of 3-5 eggs are laid. Incubation takes 2 weeks and is by both sexes, the female incubating for longer periods than the male. The young are cared for and fed by both parents, with most of the brooding carried out by the female for the first week or so. Fledging takes about one month and the young become independent a few days afterwards, although they will often roost in the nest until departure from the colony. The age of first breeding is one year old. The pair-bond is monogamous and of seasonal duration only. Birds often change mates after the first brood.

Hints on recognition: The upperparts are as blue-black as the Swallow's (for which, see that species), but have a conspicuous white rump, seen easily at some distance with the naked eye. It lacks the long tail streamers, having only a slightly forked tail. The underside of the body is entirely pure white.

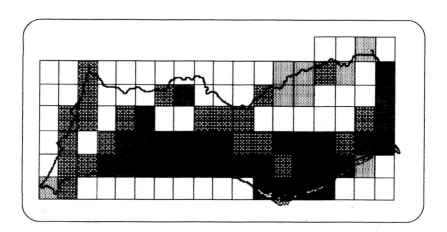

Hints on finding: Dense colonies can be found in the middle of such towns as Portimão, Silves, Loulé, Faro, and Tavira, as well as many others.

Confirmation of breeding: This species often feeds far from the nest-site, so only probable and confirmed breeding are shown on the maps.

Number of rectangles in which recorded: 62
Probable breeding: 2
Confirmed breeding: 60

ANTHUS CAMPESTRIS

TAWNY PIPIT

Portuguese name: Petinha-dos-campos.

Distribution: The Tawny Pipit breeds in the middle latitudes of the Western Palearctic and Asia, except the Far East. It is thinly distributed throughout Portugal (CEMPA).

Status in the Western Palearctic: It has decreased in the northern part of its European range, possibly because of increased arable farming in suitable habitats. Its status in Portugal is not known, but it would appear to be stable in the Algarve. It is a summer visitor, wintering in the Sahel.

Preferred habitat: Open level grasslands, such as those found on the Cape St.Vincent Peninsula, although elsewhere in Portugal it prefers the summits of mountains. It is tolerant of sandy habitats, such as the grassy areas behind sand-dunes, but avoids tall or dense vegetation, including trees, cereal crops, and maquis. It almost always breeds with larks, especially the Short-toed Lark.

Food: Mainly invertebrates, although it will take some seeds. Most prey is taken from the ground, in the stop-and-start method used by the Kentish Plover, but it will also pursue it in flight.

Breeding: Individuals return to the breeding grounds in April, upon which the male selects a territory and advertises it by song. In a typical song-flight, he ascends silently from the ground or a perch to about 20-30m. He circles the territory in characteristic undulations, singing briefly on the descent of each undulation, then descending in full song. When females are seen, the male chases them vigorously until one remains in his territory and accepts him as a mate. In May, the female, sometimes helped by the male, makes a cup of grass and leaves lined with finer material and hair, in a hollow on the ground. One clutch (sometimes two) of 4-5 eggs is laid. Incubation takes nearly 2 weeks and is by the female alone, the male guarding her. When she leaves the nest, she will often sing like the male. The young are cared for and fed by both parents, the female brooding them during the first week after hatching. If there are two clutches, the male cares for the first brood whilst the female incubates. Fledging takes nearly 2 weeks and the young become independent after a further 2 weeks, although the family often stays together for longer. The age of first breeding is one year old. The pair-bond is mainly monogamous, although polygyny is frequent. It is of seasonal duration only, but may be renewed in subsequent years owing to site-fidelity.

Hints on recognition: Pipits are in many respects half-way between larks and wagtails: they have the general colouring, type of song-flight, and nest-site as larks, but walk and stand like short-tailed wagtails. The Tawny Pipit is the only pipit which breeds in the Algarve, although other species over-winter and pass through the region on migration. The upperparts are a warm brown, only very slightly streaked, and the underparts are creamy, with a conspicuous absence of streaks.

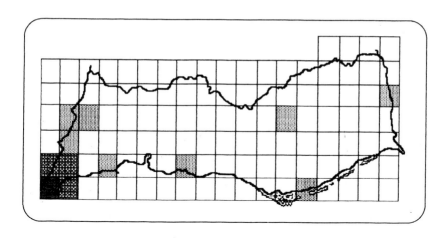

Hints on finding: The open grasslands on the Cape St. Vincent Peninsula hold good populations of Tawny Pipit. The area between the cliff-tops and the Sagres to Vila do Bispo road is criss-crossed with tracks which are easy to walk.

Confirmation of breeding:

Number of rectangles in which recorded:	12
Possible breeding:	0
Probable breeding:	4
Confirmed breeding:	8

MOTACILLA FLAVA

YELLOW WAGTAIL
(Iberian race: Blue-headed Wagtail)

Portuguese name: Alvéola-amarela.

Distribution: The Yellow Wagtail breeds in the middle and upper latitudes of the Western Palearctic and Asia, in Alaska. It is to be found everywhere in Portugal where there is suitable habitat (CEMPA).

Status in the Western Palearctic: It has decreased in some areas and increased in others, for reasons not understood. There has apparently been no recent change in its status in Portugal. It is a summer visitor to Europe, wintering in the Afrotropics.

Preferred habitat: It particularly favours all kinds of wet saline habitats and has not been found breeding outside of tidal areas in the Algarve.

Food: Small invertebrates, which it pecks from the ground or water whilst walking or running. It will also 'flycatch' and hover, using the long tail to assist its balance.

Breeding: Individuals return to the breeding grounds in March, the males 1-2 weeks before the females. The male selects a territory, which he defends and advertises by song. He begins his song-flight from a perch, then suddenly leaps into the air, ascending 4-5m before descending again, legs dangling and wings fluttering, giving a special trilling variation of the song. Just before reaching the ground, he ascends again and repeats the performance.When a female is attracted, he lands in front of her, ruffling his feathers, lowering and opening his wings and drag-ging his tail. He runs around her in this posture, frequently leaping into the air and calling. If she accepts him, she chooses a nest-site on the ground, in the base of a tussock, or in a low bush. In late March or early April, she builds a nest of grass lined with hair and wool, in which one clutch of 4-6 eggs is laid. A second clutch is laid in May or early June. Incubation takes 11-13 days and is by both sexes, although the female takes the larger share. The young are cared for and fed by both parents. Fledging takes just over a fortnight, but the chicks walk out of the nest at about 11 days old. The young become independent about a week after fledging but often remain within the territory for several weeks, the second brood possibly staying until migration. The age of first breeding is one year old. The pair-bond is monogamous and of seasonal duration only.

Hints on recogniton: The following description is for the Iberian race *M.f.iberiae*, commonly called the Blue-headed Wagtail, which is restricted to S.W. France, Iberia, and N.W. Africa. Other races have distinctly different head-patterns, including entirely yellow or almost entirely white or black heads, some of which can be seen on migration through the Algarve. This species can only be confused with the Grey Wagtail (for which, see that species). The male Yellow Wagtail is dark grey on the upperparts, strongly tinged yellow on the back, brilliant yellow on the underparts, and has pale bars across the wings. The head is pure grey with a prominent white eyebrow and throat. The female is tinged brown, lacking the contrasts of the male, and has a yellowish brown head. It has a long tail (although much shorter than the Grey Wagtail), which it constantly 'wags' up and down. Except during migration, habitat separates the two species.

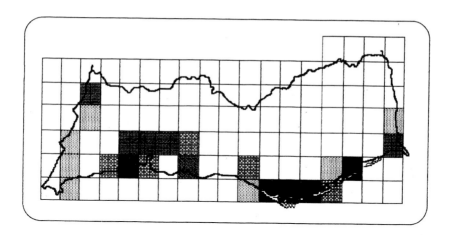

Hints on finding: This wagtail can be found in any saline environment, but it is especially conspicuous on the salt-pans of Tavira and Castro Marim.

Confirmation of breeding:

Number of rectangles in which recorded: 23
Possible breeding: 0
Probable breeding: 3
Confirmed breeding: 20

MOTACILLA CINEREA

GREY WAGTAIL

Portuguese name: Alvéola-cinzenta.

Distribution: The Grey Wagtail breeds in the middle latitudes of the Western Palearctic, including the Azores and Madeira, and in Asia. In Europe, it is mainly confined to the west and south. It is far more common in the northern half of Portugal than in the southern half (CEMPA).

Status in the Western Palearctic: It has expanded its range slightly to the north and the east of Europe this century, but is very susceptible to hard winters. There is no apparent change in its status in Portugal and the population in the Algarve would appear to be stable. It is resident, although many overwinter in Portugal from other areas as Portugal is a major wintering ground.

Preferred habitat: It particularly favours freshwater-courses with year-round fast-flowing water. In the Algarve, however, many breeding territories contain no water other than animal water-troughs or stagnant pools. It requires banks and vertical rock faces, or man-made substitutes such as buildings and bridges, for nesting. It is tolerant of human disturbance.

Food: Mainly invertebrates, which it takes from the ground or water by pecking whilst walking or running, using its long tail for balance. Other hunting techniques are fly-catching, hovering, and aerial pursuit. It will also take very small molluscs, fish, crustaceans, and amphibians.

Breeding: During the winter, the male establishes a territory which is defended and advertised by song, given from a perch or in flight. In a typical song-flight, the male flies to a high point, e.g. a tree, then descends parachute-like, with wings stretched and fluttering, giving a trilling song before landing on the ground. When a female is attracted, he struts around her, head up to show the throat pattern, and chases her whenever she attempts to leave. The male chooses a nest-site in a hole or on a ledge of a bank or wall and attempts to interest the female in the site. If she accepts, the pair builds a cup of grass, moss, and roots, which the female may line with hair. In March, the first of two or three clutches of 4-6 eggs is laid. Incubation takes nearly 2 weeks and is by both sexes. The young are cared for and fed by both parents. Fledging takes about two weeks, after which they remain dependent for several more weeks. Sometimes the brood is split between the parents and, if the female begins incubating another clutch before the brood is independent, the male will often care for them alone. The age of first breeding is one year old. The pair-bond is monogamous and of seasonal duration only.

Hints on recognition: This species is most likely to be confused with the Yellow Wagtail (for which, see that species), especially non-breeding males which have white throats. The totally different habitat and distribution will normally separate them, however. The breeding male Grey Wagtail is a pure dark grey over the entire upperparts and brilliant yellow on the underparts. The throat is black and the head shows a white eyebrow and moustache. The female is a little paler and has a grey-and-white speckled throat. The tail-length is particularly noticeable, being approx. the same as the total body-length and up to 35% longer than that of the Yellow Wagtail.

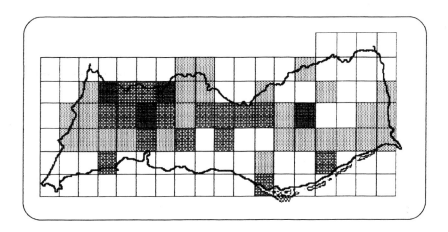

Hints on finding: It is most easily found on the River Boi and by the numerous streams running south from Monchique. There is almost always a pair to be seen near the bridge at Odelouca (see Where to watch breeding birds, D).

Confirmation of breeding:

Number of rectangles in which recorded: 46
Possible breeding: 5
Probable breeding: 15
Confirmed breeding: 26

MOTACILLA ALBA

WHITE WAGTAIL

Portuguese name: Alvéola-branca-comum.

Distribution: The White Wagtail breeds throughout Europe, including Iceland but excluding the Azores, as well as in all the northern and middle latitudes of Asia, Morocco, Greenland and Alaska. The main breeding area in Portugal is the north and centre (CEMPA) and no breeding was proved in the Algarve by the national atlas.

Status in the Western Palearctic: There has been a marked expansion in the south-west of this region, including Portugal. According to the records of Reis Jr. and Coverley, it used to breed in the north of Portugal only. Although resident in most of Europe, including Portugal, it is mainly a winter visitor to the Algarve.

Preferred habitat: It particularly favours fairly open ground or grassland, close to fresh water, but it is very adaptable and will use almost any waterside habitat or even habitats far from water. It avoids very tall or dense vegetation and prefers gently-flowing watercourses to rushing mountain streams. It is tolerant of human disturbance and will readily use man-made artefacts for nesting.

Food: Small invertebrates, which are taken from the ground or water. It pecks the prey whilst walking or running, although it will also flycatch from the ground and hover over water, using its long tail for balance. Occasionally, it will take seeds, small crustaceans and fish.

Breeding: In early March, the male establishes a territory, which he may defend and advertise by song. In typical song-flight, he ascends silently for 10-15m, then makes a near vertical 'parachute-style' or slow fluttering descent, singing strongly. Some males seldom sing, defending the territory by direct confrontation with rivals and attracting a mate by calling. Once a female is attracted, he approaches her, bobbing and bowing, showing her his bold throat pattern. He then circles her, dragging or fluttering his wings and tail. The pair chooses the nest-site, in a hole in a bank or wall, and builds the nest of twigs, grass, leaves, etc. The female alone completes the nest and lines it with hair, wool, and feathers. Two clutches of 5-6 eggs are laid. Incubation takes almost 2 weeks and is by both sexes, the female sitting throughout the night. The young are cared for and fed by both parents, the female brooding them for the first week. They fledge at about 2 weeks old and become independent shortly afterwards. The age of first breeding is one year old. The pair-bond is monogamous and of seasonal duration only.

Hints on recognition: It is entirely black, white, and shades of grey. In breeding plumage, both sexes have a white 'face' and underparts, with a black crown, nape, throat, and breast. The upperparts are grey with white 'stripes' down the wings. It is a typical wagtail, having a very long tail which it frequently 'wags' up and down. The migrant race *M.a.yarrellii*, called the Pied Wagtail, which has almost black upperparts, is occasionally seen in the Algarve.

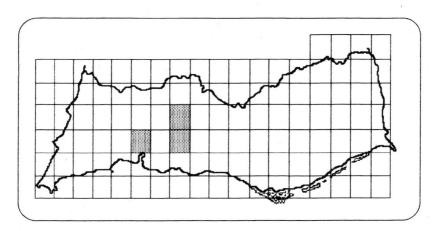

Hints on finding: This species is such an infrequent breeder that no help can be given for the breeding season. In winter, migrants from further north can be seen on golf-courses, tracks in the lowlands, rubbish-tips, and wet meadows.

Confirmation of breeding: Winter or spring migrants often remain in the Algarve for at least the beginning of the local breeding season. For this reason, only probable and confirmed breeding are shown. The records shown on the map were for one site in each rectangle and for the period prior to 1990, since when there have been no further records.

Number of rectangles in which recorded: 3
Probable breeding: 1
Confirmed breeding: 2

TROGLODYTES TROGLODYTES

<u>WREN</u>

Portuguese name: Carriça.

Distribution: The Wren is to be found in most of Europe, including Iceland but excluding the Azores, in northern Africa, the middle latitudes of Asia, and northern America. It is well-distributed and common throughout Portugal in suitable habitat (CEMPA).

Status in the Western Palearctic: Despite fluctuations in the north following hard winters, there appears to be no change in its range or abundance. In Coverley's time, it was apparently more common in the north of Portugal than in the south and the national atlas shows that this is still the case. It is resident in western Europe, including the Iberian Peninsula.

Preferred habitat: Overgrown gullies or banks, ruins and neglected walls, and extensive bramble patches. It particularly favours neglected valley-bottoms and tracts of broken scrub or woodland in the foothills, where there are patches of low thick undergrowth. It will also nest in old trees, the old nests of other species, and crevices in cliffs. Although it is tolerant of human disturbance, it avoids urbanizations.

Food: Mainly invertebrates, especially beetles, which it pecks from vegetation, trees, rocks, leaf litter, ground, etc., but also berries and weed-seeds. Occasionally, it will take prey in flight and it has been recorded taking small fish and tadpoles from water.

Breeding: In the autumn, young males select a vacant territory, which will be retained if possible for at least the breeding season and may be retained for life. The male defends and advertises the territory by a particularly loud song, given from a perch. In February, he makes several unlined nests of leaves, grass, and moss, in a hole, under overhanging roots on a bank, or in a bush such as bramble. When females are attracted, he attempts to ensure that they remain by chasing them into his territory whenever they try to leave. He leads them towards his nests, giving a special courtship song and repeatedly perching by them, extending and quivering his wings. One or more females each chooses a nest and lines it with feathers and hair. Two clutches of 5-8 eggs are laid, although not necessarily in the same nest or with the same mate. Incubation takes just over 2 weeks and is by the female alone. The care and feeding of the young are by both sexes, the female brooding them for the first week. Fledging takes 2 1/2 weeks and the young become independent about 2 weeks afterwards. The age of first breeding is not known, but is probably one year old. The pair-bond may be monogamous or polygynous and lasts for one season at most.

Hints on recognition: This is the shortest bird in the Western Palearctic, appearing to be less than half the size of a House Sparrow, with its tiny tail cocked vertically in the air. It is entirely warm brown, lightly streaked with dark brown on the upperparts, pale on the throat. It has a fairly long bill and a prominent white supercilium.

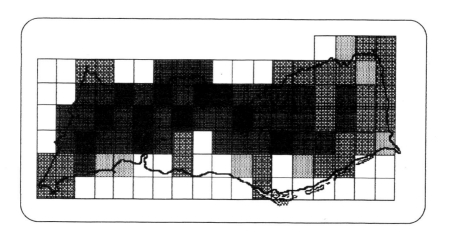

Hints on finding: Wherever there is suitable habitat in the foothills of the western mountains (see Where to watch breeding birds, D), the loud trilling song of this tiny bird can be heard. Stealth, however, is required to see this species well, as it flutters quickly from its song-perch to the depths of the nearest cover when approached.

Confirmation of breeding:

Number of rectangles in which recorded: 77
Possible breeding: 0
Probable breeding: 6
Confirmed breeding: 71

CERCOTRICHAS GALACTOTES

RUFOUS BUSH ROBIN (CHAT)

Portuguese name: Rouxinol do mato.

Distribution: The Rufous Bush Robin (or Rufous Bush Chat) breeds in the Mediterranean Basin, Africa north of the Equator, the Middle East, and south-west Asia. In Portugal, it is limited to the south-eastern part of the country and in the Algarve, it is mostly confined to the north-east. It is a summer migrant in most of its range, wintering in the northern Afrotropics, although it is a resident south of the Sahara, .

Status in the Western Palearctic: Very little is known about the status of this species, although it would appear to have declined in Israel since the 1940s as a result of the excessive use of pesticides. In Portugal, it is generally scarce (CEMPA), although it is fairly common in the north-east of the Algarve, where the population would appear to be stable.

Preferred habitat: Open freshwater-courses, with little vegetation and not necessarily with summer water. A typical nesting habitat is a wide river-bed with little or no water, a shingle and rock-strewn bottom, and the gently-sloping banks bare of vegetation except for Oleander and a spurge called *Securinega tinctoria*. It occasionally uses bare gullies in garigue, but avoids maquis, all types of woodland and sequeiro, and farmland.

Food: This species feeds almost entirely on invertebrates, including larvae and earthworms, although it will occasionally eat fruit. It catches its prey by whatever method is most appropriate, e.g. ants are pecked from the ground, earthworms are found by probing, and flies are caught in the air or taken from plants. Nestlings in Portugal have been seen to be fed on a variety of invertebrates, including beetles, small dragonflies, and grasshoppers (Beven 1970).

Breeding: In May, the male arrives before the female and claims a territory by singing from a perch near the top of a bush. The pair-bond is formed by courtship display, where the male stands in front of the female but facing away, with the wings opened sideways and the tail fanned above the body to show the black and white pattern on the tip. Both sexes help to build a nest of twigs and grass, lined with wool, hair, vegetable down, and feathers, in a dense bush. In the Algarve, the nest is almost always constructed in debris which has been caught in *Securinega tinctoria* when the river was in spate. Two clutches of 4-5 eggs are laid. Incubation is by the female alone and takes nearly 2 weeks. The chicks are cared for and fed by both parents and fledging takes 12-13 days. The young of the first brood become independent about 3 weeks after fledging, a little longer for the second brood, and breed for the first time the following year. The pair-bond is monogamous and of seasonal duration only.

Hints on recognition: It is about the same size as a Song Thrush and of a light rufous-brown colour. When perched or in flight, the prominent spots on the tail form black and white bands on the tip. It is the only species of this size and general colouring which is likely to be found in its preferred habitat in the Algarve, but there could be confusion with the Nightingale (for which, see that species) in other habitats if only seen briefly. The race *C. g. galactotes* found in Portugal is a richer rufous colour than the grey-brown race of the eastern Mediterranean.

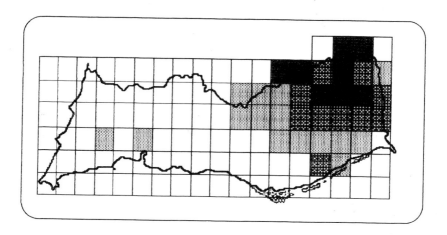

Hints on finding: It is very quiet but easily approached. Even when the observer is standing near the bird or the nest, there is little or no response. The easiest way to find it is to go to a suitable habitat (see Where to watch breeding birds, H) and listen for its song, which has a similar tone and type of phrasing to that of the Song Thrush. Contrary to its behaviour in other parts of its range, it does not favour the prickly pear.

Confirmation of breeding:

Number of rectangles in which recorded:	33
Possible breeding:	1
Probable breeding:	12
Confirmed breeding:	20

ERITHACUS RUBECULA

ROBIN

Portuguese name: Pisco-de-peito-ruivo.

Distribution: The Robin breeds mainly within the Western Palearctic, extending into parts of adjoining Asia. In Portugal, it breeds mainly to the north of the River Tagus; south of the river it has only been found breeding in the Algarve (CEMPA).

Status in the Western Palearctic: Populations fluctuate in the north, following hard winters, but there is no evidence of any change in status. Hundreds of thousands pass through Portugal every autumn, migrating to North Africa, some remaining in the Algarve over winter. The Algarve breeding population is probably resident and sedentary or dispersive.

Preferred habitat: Woodland and forests with overgrown banks for nesting, open moist ground for feeding, and numerous perches for singing and surveying the area around it. It is one of the few species to have taken advantage of eucalyptus forests, where it is particularly common. It is tolerant of human disturbance and will often nest close to habitations.

Food: Invertebrates, but also seeds and soft fruits. It takes prey mostly from the ground, by hopping and pecking. It will also swoop onto prey from a perch, catching it either on the ground or in the air. Occasionally, it has been recorded entering water to catch items such as small fish.

Breeding: By February or early March, the male has selected a territory and has begun to advertise it by means of song. He usually sings from a perch, not more than 3m above ground and generally concealed. The female approaches him calling quietly, as it is only by her behaviour that he knows she is not a rival male. He lands by her, singing loudly, and, if she still remains quiet, he retreats slowly, the female following him. Once the pair-bond is formed, the female chooses a nest-site in a hollow in a bank or tree. She makes a base of dead leaves on which she forms a nest-cup of moss, grass, and leaves, lined with fibres and hair. Two clutches of 4-6 eggs are laid. Incubation takes 2 weeks and is by the female alone. The young are cared for and fed by both parents, although the male often feeds them unaided when the female begins incubating the second clutch. Fledging takes 2 weeks and the young become independent 2-3 weeks afterwards. The age of first breeding is one year old. The pair-bond is monogamous, although bigamy sometimes occurs. It is of seasonal duration only, each bird holding a separate territory and defending it by song and direct aggression during the winter months. It is often renewed each year, however, owing to strong site-fidelity.

Hints on recognition: The familiar Robin Redbreast needs little help in identification. It is plump with relatively long legs. The upperparts are plain brown, the belly whitish, the face and breast a distinctive orange-red. The juveniles are speckled brown and buff all over. Even in silhouette, its roundish body and upright stance, interspersed with bobbing, readily distinguish it from other species found in the same habitat.

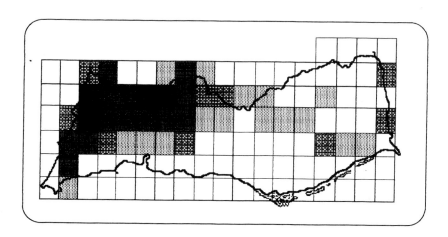

Hints on finding: Its liquid and varied song can be heard at some distance, pinpointing its presence in the eucalyptus or oak woods around Monchique.

Confirmation of breeding:

Number of rectangles in which recorded: 42
Possible breeding: 3
Probable breeding: 11
Confirmed breeding: 28

LUSCINIA MEGARHYNCHOS

NIGHTINGALE

Portuguese name: Rouxinol-comum.

Distribution: The Nightingale breeds in the middle latitudes of the Western Palearctic and western Asia. It is well-distributed and common throughout Portugal, except in the extreme north-east (CEMPA).

Status in the Western Palearctic: Although it has decreased in its numbers and range in north-western Europe, there is apparently no change in its status in Portugal. It has retreated from the south coast of the Algarve, because of urbanizations and the disturbance from tourists, but is elsewhere stable. It is a summer visitor, wintering in the Afrotropics just north of the Equator.

Preferred habitat: Fairly densely overgrown gullies, valley-bottoms, and banks of freshwater-courses, as well as thick scrub and bramble patches, etc. It will tolerate some human disturbance, often nesting close to habitations and horticulture, and will use isolated bushes in reed-beds, marshland, etc.

Food: Mainly invertebrates, especially beetles and ants, but it will also eat berries and figs. It feeds on the ground by pecking, taking prey from the earth, from low plants, or from leaf litter. Occasionally, it will drop onto prey from a perch or catch insects in flight.

Breeding: In March, both sexes return to the breeding grounds, the males a few days before the females. The male selects a territory, which he will keep for life unless a better one becomes vacant. He advertises and defends the territory by means of song, which is given from a concealed perch near the top of a bush. If a female approaches, the male lands near her, singing quietly and fanning his raised tail, then raising his wings and making small jumps in rapid succession in front of her. Once the pair-bond is formed, the female chooses a nest-site on or near the ground, in undergrowth beneath the main scrub layer. The female makes a cup of dead leaves and grass, lined with finer material and feathers, which is sometimes domed. Two clutches of 4-5 eggs are laid. Incubation takes nearly 2 weeks and is by the female alone. The chicks are cared for and fed by both parents. Often the male alone feeds them when the female begins incubating the second clutch. Fledging takes 11 days and the young become independent 2-3 weeks afterwards, although they may stay within the parents' territory until migration. The age of first breeding is probably one year old. The pair-bond is monogamous and of seasonal duration only.

Hints on recognition: It is relatively large for a song-bird, being about the same length as a Kingfisher although not so bulky. It is entirely plain warm brown, paler on the underparts, with a noticeable reddish tinge to the tail. It can be confused with the Rufous Bush Robin (for which, see that species), but it lacks the white eye-brow and spots on the tail. Except on migration, it is never found in the same habitat as the Bush Robin. The juvenile is spotted with buff, like a large Robin, but nevertheless has the reddish tail.

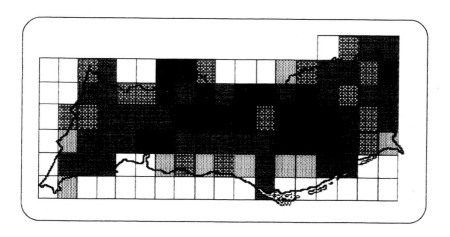

Hints on finding: Although this species is very difficult to see well, its rich and varied song emerging from dense undergrowth will quickly pinpoint its presence. During April and May, and to a lesser extent in June, it sings strongly through the day as well as the night. It can be found anywhere in the foot-hills in suitable habitat, e.g. along the Odelouca (see Where to watch breeding birds, D).

Confirmation of breeding:

Number of rectangles in which recorded: 79
Possible breeding: 0
Probable breeding: 10
Confirmed breeding: 69

PHOENICURUS OCHRUROS

BLACK REDSTART

Portuguese name: Rabirruivo-preto.

Distribution: The Black Redstart breeds in the middle latitudes of the Western Palearctic and Asia. In Portugal, it is mainly confined to the north of the River Tagus (CEMPA).

Status in the Western Palearctic: It has increased and spread in the north-west of its range during the last century, reaching Great Britain and Scandinavia in the mid-1800s. Apparently there has been no change in its status in Portugal since Coverley's time. It is resident and dispersive in Portugal, although many birds from further north overwinter in the Algarve and leave after the local population has started nesting.

Preferred habitat: Rocky sea-cliffs, especially those of the south-west coast. Occasionally it nests on inland cliffs and in ruins, stone bridges, etc., and elsewhere in its range it commonly nests in large cities. It particularly favours bare, rocky ground and avoids dense vegetation, including forests, crops, and long grass. It will tolerate some human disturbance and frequently uses habitations in winter.

Food: Invertebrates and fruit. It catches prey on the ground, by hopping and running after it, or uses a perch from which to swoop onto it. It will also catch aerial prey in short flights and hover when necessary.

Breeding: By February or early March, this species has returned to the breeding grounds, the males a week or more before the females. The male selects a territory, which he advertises and defends by means of song. When a female is attracted, the male courts her by swift chases, or by circling round her, whilst singing continuously. Apparently, the female chooses the nest-site, on a ledge or in a hole in the cliff or wall. She makes a nest of grass, moss, and other vegetation, lined with wool, hair, and feathers. Two or three clutches of 4-6 eggs are laid. Incubation takes at least 2 weeks and is by the female alone, the male in close attendance. The chicks are cared for and fed by both parents, the female brooding them for the first week after hatching. The male assumes total responsibility for them when the female begins incubating the next clutch. Fledging takes 2 to 2 1/2 weeks and the young become independent about 2 weeks afterwards, although they often stay within the territory. The age of first breeding is probably one year old. The pair-bond is generally monogamous and of seasonal duration, but sometimes lasts for one brood only, with both birds finding new mates for subsequent broods.

Hints on recognition: The male of the Portuguese race *P.o.aterrimus* is unmistakable, being Robin-like in shape and stance, but appearing mainly black. He has a light grey cap, an almost white belly, and a prominent white patch on his wing. His rump and tail are a conspicuous bright chestnut. The female can be confused with the female Redstart (for which, see that species), being entirely dusky brown with a bright chestnut rump and tail, but is darker. Both species have a distinctive manner of quivering the tail when standing but, except on migration, they use totally different habitats.

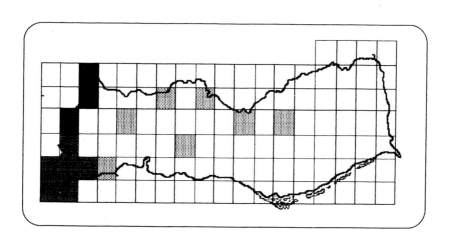

Hints on finding: The rocky coasts of the Cape St. Vincent Peninsula and the west coast are the main areas for seeing this species in the Algarve. A walk in any direction along the cliffs should produce good views.

Confirmation of breeding:

Number of rectangles in which recorded: 16
Possible breeding: 2
Probable breeding: 3
Confirmed breeding: 11

225

PHOENICURUS PHOENICURUS

REDSTART

Portuguese name:
Rabirruivo-de-testa-branca.

Distribution: The Redstart breeds in the middle and northern latitudes of the Western Palearctic, and in the middle latitudes of western Asia. It is found in very small numbers at scattered sites throughout southern Portugal (CEMPA).

Status in the Western Palearctic: There has been a marked decline in the population of many countries in recent years, probably owing to drought conditions in its winter quarters in the Sahel. Coverley mentions this species as well-known at Monchique, although neither the national atlas nor the BBA found it there. It is mainly a summer visitor, wintering in the Afrotropics north of the Equator, although some individuals apparently overwinter in the Algarve.

Preferred habitat: Stands of mature oak, with no scrub or small trees to impede its feeding. Although it is tolerant of human disturbance and will live close to habitations elsewhere in its range, it appears to shun man in the Algarve. It is mainly found around deserted villages in remote woodland.

Food: Invertebrates, which it pecks from the ground or from trees. It will also commonly flycatch or use a perch from which to swoop onto prey on the ground. Fruit is often eaten when available.

Breeding: The Redstart returns to the breeding grounds in April, the females a week or so before the males. On arrival, the male selects a territory, which he advertises and defends by means of song. When a female is attracted, he follows her, chirruping excitedly, wings and tail spread. The male chooses several nest-sites, in tree-holes, which he shows to the female. He flies into each hole, displaying his rufous tail, then turns round with his head protruding from the hole, displaying his white forehead and black throat. The female selects a hole and builds a cup of grass, moss, and other vegetation, lined with wool, hair, and feathers. Two clutches of 5-7 eggs are laid. Incubation takes nearly 2 weeks and is by the female alone. The chicks are fed and cared for by both parents, although the female takes the larger share. Fledging takes 2 weeks and the young become independent 2-3 weeks afterwards. The age of first breeding is usually one year old, but can be later. The pair-bond is generally monogamous, although bigamy sometimes occurs. It isis of seasonal duration only.

Hints on recognition: The male is unmistakable in this region. This handsome bird is blue-grey on the upperparts, with a bright chestnut tail, and vivid rufous-chestnut on the underparts, speckled white on the belly. He has a jet black throat and a pure white forehead. The female can be confused with the Black Redstart (for which, see that species), but she has a distinct rufous tinge to her underparts, whereas the other is more dusky. Both sexes have a distinctive manner of quivering the tail when perched.

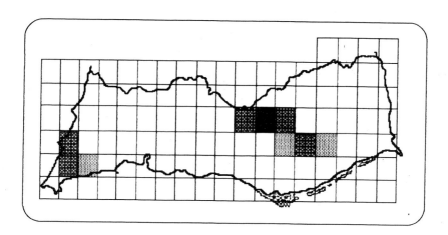

Hints on finding: The oak-woods northwest of São Braz do Alportel and northwest of Salir hold the greatest number of birds. These areas are difficult to work, however, having only rough un-signposted tracks. Although having fewer birds, the valley running due south from Pedralva, just off the Vila do Bispo-Lisbon road, is easier to explore.

Confirmation of breeding: The combination of quiet bird and difficult terrain has probably resulted in under-recording.

Number of rectangles in which recorded: 9
Possible breeding: 0
Probable breeding: 2
Confirmed breeding: 7

SAXICOLA TORQUATA

STONECHAT

Portuguese name: Cartaxo-comum.

Distribution: The Stonechat is to be found in western and southern Europe, most of Africa, and Asia. It is well-distributed throughout Portugal, but is apparently most common in the Alentejo (CEMPA).

Status in the Western Palearctic: It has declined recently in much of northern and western Europe, probably as a result of habitat changes. There would, however, appear to be no change in its status in Portugal. It is a resident, although many migrants from further north overwinter in the Algarve.

Preferred habitat:
Barlavento: It particularly favours low heathland and coastal cliff-tops, such as the Cape St. Vincent Peninsular and the area around Foia. It is also to be found in moist derelict areas, e.g. abandoned valleys where pasture and horticulture have reverted to nature.
Sotavento: The sides of rocky gorges and steep banks overlooking dry river-beds, such as are found in the north-east.

Food: Invertebrates, which it takes by swooping onto them from a perch and catching them on the ground. It will also take prey in aerial pursuit and by hovering, including hovering over water for small fish. It has been recorded eating small lizards.

Breeding: During the winter months, the male establishes a territory. In early February, he advertises his possession by means of song, which may be given from a perch or from flight. In a typical song-flight, he flutters erratically, legs dangling, before returning to a favoured perch. When a female is attracted, he continues his song-flight just above her, hovering so that his white markings are displayed. He then lands by her, bowing with wings drooped and tail fanned. Once the pair-bond is formed, it is probably the female who chooses the nest-site and builds the nest, although the male may assist. She builds a loose cup of grass and leaves, lined with hair and feathers, on the ground or on a bank. It is hidden by vegetation at the base of a bush or tussock and the pair approach it by means of 'tunnels' through the vegetation. In the Sotavento, nests are often built inside holes, screened by tufts of vegetation, on sheer cliff-faces. Three clutches of 4-6 eggs are laid. Incubation takes 2 weeks and is by the female alone. The chicks are fed and cared for by both parents, although the male assumes responsibility when the female begins incubating another clutch. Fledging takes 2 weeks and the young become independent about 2 weeks after- wards. The age of first breeding is at one year old. The pair-bond is generally monogamous, although polygyny occurs and mates sometimes change between broods. It is usually of seasonal duration only, although pairs will often remain together for longer.

Hints on identification: This species is slightly smaller than a Robin, but with a similar shape and stance. The male is a handsome bird, with very dark brown upperparts, paler on the rump, and with rufous underparts. He has a black face and throat, a slash of white down the wing, and a prominent white patch on the sides of his neck forming a half-collar. The female has a similar pattern but in more muted colours.

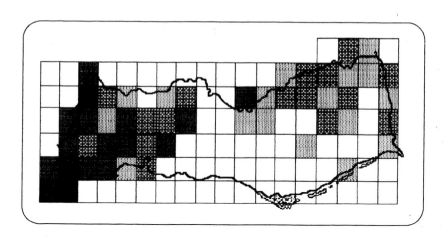

Hints on finding: Ditches and banks beside tracks on the Cape St. Vincent Peninsula provide good habitat for this species. It is also easy to find on the top of Foia.

Confirmation of breeding:

Number of rectangles in which recorded:	50
Possible breeding:	2
Probable breeding:	7
Confirmed breeding:	41

OENANTHE OENANTHE

WHEATEAR

Portuguese name: Chasco-cinzento.

Distribution: The Wheatear breeds in most of Europe, the middle and northern latitudes of Asia, northern Africa, and the northern latitudes of America. It is restricted to the north-east of Portugal and was not found breeding in the Algarve by the national atlas. The records for the BBA represent the first known breeding in southern Portugal.

Status in the Western Palearctic: There has been a decrease in range and population in north-west Europe, mainly as a result of habitat changes. It would appear to have been more common in Coverley's time in northern Portugal than it is today, but coastal development and mountain afforestation have reduced it markedly (CEMPA). It is a summer visitor, with the entire world population (including Nearctic) wintering in Africa, mainly between the Sahara and the Equator.

Preferred habitat: Open and broken slopes in sparse heathland. It particularly favours areas of short grass, close to rocky slopes or broken walls for nesting, and avoids forests and wetlands. It will tolerate some human disturbance, but has not adapted to man and will not use horticulture or grassland within settlements.

Food: Mainly insects, but also other invertebrates, molluscs, and berries. It takes prey from the ground by running and pecking or by swooping onto it from a low perch. Aerial prey is caught by flycatching or by fluttering pursuit. Occasionally, it will hover, probe the ground or animal droppings, or snatch prey from the air by jumping.

Breeding: Males arrive at the breeding grounds in March, a few days before the females, and immediately establish their territories. Defense against rivals and the attraction of a mate are by song, given from a perch or in song-flight. When a female is attracted, the male bounces towards her and appears to dance. In this dancing display, he leaps quickly and erratically from side to side over the female, feathers ruffled, like a ball of feathers being jerked to and fro on a string. If the female accepts him, she inspects several possible nest-holes, in a wall, amongst stones, or down a burrow, before choosing one. In early April, she makes a foundation of dry plants, on which she makes a nest-cup of grass, leaves, moss, and lichen, lined with feathers and hair. One or two clutches of 4-6 eggs are laid. Incubation takes 2 weeks and is by the female. The chicks are cared for and fed by both parents. Fledging takes 2 weeks, although the young often leave the nest at 10 days old. They become independent at about one month old and breed for the first time at one year old. The pair-bond is monogamous and is often renewed in subsequent years owing to strong site-fidelity.

Hints on recognition: The male is distinctive, being light blue-grey on the upperparts and creamy white on the underparts. He has a black 'mask', mostly black wings, and a black $\perp$ on the end of a white tail. The female closely resembles the female Black-eared Wheatear (for which, see that species). She has the male's tail-pattern, but is grey-brown on the upperparts, dark brown on the wings, and buff on the underparts, although the Iberian race *Oenanthe o. libanotica* can often resemble the male.

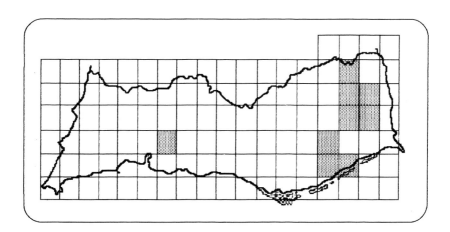

Hints on finding: This species is scarce in the Algarve, with only one pair recorded in each rectangle. The Beliche Reservoir area and the upper reaches of the Odeleite would be good areas to search.

Confirmation of breeding: The female Wheatear can be confused with the Black-eared Wheatear, which may have led to under-recording.

Number of rectangles in which recorded: 9
Possible breeding: 2
Probable breeding: 4
Confirmed breeding: 3

OENANTHE HISPANICA

BLACK-EARED WHEATEAR

Portuguese name: Chasco-ruivo.

Distribution: The Black-eared Wheatear breeds only in the Mediterranean Basin and the adjoining regions of south-west Asia. It is absent from north-western and north-central Portugal, and is particularly abundant in the south (CEMPA).

Status in the Western Palearctic: Although the range of this species has decreased in France, its general status is not known. There has apparently been no change in Portugal since Coverley's time and the Algarvian population would appear to be stable. It is a summer visitor, wintering in northern tropical Africa.

Preferred habitat: Dry, broken ground with sparse vegetation. It particularly favours the broken banks of newly-made or newly-repaired tracks and terraces, but also uses the sides of dried-up water-courses, banks of ditches, rough stony terrain, and piles of stones. It is tolerant of some human disturbance but generally avoids habitations.

Food: Mainly insects, but also other invertebrates and berries. Most prey is taken from the ground or low vegetation, the bird swooping onto it from a perch. This species will also catch prey in aerial pursuit, by fly-catching, by hovering over dense vegetation, and by deliberately flushing it from hiding places.

Breeding: It arrives at its breeding grounds in March, the males at least some days before the females. The male establishes a territory, which he advertises by song given from a perch or in flight. In a typical song-flight the male flutters upwards, singing, with tail fanned, circling and jinking over his territory, before plummetting down with wings closed. When a female is attracted, the male approaches her silently in a series of gliding and quick flapping. He then alternates displays of flying rapid figure-of-eights with raising his head and quivering his wings. In both displays he often swinging his body up and down violently. He shows her potential nest-sites, both sexes singing, from which she either chooses one or moves on to a different male. Once a site is chosen, she builds a cup of grass and moss, lined with hair and fine grass, in a hollow or depression in a bank, with long pieces of vegetation arranged down the bank below the nest. Two clutches of 4-5 eggs are laid. Incubation takes 2 weeks and is by the female alone. The chicks are fed and cared for by both parents. Fledging takes 11-12 days and the young become independent at about 3 weeks old. The age of first breeding is one year old. The pair-bond is monogamous and probably of seasonal duration only.

Hints on recognition: The male is found in two morphs, a black-throated form and a light-throated form. His body colour can be any shade between a rich biscuit and a creamy white, with a white forehead contrasting with a jet black 'mask' (or face and throat in the black-throated form). His wings are jet black, and his rump and tail are white with a jet black $\perp$ on the end of the tail. The female is entirely sandy brown, with dark brown wings and a similar tail-pattern to the male (and can have a dusky throat). She can resemble a female Wheatear (for which, see that species).

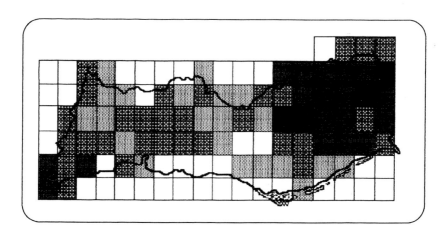

Hints on finding: It is most abundant in the Serra do Caldeirão, where the interior is being opened up with numerous new tracks and roads. An exploration to either side of the Barranco do Velho (north of São Braz) to Alcoutim road or the roads running east from Azinhal (north of Castro Marim) should quickly provide good views of this species. It can also be easily found on the Cape St. Vincent Peninsula, away from the tourist stops.

Confirmation of breeding:

Number of rectangles in which recorded:	73
Possible breeding:	1
Probable breeding:	13
Confirmed breeding:	59

OENANTHE LEUCURA

BLACK WHEATEAR

Portuguese name: Chasco-preto.

Distribution: The Black Wheatear is mainly restricted to northern Africa and Spain, with a few breeding sites in neighbouring areas of Portugal and France. In Portugal, it is confined to the extreme eastern border with Spain and was not found breeding in the Algarve by the national atlas.

Status in the Western Palearctic: There would appear to be a marked decrease in the population of both Portugal (CEMPA) and France (BWP, 1988), although the records shown in this Atlas represent the first known breeding for the Algarve. It is resident.

Preferred habitat: Dry, rocky slopes or cliffs, with little or no vegetation. It readily uses rocky gorges, crags, and ruins, but avoids flat terrain, forests, wetlands, crops, horticulture, sand-dunes, and habitations.

Food: Mainly insects, which it catches on the ground, whilst hopping along or by searching in likely hiding places. It will also take prey in flight. Other invertebrates are also eaten, as well as lizards, scorpions, and berries.

Breeding: Unpaired males establish their territories in autumn. In mid-winter, the male begins to advertise his territory by song, given in flight. In typical song-flight, he begins by singing from an exposed perch, then flutters upwards, tail fanned and legs dangling, before gliding down to another perch. When a female approaches, he lands by her and slowly raises and fans his tail, to show his only conspicuous markings. He moves rhythmically in front of the female, gradually enticing her to follow him to one of the nest-holes which he has already selected. By the end of February, the pair-bond is formed and the female chooses the nest-hole, which may be in a cliff or a wall. The male, later helped by the female, brings large numbers of small stones to the entrance of the hole, to form a platform, which may become extensive (often consisting of many hundreds of stones) after several years' usage. The pair constructs a nest-cup of grass, feathers, and wool inside the hole. One clutch (sometimes two) of 3-5 eggs is laid. Incubation takes 2 to 2 1/2 weeks and is by the female alone. The chicks are fed and cared for by both parents, the female brooding them while they are small. Fledging takes 2 weeks and the young become independent about 2 weeks afterwards, although they may stay with the parents for several months. The age of first breeding is one year old. The pair-bond is monogamous and may last for life.

Hints on recognition: This species has unique plumage in Europe, being entirely black (the female a very dark brown) with a white tail, having the typical black $\perp$ terminal pattern of the wheatear family. As with the other wheatears, it has the general shape and stance of a Robin.

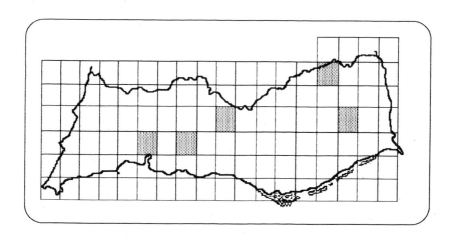

Hints on finding: This species is so scarce in the Algarve that no help can be given in this section.

Confirmation of breeding: One pair was found in each of the rectangles marked on the map, for one year only in each case.

Number of rectangles in which recorded: 5
Possible breeding: 1
Probable breeding: 2
Confirmed breeding: 2

MONTICOLA SOLITARIUS

BLUE ROCK THRUSH

Portuguese name: Melro-azul.

Distribution: The Blue Rock Thrush breeds mainly around the Mediterranean Basin, in the middle latitudes of Asia, and in Malaysia. In Portugal, it is to be found along the entire eastern border with Spain, as well as several places along the south-west coast (CEMPA).

Status in the Western Palearctic: It has decreased in France and Switzerland, but would appear to be stable elsewhere in its range. There is no evidence of any change in its status in the Algarve. It is resident, although there is considerable local dispersal in winter.

Preferred habitat: Broken cliffs, both coastal and inland, and steep rocky slopes. In the west, it particularly favours the sea-cliffs, whilst in the east it favours gorges and the rocky sides of small river-valleys. It will also use ruins or piles of stones for nesting in less broken terrain. Although shy in the breeding season, it will live on the roofs of houses in winter in the Algarve and breeds in the middle of cities in other parts of its range.

Food: Mainly invertebrates, but also small lizards, snakes, and fruit. It will feed on the ground, use a perch from which to pounce onto prey, or catch flying prey in aerial pursuit.

Breeding: In late December or early January, both sexes return to the breeding grounds. The males establish their territories, which they defend and advertise by song, given from a perch or in flight. In typical song-flight, the male glides upwards, spreading his wings and tail to gain up-lift, singing. He then either glides down or flutters down with legs dangling. When a female approaches, the male lands by her, bill pointing skywards. He may then droop his wings and fan his raised tail, or he may alternately bow and stretch in front of her. The female may also sing, but not so strongly as the male. In late March or early April, the female makes a nest of grass and moss, lined with fine grass and other soft materials, in a hole or on a ledge inside large holes. During the course of fieldwork for the BBA, one nest was found on a dresser-shelf in a ruin. Two clutches of 4-5 eggs are laid. Incubation takes 2 weeks and is by the female alone. The chicks are fed and cared for by both parents, the female brooding them while they are small. Fledging takes 2 1/2 weeks and the young become independent shortly afterwards, although the family frequently remains together for some time. Often the male looks after the fledged young whilst the female begins incubating the second clutch. The age of first breeding is probably one year old. The pair-bond is monogamous and of seasonal duration only.

Hints on recognition: When it is standing on a perch, the male looks like a blue Blackbird, with dark brown wings and bill. The female is light brown, strongly barred and streaked on the underparts, lightly tinged blue-grey on the upperparts. When it is seen hiding, behind rocks or the chimney of a house, it appears black. It has a distinctive manner of craning its neck around or over an obstacle, appearing long, sleek, and thin.

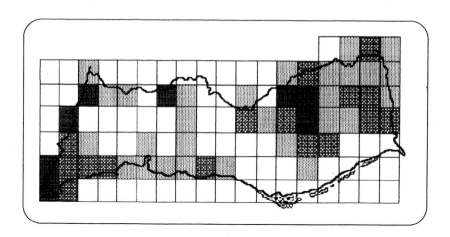

Hints on finding: A walk along the cliffs of the Cape St. Vincent Peninsula, away from the tourist stopping-points, should quickly provide good views of this species.

Confirmation of breeding:

Number of rectangles in which recorded: 52
Possible breeding: 3
Probable breeding: 14
Confirmed breeding: 35

TURDUS MERULA

BLACKBIRD

Portuguese name: Melro-preto.

Distribution: The Blackbird is to be found throughout the Western Palearctic, except the extreme north and south, and in the middle to lower latitudes of Asia south to Sri Lanka. It was introduced into Australasia in 1862. It is well distributed and fairly common throughout Portugal (CEMPA).

Status in the Western Palearctic: This species has increased in many parts of its range over the past 100 years, mainly owing to its ability to live close to man and colonise towns. Its status in the Algarve is not known, but it would appear to be stable or slightly increasing. It is resident in Portugal, although many birds migrate from northern Europe to the Algarve in winter.

Preferred habitat: The Blackbird will live almost anywhere that has a suitable nest-site and at least some bushes. It will tolerate habitats as diverse as sand-dunes, wetlands, cities, sea-cliffs, forest, horticulture, and grasslands. It is very tolerant of man and freely lives close to him.

Food: Mainly insects and earthworms, but also fruit. It mainly catches prey on the ground by: hopping and locating it visually, digging with the feet, foraging through leaf-litter with the bill, locating earthworms underground by listening.

Breeding: During the winter months, the male establishes a territory, which is defended and advertised by means of song. Most song is given early in the morning, before daylight, or late in the evening, and is delivered from a high perch. If a female approaches on the ground, he moves around her, tail lowered and fanned, rump feathers ruffled to form a conspicuous hump, occasionally leaping and twirling in front of her. Then, both sexes search for prospective nest-sites, the male often showing the female likely places, although she has the final choice. In early March, the female makes a nest of grass and twigs on a base of moss, lined firstly with mud and then with fine grass. The nest is sited in the branches of a tree or bush, including in bramble, but also used are buildings, piles of debris, tree-stumps, ledges on banks, etc. Two or three clutches of 3-5 eggs are laid. Incubation takes almost 2 weeks and is by the female alone. The chicks are fed and cared for by both parents, the female brooding them while they are small. Fledging takes about 2 weeks and the young become independent about 3 weeks afterwards, the brood often being split between the parents. The age of first breeding is one year old. The pair-bond is monogamous and can be of seasonal duration only or can be for life.

Hints on recognition: The male, with his glossy black plumage and brilliant yellow-orange bill and eye-ring, is well-known. The female, however, differs from her northern counterparts in being slate-grey and having a bill and eye-ring almost as orange as the male. Her throat is often pale grey speckled with dark grey. Juveniles are brown, spotted and streaked with buff and showing variable amounts of black or grey.

238

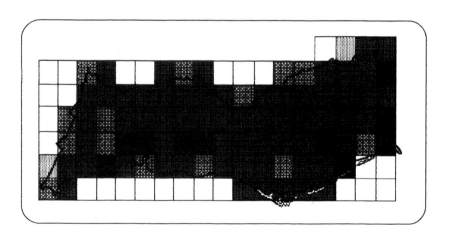

Confirmation of breeding:

Hints on finding: This ubiquitous species can be found in any suitable habitat.

Number of rectangles in which recorded:	83
Possible breeding:	0
Probable breeding:	1
Confirmed breeding:	82

TURDUS VISCIVORUS

MISTLE THRUSH

Portuguese name: Tordeia.

Distribution: The Mistle Thrush is to be found in most of the Western Palearctic and the middle latitudes of western Asia. It is well distributed throughout Portugal but is nowhere very common (CEMPA).

Status in the Western Palearctic: There has been a marked increase in parts of northern Europe, although it has decreased in Finland. There appears to be no general change in its status in Portugal, but there has been some recent decrease in the Algarve population, probably owing to the destruction of cork oaks and to the increase in eucalyptus planting. It is resident but dispersive in Portugal.

Preferred habitat: Open, mature oakwoods, with sparse under-storey and with easy access to fruit and short grass. It avoids dense forest, treeless terrain, wetlands, and tall vegetation. It is not tolerant of human disturbance and generally avoids the close proximity of man.

Food: Invertebrates, but also considerable quantities of fruit in autumn and winter. It mainly feeds on the ground in a similar manner to the Blackbird (for which, see that species), but it will also taking flying prey in aerial pursuit and feed in trees.

Breeding: The winter is spent in small flocks, which break up in December or January. The male establishes a territory, which he defends and advertises by song, given from a high perch. He may also leave his perch to fly, singing, over his territory.

Singing starts before dawn and continues almost without interruption until sunset. As with many other species where the female resembles the male, approaching females are at first met with aggression by the male. He chases her from branch to branch, and she may chase him, the male repeatedly raising his wings to show the white linings and fanning his tail to show the white tips. Feeding of the female by the male is an essential part of courtship. By February the pair is formed and the female has chosen the nest-site, which may be in a tree, in a fork of thick branches or in a fork between a branch and the trunk, but may sometimes be in a building or on a bank. In early March, the female builds a nest of twigs, grass, moss, and leaves, lined with mud mixed with vegetation and rotten wood, which is then lined with fine grass. Two clutches of 3-4 eggs are laid. Incubation takes 2 weeks and is by the female alone, occasionally helped by the male. The chicks are fed and cared for by both parents, the female brooding them while they are small. Fledging takes 2 weeks and the young become independent about 2 weeks later, the male assuming sole responsibility when the female begins incubating the next clutch. The first brood often remains close to the nest, forming a group with the second brood when it fledges. The age of first breeding is probably one year old. The pair-bond is monogamous and may be of seasonal duration only or may last longer.

Hints on recognition: This species can be confused with the Song Thrush, which is common in winter. The Mistle Thrush is larger, with very light brown upperparts, white feathers at the sides of the tail, and in flight shows whitish undersides to the wings. The Song Thrush is medium-brown on the upperparts, has no white on the tail, and in flight shows warm golden-brown on the undersides of the wings.

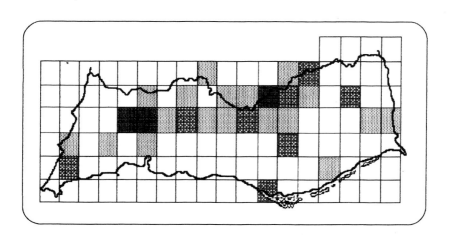

Hints on finding: It is often difficult to find as it tends to perch at the top of the tallest tree when approached. The mature oakwoods between Monchique and Alferce (east of Monchique) have easy access, however. It can also be observed at Quinta do Lago (see Where to watch breeding birds, E).

Confirmation of breeding:

Number of rectangles in which recorded:	29
Possible breeding:	2
Probable breeding:	10
Confirmed breeding:	17

CETTIA CETTI

CETTI'S WARBLER

Portuguese name: Rouxinol-bravo.

Distribution: The Cetti's Warbler is restricted to temperate western Europe, the Mediterranean Basin, and Central Asia. It is to be found everywhere in Portugal except the north-west (CEMPA).

Status in the Western Palearctic: It has increased and spread markedly over the last 30 years, crossing the English Channel to breed for the first time in the U.K. in 1972. There is apparently no change in its status in Portugal since Coverley's time. It is resident and sedentary in the Algarve.

Preferred habitat: Dense vegetation by rivers, freshwater-ditches, seasonal watercourses, marshes, etc., in warm situations. It particularly favours patches or lines of low dense vegetation, through which it may travel without having to break cover, especially in valley bottoms or other flat terrain. It avoids tall vegetation and all open situations. It is tolerant of some human disturbance.

Food: Mainly insects, but also other invertebrates, including aquatic prey. It mostly catches its prey on or near the ground, by pecking or by fluttering, but will also extract invertebrates from rotten wood or damaged plants.

Breeding: Any time from autumn onwards, the male establishes a main territory, within which one or more females may have their own territories. He defends and advertises his territory by flying from one perch to another, singing loudly from each, around or along the area claimed. If an unpaired female enters his territory, the male calls softly to her and she answers, both birds quivering their wings. If the female accepts him and stays, she will defend her own territory and rarely helps him to expel intruders. In March, she builds a bulky nest of leaves and stems or roots, lined with feathers, hair, and other fine material, in thick vegetation. Two clutches of 4-5 eggs are laid. Incubation takes 16-17 days and is by the female alone. The chicks are brooded and cared for by the female only, and are also fed mostly by her, although the male will sometimes help to feed them. Fledging takes 2 weeks and the young become independent at about one month old, the male often assuming feeding responsibilities when the female begins incubating the next clutch. Family bonds are often maintained until the young are about 5-6 weeks old. The age of first breeding is one year old. Some pair-bonds are monogamous, but more often they are polygynous. Although the males and females often retain the same territories throughout the year and in successive years, there is little association between the male and his mate/mates, even during the breeding season.

Hints on recognition: This species is often heard but rarely seen. It is a rich reddish brown on the upperparts and buff on the underparts. It has a prominent white supercilium and a distinctive way of holding its tail almost always fanned, even in its normal weak fluttering flight.

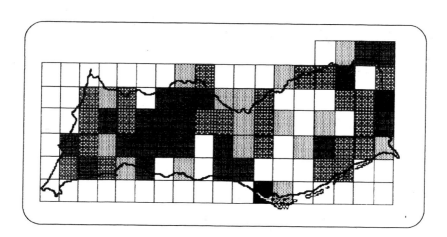

Hints on finding: This species is very rarely seen, as it stays always in deep cover. Its loud and distinctive song of "chee chee chi-chooweechoowee-chwee", or variations, quickly pinpoints its presence. It can easily be found at Ludo, and at such places as the hide at Quinta do Lago and the banks of the Odelouca (see Where to watch breeding birds, E and D).

Confirmation of breeding:

Number of rectangles in which recorded: 63
Possible breeding: 1
Probable breeding: 13
Confirmed breeding: 49

CISTICOLA JUNCIDIS

FAN-TAILED WARBLER

Portuguese name: Fuinha-dos-juncos.

Distribution: The Fan-tailed Warbler is to be found mainly around the Mediterranean Basin (but see Status for spread in France), in most regions of Africa, most of southern Asia, and Australia. It inhabits all of Portugal, except for the north-east, but is most common in the south (CEMPA).

Status in the Western Palearctic: It has spread north-westwards in Europe during this century, reaching the north coast of France in the 1970s. There would appear to be no recent change in its status in Portugal. It is resident but dispersive and it is possible that some may migrate to overwinter in Morocco.

Preferred habitat: Grass, fallow horticulture, and marshland with low vegetation. It particularly favours grass and non-woody vegetation less than 1m high on mainly level terrain. It avoids reeds, bull-rushes, bamboos, and other tall vegetation, except for the peripheries, and avoids all trees completely. It is tolerant of human disturbance.

Food: Mainly insects, which are taken on or near the ground. It will also flycatch from a high perch, such as overhead wires. Other invertebrates, such as spiders, are occasionally caught.

Breeding: Males, which have dispersed or migrated during the winter, return to the breeding grounds in February or early March, whereas the females can arrive up to a month later. The male advertises his territory by song, given from a perch or in flight. The song-flight is conspicuous, whereby he appears to be jerked up and down on the end of a string suspended from the sky, singing "Zip zip" in time with the jerks. As well as singing, he constructs several basic nests of grass, each literally sewn (he punctures each blade of grass with his bill and threads a strand of cobweb through it) and glued together with cobwebs, to which he tries to attract one or more females. The nest is pear or bottle shaped and is sited low down in a clump of vegetation. As soon as a female accepts one, he often destroys all the others and uses the material, especially the essential cobwebs, to make new ones. The female lines the chosen nest with cobwebs, hair, flowers, and down, and lays 4-6 eggs. Incubation takes nearly 2 weeks and is by the female alone. The care of the chicks is also by the female, although occasionally the male will help to feed them. Fledging takes 2 weeks and the young become independent 2-3 weeks later. Two or three clutches may be laid, but each is almost always with a different male. The age of first breeding for females can be as little as one month old, and juveniles from early broods often breed later in the same season, whereas males are not known to breed until they are one year old. The pair-bond is polygynous and weak, with little association between the sexes beyond the initial nest-building and mating. In one study, recounted in BWP (1992), the average number of females per male was 4 and one male had as many as 11 females.

Hints on recognition: The distinctive song-flight is particularly diagnostic. This bird is tiny, but when seen perched, its buff plumage, strongly striped with black on the upperparts, and its cocked and fanned tail, tipped with black and white, can be observed.

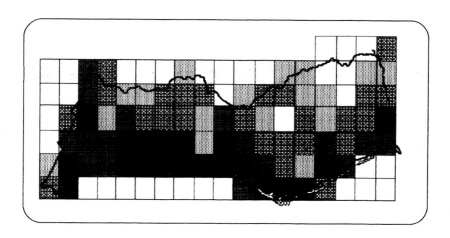

Hints on finding: It can be found in suitable habitat anywhere in the lowlands, including by the sea-wall at Alvor and near the hide at Quinta do Lago (see Where to watch breeding birds, B and E).

Confirmation of breeding:

Number of rectangles in which recorded: 78
Possible breeding: 0
Probable breeding: 12
Confirmed breeding: 66

ACROCEPHALUS SCIRPACEUS

REED WARBLER

Portuguese name:
Rouxinol-pequeno-dos-caniços.

Distribution: The Reed Warbler breeds in temperate Europe, northern Africa, southwest Asia, and Central Asia. It is to be found throughout the Portuguese littoral but is not common south of the Sado (CEMPA).

Status in the Western Palearctic: Although its range has spread in northern Europe, it has declined markedly almost everywhere, mainly because of habitat destruction. In the Algarve, too, it has declined drastically, owing to the extensive removal of reed-beds for urbanizations and golf-courses, and to the total neglect and over-grazing of most of the remaining reed-beds. It is a summer visitor, wintering in the equatorial regions of Africa.

Preferred habitat: Reed-beds, as its name would suggest. Generally, it requires more extensive and mature beds than those required by the Great Reed Warbler and, unlike that species, will not use other wetland vegetation.

Food: Mainly insects and spiders, but also other invertebrates and small fruits. It catches most of its prey by pecking, either directly from the vegetation or by hovering and pecking. It will also flycatch, leap from a perch after aerial prey, and leap upwards to take prey from the underside of foliage.

Breeding: This species arrives at the breeding grounds in March, the males 2-3 weeks before the females. Young males tend to return to their natal site or to the area where they lived just after fledging. Most older males return to the same reed-bed every year; females are less site-faithful. Possession of a territory by a male is advertised by song, given from the top of a reed. If a female is attracted to him, the male stops singing and follows her everywhere she goes, only moving in front of her when she tries to leave his territory. If she accepts him, she builds a nest of grass and reed, interwoven with down and cobwebs, lined with finer material, and attached to plant stems. While she is building, the male perches near her, fluttering his wings and continuously calling. One clutch (sometimes two) of 3-5 eggs is laid. Incubation takes 10-11 days and is by both parents, although the female takes the greater share and mostly sits at night. The care and feeding of the chicks are by both parents, both brooding them for the first week after hatching. Fledging takes 10-12 days and the young become independent about 2 weeks afterwards. The age of first breeding is one year old. The pair-bond is monogamous and is often renewed in subsequent years, although sometimes the female deserts her mate in favour of a neighbouring male, even while incubating the first clutch.

Hints on recognition: In the Algarve during the breeding season, this species can only be confused with the Cetti's Warbler and the Great Reed Warbler (for which, see those species). The only time it is seen is when it is singing on top of a reed, which the Cetti never does. It is smaller than the Great Reed, being between the Blue Tit and the Great Tit in size, and is also noticeably slimmer. It is more rufous than the Great Reed, especially on the rump, and has a long sloping forehead, leading without any apparent demarcation onto its thin bill.

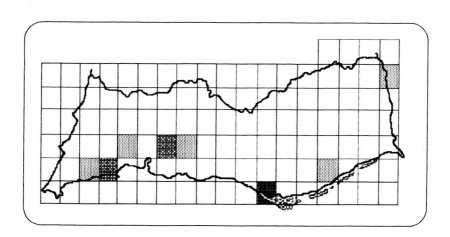

Hints on finding: This species is to be found easily only at Ludo (see Where to watch breeding birds, E), as it does not always breed at the other sites marked on the map.

Confirmation of breeding:

Number of rectangles in which recorded:	8
Possible breeding :	3
Probable breeding :	2
Confirmed breeding :	3

ACROCEPH. ARUNDINACEUS

GREAT REED WARBLER

Portuguese name:
Rouxinol-grande-dos-caniços.

Distribution: The Great Reed Warbler breeds in all the middle latitudes of the Western Palearctic and Asia, although the East Asian race is often given species status. It is fairly common throughout the Portuguese littoral where there is suitable habitat, being largely absent only from the north-west (CEMPA).

Status in the Western Palearctic: It has expanded its range to the north and east of Europe, but has decreased markedly in parts of western Europe. There is apparently no change in its general status in Portugal, although it is declining in the Algarve owing to the destruction of its nesting habitat. It is a summer visitor, wintering in equatorial and southern Africa.

Preferred habitat: Reed-beds, but also bamboo, bulrush, and other similar types of vegetation. It will tolerate small remnant clumps of reeds, which the Reed Warbler shuns, as well as tall riparian vegetation along ditches.

Food: Mainly invertebrates, but also small fruits and vertebrates such as fish fry. It takes prey from: vegetation by searching and pecking, the ground by pouncing on it from vegetation, the air by flycatching or leaping, and the edge of water by hovering and pecking.

Breeding: Individuals arrive at the breeding grounds at the end of March or in early April, the males at least a few days before the females. The male establishes a territory, which is advertised by song given from an exposed perch or in flight. When a female approaches, he immediately stops singing and approaches her. He courts her aggressively, following her everywhere, and she may respond aggressively to him. If she accepts him, she begins depositing material at several prospective nest-sites, eventually choosing one. She makes a nest of leaves and stems, interwoven with plant down and cobwebs, lined with finer material, and attached to plant stems. One clutch (sometimes two) of 3-5 eggs is laid. Incubation takes 2 weeks and is by the female alone, the male guarding the nest and bringing food to the female. The chicks are fed and cared for by both parents, the female brooding them for the first week after hatching. The male assumes responsibility for feeding them if the female begins building a second nest. Fledging takes nearly 2 weeks and the young become independent about 2 weeks later, leaving the breeding grounds completely after a further 2-3 weeks. The age of first breeding may be at one year or two years old. The pair-bond is often monogamous, although polygyny is frequent. It is of seasonal duration only, the pair separating when the young fledge, and most females will desert their mates for new ones if a nest is unsuccessful.

Hints on recognition: This species can only be confused with the Reed Warbler (for which, see that species), which is much smaller. It is 50-60% bigger than the Reed Warbler, with a thicker bill and generally bulkier appearance. It is a lighter and less warm brown, and has a more strongly marked supercilium.

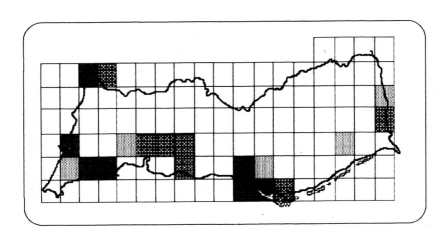

Hints on finding: This species is most easily found at Ludo and in front of the hide at Quinta do Lago, but can also be observed at Boca do Rio (see Where to watch breeding birds, E and A). Other easily reached sites are Carrapateira, Sargaçal to the northeast of Lagos, and Fontes between Silves and Estômbar.

Confirmation of breeding:

Number of rectangles in which recorded:	19
Possible breeding:	1
Probable breeding:	6
Confirmed breeding:	12

HIPPOLAIS PALLIDA

OLIVACEOUS WARBLER

Portuguese name: Felosa-pálida.

Distribution: The Olivaceous Warbler breeds in southern Europe, the northern half of Africa, the Middle East, south-west Asia, and Central Asia. It is known to breed only in the south-east of Portugal, where it is very scarce (CEMPA).

Status in the Western Palearctic: There is little recorded about its general status, although it is known to have increased in a few places. Coverley does not mention this species as having been seen in Portugal, but few observers visited the south-east in his time. There has certainly been no change in its status in the Algarve since the beginning of the national atlas. It is a summer visitor, wintering in West Africa.

Preferred habitat: Edges of groves or horticulture, close to farms or small villages. It particularly favours small streams, with or without water, overhung with trees. It is very tolerant of human disturbance.

Food: Mainly invertebrates, but also some fruit. It principally forages amongst the foliage in the upper half of bushes and trees, taking insects by pecking or by short flights. It will also occasionally drop onto prey on the ground.

Breeding: Individuals arrive at the breeding grounds in April, the males a few days before the females. The male quickly estab-lishes a territory, which he defends and advertises by singing. His song is given in flight or from a concealed perch near the top of a bush yet within the foliage. In typical song-flight, the male rises almost vertically, singing, before descending, still singing, to a new perch. When a female is attracted, the male follows her, with drooped and quivering wings, sometimes chasing her, occasionally singing quietly, until she accepts him. The degree of participation of the sexes in nest-building varies from pair to pair. Sometimes the male begins building before he has a mate, sometimes both birds build, and sometimes the male builds the cup and the female completes the lining. The nest is constructed of twigs and plants, and is lined with fine materials, such as hair and plant down. It is situated in a tree or bush, about 1m above ground. One clutch (sometimes two) of 2-5 eggs is laid. Incubation takes almost 2 weeks and is usually by the female alone, although sometimes the male will help. The chicks are fed and cared for by both parents, but, as with nest-building, the role of each sex can vary from pair to pair. Fledging takes almost 2 weeks and the young become independent about two weeks afterwards. The age of first breeding is probably one year old. The pair-bond is monogamous and of seasonal duration only.

Hints on recognition: In shape and size, this species closely resembles the Reed Warbler and the Melodious Warbler (for which, see those species). It is dull greyish-brown on the upperparts and whitish on the underparts, with a pale supercilium reaching only to a whitish eye-ring. The outer tail-feathers are very pale, almost white. It never has the warm brown of the Reed Warbler nor the yellowish tinge which even the palest Melodious Warblers have.

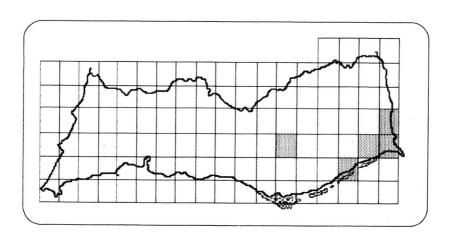

Confirmation of breeding:

Hints on finding: As this species is so sparsely distributed in the Algarve, no help can be given in this section.

Number of rectangles in which recorded:	5
Possible breeding:	0
Probable breeding:	4
Confirmed breeding:	1

251

HIPPOLAIS POLYGLOTTA

MELODIOUS WARBLER

Portuguese name: Felosa-poliglota.

Distribution: The Melodious Warbler breeds in south-west Europe and north-west Africa only. It is well-distributed throughout Portugal and is fairly common everywhere (CEMPA).

Status in the Western Palearctic: It has increased markedly northwards and north-eastwards over the past 50 years. For example, only one year after the first record, there was estimated to be 100 pairs breeding in Saarland, Germany (Melchior 1988). The population and range in Portugal would appear to be stable. It is a summer visitor, wintering in West Africa.

Preferred habitat: Small clumps of scrub, bramble, or bushes in open woodland or in otherwise open countryside, especially along seasonal water-courses. It particularly favours streams overgrown with scrub, with few or no trees, such as those found along the northern borders. It avoids forests and close proximity with habitations, but will tolerate wetlands where there is suitable cover.

Food: Mainly insects, but it will also take other invertebrates and small fruits. It feeds within the foliage of the bush, pecking prey from the leaves or snatching flying insects as they pass. It will also flycatch from the top of bushes and forage amongst roots for larvae, etc.

Breeding: Individuals arrive at the breeding grounds in April, the males a few days before the females. The male immediately establishes a territory, which he defends and advertises by song, given normally from an exposed perch. When a female is attracted, he follows her, sometimes fluttering from one perch to another singing excitedly. There is little time spent in courtship and, towards the end of April, the female makes a nest of plant stems and leaves, interwoven with and lined with plant-down and cob-webs. It is sited in a fork of a bush or small tree, about 1 1/2m above ground. One clutch (or sometimes two) of 4-5 eggs is laid. Incubation takes almost 2 weeks and is by the female alone. The chicks are fed and cared for by both parents, the female brooding them when they are small. Fledging takes almost 2 weeks and the young become independent about two weeks later, after which the family leaves the territory. The age of first breeding is probably one year old. The pair-bond is monogamous and of seasonal duration only.

Hints on recognition: It closely resembles the Reed Warbler and the Olivaceous Warbler (for which, see those species), but even the palest individuals have at least a yellowish tinge. In spring, when it has just arrived, it is yellowish-brown on the upper-parts and brilliant yellow on the underparts. Note that, unlike the Olivaceous Warbler, the yellowish supercilium reaches well behind the eye and that it does not have white side-tail feathers. The alarm-call is similar to that of the House Sparrow. The song is very UNmelodious, being a rapid stream of notes, usually preceded or interrupted by a few single notes.

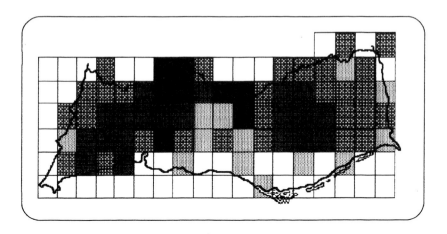

Hints on finding: The observer should be able to find this warbler in any suitable habitat away from the coast. The area of highest density is around São Marcos da Serra, near the centre of the northern border. It can also be readily found on the banks of the Odelouca away from the areas of bamboo (see Where to watch breeding birds, D).

Confirmation of breeding:

Number of rectangles in which recorded:	70
Possible breeding:	0
Probable breeding:	11
Confirmed breeding:	59

SYLVIA UNDATA

DARTFORD WARBLER

Portuguese name: Felosa-do-mato.

Distribution: The Dartford Warbler breeds in south-west Europe and north-west Africa only, reaching as far east as Italy. It is well distributed throughout Portugal, except for the Alentejo where there is insufficient suitable habitat (CEMPA).

Status in the Western Palearctic: There is no evidence for any general decline, although there has been some decrease in range in Great Britain and it fluctuates markedly following hard winters. Despite some loss of habitat to afforestation and urbanizations, the population in the Algarve would appear to be stable. It is mostly resident or dispersive, although some (possibly young birds) migrate in winter as far south as West Africa.

Preferred habitat: Scrub of uniform height and density with plentiful furze and heather, generally in sloping terrain. It is also commonly found in sparse ground-cover, e.g. on the west coast and on the edges of groves or plantations in hilly areas, as well as in isolated bramble clumps. It does not favour extensive agriculture, forests, wetlands, or mountain-tops. It will tolerate limited human disturbance and sometimes uses gardens.

Food: Chiefly invertebrates, especially caterpillars when in season, but also fruit. It feeds mainly in low scrub, searching slowly and thoroughly for prey. It will also peck from the ground and flycatch from an exposed perch.

Breeding: The unpaired males which have remained on the breeding grounds select territories in autumn; dispersive or migrant males take up unclaimed territories in January. An established pair will retain the same territory for life. The male advertises his presence by song, given from a perch or in flight. In typical song-flight, the male begins singing on an exposed perch, then flutters to about 6-7m above the bushes, still singing, and continues fluttering in an arc or a circle before descending to another perch. In late February or early March, the pair makes a nest of grass, plants, plant-down, and cobwebs, lined with hair and other fine material. It is sited in a dense bush, e.g. amongst the spikes of a gorse-bush or the prickly stems of bramble. Sometimes the male will make cock-nests, from which the female may choose one to complete. Two clutches of 3-5 eggs are laid. Incubation takes nearly 2 weeks and is mainly by the female, especially at night, but the male often helps. The chicks are fed and cared for by both sexes, sometimes assisted by an unmated male. Fledging takes about 12 days and the young become independent about 2 weeks afterwards, with the brood sometimes split between the parents. The age of first breeding is one year old. The pair-bond is monogamous and, in the case of sedentary pairs, for life.

Hints on recognition: It is a tiny wary bird, usually seen only briefly, fluttering weakly, tail flicking up and down, before diving into a bush. It is slate-grey on the upperparts, a rich rufous-red on the underparts, with a whitish belly and white spots on the throat. Its legs and eyes are red and it has a distinctive manner of cocking its tail when perched. Both sexes are similar, but the female is less strongly coloured.

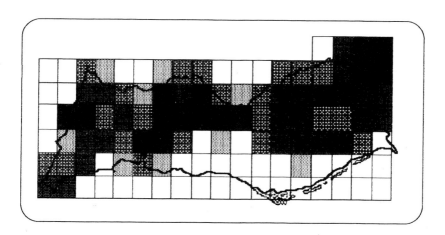

Hints on finding: It is particularly numerous in the foothills of the western serras, although the observer usually has to scramble through dense scrub to obtain good views. The distinctive wheezing alarmcall "zäärr-zäärr" helps to locate this species. Access is reasonably easy from the Odelouca Valley or from the Azinhal area (see Where to watch breeding birds, D and G).

Confirmation of breeding:

Number of rectangles in which recorded: 71
Possible breeding: 2
Probable breeding: 6
Confirmed breeding: 63

SYLVIA CONSPICILLATA

SPECTACLED WARBLER

Portuguese name: Toutinegra-tomilheira.

Distribution: The Spectacled Warbler breeds around the Mediterranean Basin and on the north-west coast of Africa only, reaching as far south as the Cape Verde Islands. The national atlas proved breeding on the north-east border of Portugal only.

Status in the Western Palearctic: There is little recorded on the population trends of this species and its status is unclear. Coverley mentions that he had never seen any in Portugal and he regarded it as scarce, which agrees with its position in Portugal today. The European population is mainly migratory, wintering in north-west Africa.

Preferred habitat: Very low but very dense scrub. It particularly favours the stunted scrub which is to be found on the wind-swept summit of Foia and the *Salicornia* growing on the dried-out mud of the eastern salt-marshes.

Food: Mainly invertebrates, but also fruits on migration. It moves through the vegetation, searching assiduously for prey, and forages on the ground amongst the roots. Occasionally, it will take insects in flight.

Breeding: Semi-colonial. Individuals, some of which may already be paired, arrive at the breeding grounds in March. The male quickly establishes a territory, which he advertises by song, given from an exposed perch on top of a bush or in flight. In typical song-flight, the male ascends silently from a prominent perch, then descends slowly, singing, with tail fanned and wings beating rapidly, before plunging into a bush. Sometimes, the male makes the nest and entices the female to add the lining. He may also build the nest for the second clutch whilst the female is still caring for the first brood. Otherwise, the pair constructs it from grass, roots, and leaves, and lines it with plant-down, before adding a final lining of hair and other fine material. It is situated in low, dense vegetation, close to or on the ground. Two clutches (sometimes three) of 3-5 eggs are laid. Incubation takes almost 2 weeks and is by the female alone. The chicks are fed and cared for by both parents, the female brooding them for the first week. Fledging takes 11-12 days and the young become independent about 2 weeks afterwards. The age of first breeding is probably one year old. The pair-bond is monogamous and may be of seasonal duration only.

Hints on recognition: It sounds and looks like a miniature Whitethroat, which occurs on migration and may breed, but does not use the same habitat. The male is light brown on the back, greyish on the rump and head, with a well-marked dark-grey 'mask' contrasting with a white eye-ring. His wings are a rich chestnut and his under-parts are pinkish, contrasting with a prominent white throat. The female lacks the grey markings and is buffish on the underparts, with a whitish throat. She may be confused with the juvenile male Subalpine Warbler (for which, see that species), which also shows a whitish throat but does not have such rich chestnut wings. The alarm-call is a harsh, wheezing chur, similar to that of the Whitethroat.

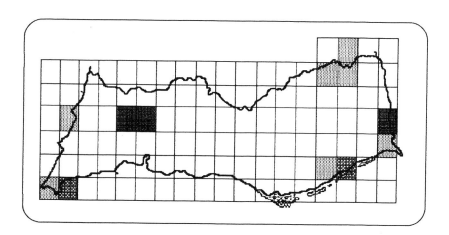

Hints on finding: The easiest place to find this species in the west is on Foia, to the north of the road. In the east, it is common along the southern banks of the Guadiana (see Where to watch breeding birds, G).

Confirmation of breeding:

Number of rectangles in which recorded:	12
Possible breeding:	0
Probable breeding:	6
Confirmed breeding:	6

SYLVIA CANTILLANS

SUBALPINE WARBLER

Portuguese name: Toutinegra-carrasqueira.

Distribution: The Subalpine Warbler breeds around the northern and western Mediterranean only. In Portugal it is restricted to the eastern borders with Spain and to the Algarve (CEMPA).

Status in the Western Palearctic: There is little recorded information on the status of this species. It has recently expanded its range to Rumania and it is being more frequently observed outside of its normal range than formerly. Coverley knew only from hearsay that it was common in the Algarve. Breeding numbers fluctuate from year to year throughout its range, following drought in its winter quarters. It is a summer visitor, wintering in Africa along the southern edge of the Sahara.

Preferred habitat: Clumps of bushes and dense scrub amongst thinner scrub, or clumps of bushes or small trees along watercourses. It particularly favours the banks of dried-out, or partially dried-out, rivers in the north-east.

Food: Mainly insects, but also other invertebrates. It is particularly dependent on fruit on migration (Vowles and Vowles, 1993). It feeds low down in bushes as well as in the canopy of tall trees, pecking prey from leaves, including galls from oak-leaves. Occasionally, it will flycatch from an exposed perch.

Breeding: Individuals arrive at the breeding grounds by mid-March, the males at least several days before the females. Each male establishes a territory, which is advertised by song given from a perch or in flight. On first arrival, the male tends to sing from an exposed perch or in flight, later he sings from deep cover. In typical song-flight, the male begins singing from one exposed perch then flutters, singing, to another exposed perch, where he continues singing. In April, the pair constructs a nest of grass, leaves, and plants, with cobwebs on the outside and a lining of hair and fine materials. It is sited in a bush, less than a metre above ground. The male often constructs cock nests, which are not used for laying and which he continues to make while the female is incubating. Two clutches of 3-4 eggs are laid. Incubation takes 11-12 days and is by both sexes. The chicks are fed and cared for by both parents. Fledging takes 11-12 days and the young become independent about 2 weeks afterwards, the male possibly feeding them until independence if the female begins incubating another clutch. The age of first breeding is probably one year old. The pair-bond is monogamous and of seasonal duration only.

Hints on recognition: The male is blue-grey on the upperparts, with some brown on the wing. The underparts are reddish and are separated from his grey head by prominent white streaks leading from the bill, like a moustache. The female is light brownish-grey on the upperparts and pinky-buff on the underparts, with pale eye-rings and barely perceptible white streaks. Young males can resemble the female Spectacled Warbler (for which, see that species), but have a brown patch on the wing, not chestnut.

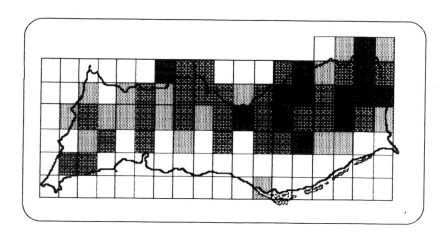

Hints on finding: It is particularly common along suitable stretches of the Foupana and Cadavais (Alcoutim) Rivers and the Odeleite. The Odeleite is easily accessible from the town of Odeleite, on the Castro Marim to Alcoutim road. This same road crosses the Foupana a short way further north.

Confirmation of breeding:

Number of rectangles in which recorded:	57
Possible breeding:	2
Probable breeding:	17
Confirmed breeding:	38

SYLVIA MELANOCEPHALA

SARDINIAN WARBLER

Portuguese name:
Toutinegra-de-cabeça-preta.

Distribution: The Sardinian Warbler breeds around the Mediterranean Basin and the north-west coast of Africa (including the Canaries) only. It is well-distributed throughout Portugal, but is more common in the south than in the north (CEMPA).

Status in the Western Palearctic: It has apparently extended its range and increased over the past century, but there is no evidence of any change in its status in Portugal. It is mainly resident or dispersive, although there is some migration into northern Africa.

Preferred habitat: This is the least discriminating of all the species breeding in the Algarve and is the only one to be represented in all rectangles. It will use all kinds of scrub, saltings, sand-dunes, salt-marsh vegetation on the banks of salt-pans, woodlands, sequeiros, reed-beds, gardens, fallow fields with at least one nesting-place, banks of rivers (with or without water), horticulture, etc. It is tolerant of human disturbance.

Food: Mainly invertebrates, but also seasonal berries or seeds. It feeds at all levels, from the ground to the canopy of tall trees, searching the foliage for prey, including galls on oak-leaves. It will also flycatch from an exposed perch and peck small invertebrates from crevices in stone walls.

Breeding: Older males and females remain on territory, or close to it, throughout the year, although members of a pair rarely stay together. Young birds disperse during the winter, often establishing territories at some distance from the natal area. By January, the males are defending and advertising their territories by song, given from a perch (concealed or exposed) or in flight. In a typical song-flight, the male begins singing from a perch, then ascends vertically, fluttering in an erratic circle whilst still singing, before returning to the same perch or near it. In February, the pair makes a nest of grass, plants, and cobwebs, lined with finer grasses, which is often used for more than one clutch. It can be sited in a bush, tree, or clump of herbage. The male often makes cock nests, which are not used for laying. Three clutches of 3-5 eggs are laid. Incubation takes about 2 weeks and is by both sexes, although the female takes the greater share. The chicks are cared for and fed by both parents, both of whom brood them for the first week after hatching. Fledging takes almost 2 weeks and the young become independent 2-3 weeks later. The parents then chase them away from the territory if there is to be another clutch laid. The age of first breeding is one year old. The pair-bond is monogamous and of seasonal duration only.

Hints on recognition: The male can be confused with the Orphean Warbler (for which, see that species), but which is much larger and has a white eye. The Sardinian Warbler has dark-grey upperparts, with a jet black head contrasting with bright red eye-rings. The underparts are light grey with a conspicuous white throat. The female is less strongly marked, with grey-brown upperparts, greyish head and reddish eye-rings. Her underparts are buff, except for a white throat like the male's.

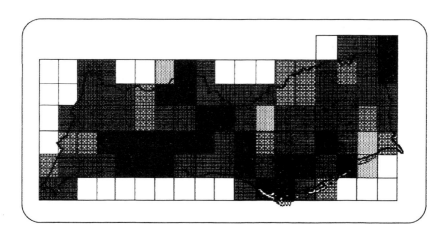

Hints on finding: As indicated under Preferred habitat, the Sardinian Warbler (or 'Sardine' as resident bird-watchers call this species), can be found almost everywhere.

Confirmation of breeding: It is the only species to have been found in all 88 rectangles.

Number of rectangles in which recorded: 88
Possible breeding: 0
Probable breeding: 4
Confirmed breeding: 84

SYLVIA HORTENSIS

ORPHEAN WARBLER

Portuguese name: Toutinegra-real.

Distribution: The Orphean Warbler breeds only in the Mediterranean Basin and in the adjoining regions of south-west Asia. It is sparsely distributed throughout Portugal and was not proved to breed in the Algarve by the national atlas.

Status in the Western Palearctic: It is apparently spreading north-eastwards in Europe, while decreasing in Italy. Coverley states that it was abundant in the Algarve and should be considered a bird of the south, whereas the national atlas considered it most common in the north-east. It is a summer visitor, wintering in Africa just south of the Sahara.

Preferred habitat: Grasslands with mature cork oaks. It particularly favours parkland with little or no scrub, such as the open oak-woods of the eastern Algarve, and avoids all areas without mature trees. It is not tolerant of human disturbance.

Food: Mainly invertebrates, but also berries. It feeds almost entirely within the canopy of trees and large bushes, pecking insects from the foliage and branches. Occasionally, it will also catch flying prey.

Breeding: In April, the males arrive at the breeding grounds at least a few days before the females. Each male establishes a territory, which is defended and advertised by song, given from a perch just within the canopy of a tall tree or from flight. Song-flights are rare, given mostly in response to the presence of a rival, and consist of the male flying, singing, from one tree to another tree some distance away. Either the male may select the nest-site and commence building whilst waiting for the arrival of the female, or the pair makes the nest after pair-formation. It is constructed of grass and plants, bound with cobwebs, plant down, and moss, and lined with finer materials. It is sited at a little over 1m above ground, in the branches of a bush or small tree. As with many other warblers, the male often makes cock nests which are not used for laying. One clutch of 3-5 eggs is laid. Incubation takes almost 2 weeks and is by both sexes, although the female takes the greater share. The chicks are fed, cared for, and brooded for the first week after hatching by both parents. The young leave the nest at 11-13 days old, when they are only able to flutter. They are fed for nearly a week out of the nest, until they can fly, after which they disperse and leave the parents' territory. The age of first breeding is probably one year old. The pair-bond is monogamous and is thought to be of seasonal duration only.

Hints on recognition: It is much larger and bulkier than any other warbler in this region, being between the House Sparrow and the Woodchat Shrike in size. In colouring it is similar to the Sardinian Warbler (for which, see that species). The head and upperparts are greyish and it has a dark forehead and mask, which contrast strongly with its white eyes. The female is similar to the male but has slightly less dark colouring on the head. The loud and repeated phrases of 2 or 3 notes, given from just within the canopy of a tall tree, are diagnostic.

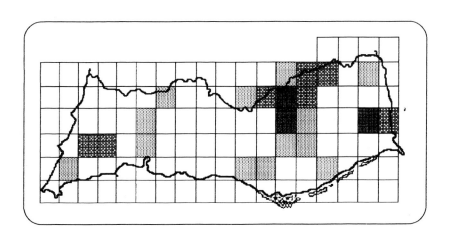

Hints on finding: This warbler spends most of its time hidden in the canopy of tall trees and tends to leave a tree on the opposite side to the observer. The loud and repetitive song of 2 or 3 notes, however, pin-points its whereabouts. It is particularly common in the region of Ameixal, but it can also be heard near Azinhal (see Where to watch breeding birds, G), and in a small valley just north of Alportel (near São Braz de Alportel), sign-posted to a spring and car-park.

Confirmation of breeding:

Number of rectangles in which recorded:	23
Possible breeding:	3
Probable breeding:	7
Confirmed breeding:	13

SYLVIA BORIN

GARDEN WARBLER

Portuguese name: Felosa-das-figueiras.

Distribution: The Garden Warbler breeds in most of Europe, being absent from parts of the extreme north and south only. It also breeds in adjoining regions of central and south-west Asia. The national atlas found it on the extreme northern borders of Portugal but not in the Algarve, although it apparently breeds in that part of Spain adjoining the Algarve (BWP, 1992).

Status in the Western Palearctic: Despite some recent spread northwards in Europe, it has decreased in Spain. Coverley mentions this species breeding in Portugal and intimates that it was scarce in his time, but gives no information on distribution. It is primarily an abundant passage migrant, especially in autumn when many thousands pass through the Algarve on their way to the wintering grounds in the southern half of Africa.

Preferred habitat: Open woodland, with plentiful scrub. It avoids dense forests, wetlands, urbanizations, very dry places such as sand-dunes, and terrain without trees or scrub. It is not tolerant of human disturbance.

Food: Mainly insects in the breeding season, although it is heavily dependent on fruit during migration (Vowles & Vowles, 1993). Other invertebrates are also included in the diet. It searches for and pecks insects from the foliage or branches of low scrub, as well as occasionally hovering or flycatching.

Breeding: In April, the males arrive a few days before the females and establish their territories. Defence and advertisement of the territory is by song, given from a concealed perch deep within dense scrub. When a female approaches, the male follows her, frequently fanning and wagging his tail up and down whilst shivering his wings. The male builds numerous flimsy cock nests, which he shows to the female. She usually chooses one and completes it, although she may reject them all. The nest is constructed of grass, leaves, and roots, mixed with plant down and cobwebs, and lined with hair and other fine material. It is sited in a low bush, especially bramble, up to 1m above ground. One clutch (sometimes two) of 4-5 eggs is laid. Incubation takes 11-12 days and is by both sexes, although the female takes the greater share, especially at night. The chicks are fed and cared for by both sexes, both parents brooding them for the first week after hatching. The young leave the nest at 10-11 days old, before they are able to fly, and become independent almost 2 weeks later. The age of first breeding is one year old. The pair-bond is monogamous, but its duration is not known in the Algarve.

Hints on recognition: It is plain brown on the upperparts, buff on the underparts, slightly paler on the throat, and has very faint white eye-rings. It is a plump bird, with no obvious markings anywhere, about the size of a Robin but with much shorter legs. The forehead is rounded, not sloping like the Olivaceous and Reed Warblers (for which, see those species), and the bill is relatively short. It is quiet and unobtrusive and rarely seen well.

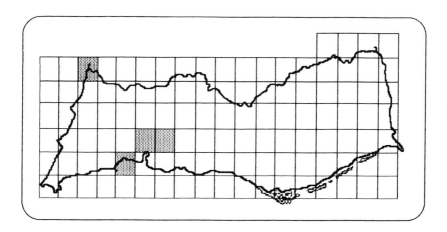

Hints on finding: This species is so scarce as a breeding species in the Algarve that no help can be given in this section. In the autumn, however, it can be found in almost any habitat.

Confirmation of breeding: The 2 rectangles with confirmed breeding involved one family party with newly-fledged young in each, in different years. The 2 probable breedings involved one trapped female with a brood-patch and one pair holding territory.

Number of rectangles in which recorded: 4
Possible breeding: 0
Probable breeding: 2
Confirmed breeding: 2

265

SYLVIA ATRICAPILLA

BLACKCAP

Portuguese name:
Toutinegra-de-barrete-preto.

Distribution: The Blackcap breeds in all Europe, except the extreme north, in the coastal areas of north-west Africa, and in parts of central and south-west Asia. It is well-distributed throughout Portugal, although it is scarce in the south-east (CEMPA).

Status in the Western Palearctic: It has increased and spread recently in much of Europe, possibly because of an increase in suitable habitat, but is declining or becoming extinct in the Cape Verde Islands. It is resident in Portugal, although hundreds of thousands of migrants from further north pass through the Algarve in autumn, some overwintering.

Preferred habitat: Overgrown valley-bottoms in all types of habitats, especially where there is some water or at least moisture even in the summer. It particularly favours river-banks with mature trees and patches of bramble. It is tolerant of human intrusion and freely uses gardens.

Food: Mainly insects, although it is heavily dependent on fruit whilst migrating (Vowles & Vowles, 1993) and on olives in the winter. Other invertebrates are also taken. It searches the foliage and branches of shrubs or trees for prey, pecking them off or taking them in short flight. It will also feed on the ground or hover.

Breeding: During the winter months, males select suitable territories and begin to advertise them by song in early March. The song is given almost exclusively from a concealed perch, which can be at any height, from a low bush to the canopy of a tall tree. When a female is attracted, the male flutters toward her whilst giving a special courtship-song. He lands by her, alternately raising and lowering his crown feathers, waving his wings and tail up and down. If she accepts him, the male shows her the rudimentary nests which he has already made. If she chooses one, she adds a little material immediately, otherwise she chooses her own nest-site. The pair completes the nest (or builds a new one) from grass and rootlets, bound with spiders' webs and cocoons, and lined with hair and other fine material. It is sited in a bush. Two clutches of 4-5 eggs are laid. Incubation takes about 2 weeks and is by both sexes, although the female takes the greater share. The chicks are fed and cared for by both parents, being brooded for the first week after hatching. Fledging takes 11-12 days and the young become independent about 2 weeks afterwards. The female may then leave the territory with them. The age of first breeding is one year old. The pair-bond is monogamous and of seasonal duration only.

Hints on recognition: It is grey-brown on the upperparts, pale buff or almost white (the male) or light brown (the female) on the underparts. The male has a black cap, whilst the female and juveniles have a rich chestnut one.

266

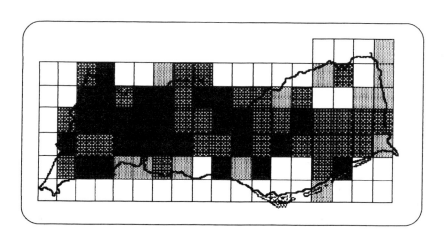

Hints on finding: The Blackcap is common in any suitable habitat, but is most easily found on the banks of the Odelouca or Arade, above tidal influence. The song is a rapid warble, interspersed with bursts of loud melodious notes, and the alarm-call is a sharp "tack".

Confirmation of breeding:

Number of rectangles in which recorded: 70
Possible breeding: 1
Probable breeding: 10
Confirmed breeding: 59

PHYLLOSCOPUS BONELLI

BONELLI'S WARBLER

Portuguese name: Felosa-de-bonelli.

Distribution: The Bonelli's Warbler is mainly restricted to the Mediterranean Basin, although a few pairs breed outside of this range, reaching as far north as the Netherlands and possibly Poland. Its principal breeding area in Portugal is the northeast (CEMPA). The national atlas did not prove any breeding in the Algarve.

Status in the Western Palearctic: The spread northwards of this species began towards the middle of this century, albeit in very small numbers. There would appear to be no change in its status in Portugal since Coverley's time. It is a summer visitor to Portugal, wintering along the southern edge of the Sahara. In the Algarve, it is mainly a common passage migrant.

Preferred habitat: In the Algarve, it has only been found breeding in secluded broadleaf valleys with plentiful ground-cover. Elsewhere in its range it will use pinewoods and appears to be tolerant of some human disturbance.

Food: Invertebrates. Unlike most other migrants, it apparently does not feed on fruit even on migration, but relies exclusively on animal matter. It forages mostly near the top of trees, searching even the tiniest twigs for prey. It will frequently hover, hang upside down like a tit, take prey in aerial pursuit, or flycatch.

Breeding: At the end of March or the beginning of April, both sexes return to the breeding grounds. The males quickly take up territories, which are defended and advertised by song. The male sings from a perch near the top of a tree, quivering the length of his body and with bill pointed upwards. When a female approaches him, she crouches, quivering her drooped wings and spread tail, which helps to appease his aggression. The female immediately searches his territory for a suitable nest-site. If she finds one, she accepts him and his territory, otherwise she leaves. The female alone builds the domed nest of grass, leaves, and moss, lined with hair and other fine material. One clutch (occasionally two) of 5-6 eggs is laid. Incubation takes almost 2 weeks and is by the female alone. The chicks are brooded by the female for the first week, then both sexes feed and care for them. Fledging takes nearly 2 weeks and the young become independent soon afterwards, although they will often stay with the parents for several weeks at least. The age of first breeding is probably one year old. The pair-bond is monogamous and of seasonal duration only.

Hints on recognition: If not seen very clearly, this species can easily be confused with the Chiffchaff or the Willow Warbler (for which, see those species). It is tiny, being smaller than a Blue Tit, with the upperparts yellowish-grey and the underparts entirely whitish. Unlike the other two mentioned warblers, it has no noticeable supercilium, but has a strongly marked greenish-yellow rump (which is not always visible) and a greenish-yellow panel on the wing (which is easily visible even at a distance). The song is a trill, totally different to other similar warblers.

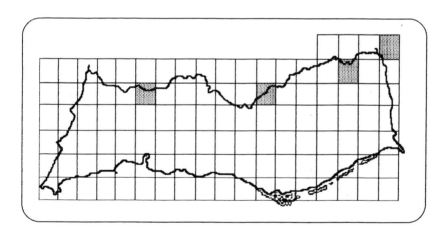

Hints on finding: The Bonelli's Warbler is a very scarce breeder in the Algarve and is therefore difficult to find. The northern borders with the Alentejo provide the best chances of observing it on the breeding grounds. It is easier to find it on autumn migration, when it can be seen in many coastal habitats in late August or early September.

Confirmation of breeding: The two con-firmed records of breeding were a nest with eggs in the confluence of the Vascão with the Guadiana and a family party with small young north of Monchique. There was also a breeding record of a nest with young near Odelouca, Silves, in 1984.

Number of rectangles in which recorded:	4
Possible breeding:	0
Probable breeding:	2
Confirmed breeding:	2

PHYLLOSCOPUS COLLYBITA

CHIFFCHAFF

Portuguese name: Felosa-comum.

Distribution: The Chiffchaff breeds in most of Europe, the middle-to-northern latitudes of Asia, and a few sites in north-west Africa and south-west Asia. It is to be found breeding the length of Portugal, although absent from a few small areas, especially from the Alentejo (CEMPA).

Status in the Western Palearctic: It has increased and spread northwards since the middle of this century. The current status of this species in Portugal is not well-documented but, according to residents of the Algarve, it is increasing in this region. The local population is partially resident, partially migratory, wintering at least as far south as north-western Africa. Large numbers of migrants from north of the Pyrenees overwinter in the Algarve.

Preferred habitat: Broadleaf woodlands, pinewoods, and open eucalyptus forests, where there is plentiful medium-height ground-cover. It is one of the few species to have fully accepted and made use of the Monchique eucalyptus plantations, where the trees are not too densely planted. It avoids all treeless terrain, even where there are numerous large bushes, and does not favour sequeiros. It is tolerant of some human disturbance.

Food: Mainly insects, but also other invertebrates. It pecks prey from the foliage and small twigs of trees, often hanging upside down like a tit. It will also take prey from the ground, hover, or catch it in aerial pursuit. Frequently it will sip nectar from flowers, such as the eucalyptus flower, and eat small berries.

Breeding: At the end of February or early in March, the males begin to advertise their territories by song, which is given either from a high perch or in flight from one perch to another. Periodically, the male searches lower in the tree for the presence of a female, which he recognizes by her keeping to the lower foliage and not singing. He flutters round her with tail fanned, either silently or giving a special courtship song. If she accepts him, she builds a domed nest of dry grass, leaves, and moss, lined with fine grass and feathers. She sites it on or just above the ground in vegetation. Two clutches of 4-7 eggs are laid. Incubation takes 2 weeks and is by the female alone. The chicks are fed and cared for by both parents, the female brooding them for the first week after hatching. Fledging takes a little over 2 weeks and the young become independent about 2 weeks afterwards, the second brood often staying with the parents until the autumn. The age of first breeding is one year old. The pair-bond is mainly monogamous, but is possibly occasionally polygynous, and is of seasonal duration only.

Hints on recognition: It is similar to the Bonelli's Warbler and the Willow Warbler (for which, see those species). It differs from the Bonelli's Warbler in being buff or yellowish-grey on the underparts, having a pale but noticeable supercilium and no pale greenish wing-panel or rump. It differs from the Willow Warbler by being generally browner, having a less obvious supercilium (never yellow), and dark almost black legs. The song of the migrant races consists of random "chiff" and "chaff" on 2 notes. The Iberian race *P.C. brehmii* is also on 2 notes but has a definite pattern, varying from bird to bird but usually "chip-chip-chip" (lower note) "chip-chip-chip" (higher) followed by a trill (lower).

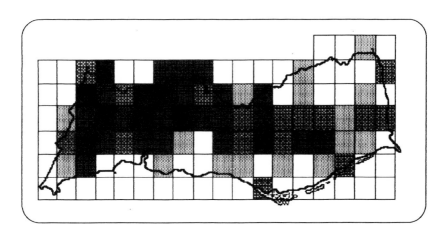

Hints on finding: This species is particularly common on the Serra de Monchique, where it can be found in broadleaf woodlands as well as in open eucalyptus plantations. Its sharp alarm-call "weet" or its distinctive song will guide the observer to its whereabouts.

Confirmation of breeding:

Number of rectangles in which recorded: 61
Possible breeding: 2
Probable breeding: 13
Confirmed breeding: 46

PHYLLOSCOPUS TROCHILUS

WILLOW WARBLER

Portuguese name: Fuim.

Distribution: The Willow Warbler breeds in almost all the northern latitudes of Europe and Asia. In Europe, the furthest south that it normally reaches is the extreme north of Spain. It was not found breeding anywhere in Portugal by the national atlas.

Status in the Western Palearctic: There has been a slight spread in Europe, northwards, westwards, and south-eastwards during this century. Coverley mentions, from hear-say, that it may have bred in southen Spain, but there would appear to be no record of it having bred in Portugal prior to the BBA. It is normally a passage migrant through the Algarve, especially in autumn, moving between its northern breeding grounds and its wintering quarters in the southern half of Africa.

Preferred habitat: All the Algarvian records came from the neighbourhood of medium-sized rivers, where there were plentiful ground-cover, mature broadleaf trees on the banks, and some scrub on the surrounding hillsides.

Food: Mainly insects, but also other invertebrates. It mostly pecks the prey from the foliage and branches of bushes or trees, but it will also flycatch, hover, and take food in short flights.

Breeding: Spring migrants pass through the Algarve in April, some remaining and singing until May. The breeding records which were obtained for the Algarve were for May-June. All the following information has been obtained from its normal breeding range. Males arrive at the breeding grounds 1-2 weeks before the females and establish their territories. They advertise their presence by song, given from an exposed perch near the top of a tree or bush. When a female enters the territory, the male stretches his head forwards, wings drooped, and twitters. If the female is attracted, she searches for a suitable nest-site, the male fluttering around her excitedly. If she does not find a site to her liking she leaves, otherwise she builds a domed nest of dry grass, leaves, moss, etc., lined with hair, feathers, and fine grass. One clutch of 4-8 eggs is laid. Incubation takes about 2 weeks and is by the female alone. The chicks are fed and cared for by both parents, the female brooding them for the first week after hatching. Fledging takes 11-15 days and the young become independent about 2 weeks afterwards, with the brood sometimes split between the parents until independence. The age of first breeding is one year old. The pair-bond may be monogamous or polygynous and is of seasonal duration only, although it can be renewed in subsequent years owing to site-fidelity.

Hints on recognition: This species can easily be confused with the Chiffchaff or the Melodious Warbler (for which, see those species). It is a little larger and bulkier than the Chiffchaff and more yellow. It has a strongly defined yellow supercilium and light brown legs. It is smaller than the Melodious Warbler and less yellow. The head is rounded with a relatively short fine beak, lacking the long sloping forehead of the Melodious Warbler. The song is a plaintive cascade of notes down the scale.

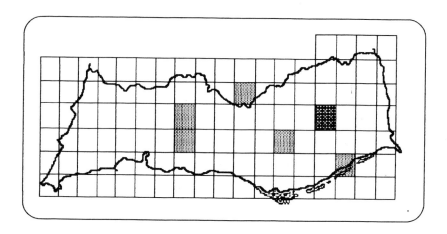

Hints on finding: Owing to the extreme scarcity of this species, no help can be given in this section for breeding birds. It can be readily seen on autumn migration, however, especially in September-October, when it can be found almost anywhere that has trees and scrub.

Confirmation of breeding: One nest with young was recorded in May 1989. All the other records were for the same year. There is no evidence to suggest that it has bred outside of that year.

Number of rectangles in which recorded:	6
Possible breeding:	2
Probable breeding:	3
Confirmed breeding:	1

REGULUS IGNICAPILLUS

FIRECREST

Portuguese name:
Estrelinha-de-Cabeça-listada.

Distribution: The Firecrest is entirely restricted to the temperate latitudes of Europe, the north-west coast of Africa, and Asia Minor. The national atlas shows it as breeding in the northern half of the country only, with no records south of Lisbon.

Status in the Western Palearctic: It has spread and increased this century in many parts of Europe. Coverley states that he knew of no nest having been discovered for this species anywhere in Portugal, whereas the national atlas found it in several areas in the north and the BBA proved breeding in the Algarve, perhaps indicating a spread in Portugal. Those that breed in the Algarve are probably resident, although it is also a common winter visitor to the region.

Preferred habitat: Very secluded mature oak-woods. It avoids open grass, farmland, eucalyptus plantations, and coastal habitats, although it can be found in these habitats on migration.

Food: Arthropods, especially springtails, spiders, and aphids (BWP, 1992). It pecks its prey from the branches and foliage of trees or large bushes, or catches it by hovering. There is no record of it taking fruit or other vegetable matter.

Breeding: In March or early April, both sexes arrive almost simultaneously on the breeding grounds. The male establishes a territory and advertises it by song, given whilst foraging. He may also advertise it by display flights, diving suddenly and silently almost to the ground, before swiftly ascending again. When a female approaches him, the two birds perch at right-angles to one another, body feathers ruffled. Each will give little jumps, remaining motionless between the jumps. Then each bird may point its beak at the other, crest raised, displaying the striking head pattern, sometimes fanning the tail and raising the wings to show the pale undersides. The male chooses the nest-site and shows it to her, even though she builds the nest unaided. The nest is a tiny elastic cup (which stretches as the chicks grow), made from moss, lichens and cobwebs, lined with more moss, with an inner layer of up to 3,000 feathers (BWP, 1992). It is suspended near the tip of a branch, concealed amongst fine twigs. Incubation takes a little over 2 weeks and is by the female alone, although the male will feed her on the nest. The chicks are cared for and fed by both parents, the female brooding them for more than a week after hatching. Fledging takes about 3 weeks and the young become independent 2-3 weeks afterwards. The age of first breeding is probably one year old. The pair-bond is monogamous and may be of seasonal duration only.

Hints on recognition: It is the second smallest bird in the Western Palearctic, the smallest being the similar Goldcrest *Regulus regulus*, which is a scarce winter visitor. It is greenish-brown on the upperparts, with 2 pale wing-bars, and pale whitish-buff on the underparts. The face and throat are white, with a black moustache and a black streak through the eye to the beak. The crown of the male is brilliant orange, edged with yellow and bordered with jet black. The crown of the female is similar but is mainly yellow with little or no orange. The song is an extremely high-pitched and faint jingle.

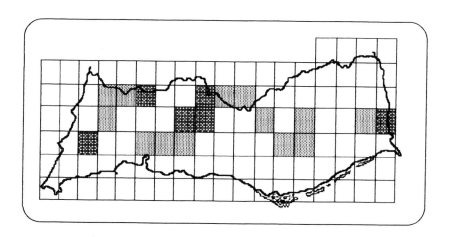

Hints on finding: This tiny and shy bird is easily overlooked. In the course of fieldwork for the BBA, it was found mainly in remote valleys, with plentiful unmanaged oak-trees and no vehicular access. Such valleys exist north of Monchique, on the upper reaches of the Arade, in the forests north of São Braz de Alportel, and near Azinhal (see Where to watch breeding birds, G).

Confirmation of breeding:

Number of rectangles in which recorded:	19
Possible breeding:	0
Probable breeding:	8
Confirmed breeding:	11

MUSCICAPA STRIATA

SPOTTED FLYCATCHER

Portuguese name: Papa-moscas-cinzento.

Distribution: The Spotted Flycatcher breeds in most of Europe, the temperate regions of the western half of Asia, and north-west Africa. The national atlas found it at scattered sites the length and breadth of Portugal.

Status in the Western Palearctic: It has decreased recently in many parts of Europe, including in Spain, yet has increased in Finland. Coverley mentions having seen a nest and several birds in the 'Quarteira woods', which area is now completely urbanized. It is a summer visitor and passage migrant, wintering in the southern half of Africa.

Preferred habitat: Mature oakwoods, especially copses near quiet farmsteads or remote villages. It avoids both dense forests and treeless terrain, as well as woodland with excessive scrub which impedes its hunting. It is fairly tolerant of human disturbance.

Food: As the name would suggest, this species feeds mainly on flies and other aerial insects. It does, however, take some berries, especially on migration. As the name would also suggest, prey is caught mainly by 'flycatching', although it will also take food from the ground or directly from foliage and branches.

Breeding: Both sexes return to the breeding grounds in May, often the males a few days before the females, although sometimes they arrive already paired. The male establishes a territory, which is advertised by a very quiet song, given from an exposed but relatively low perch. When a female approaches, the male, with crown and throat feathers ruffled, shows her the prospective nest-sites that he has found, bowing so low that his bill nearly touches the site. He shuffles around, flicking his tail and singing quietly, until the female has made her choice. She then constructs a loose cup of fine twigs, dry grass, moss, and lichens, lined with hair and feathers. It can be sited on any type of ledge, but rarely more than 10m above ground. There must be a good overall view from the ledge for the incubating bird and an overhang for shelter. One or two clutches of 4-6 eggs are laid. Incubation takes 2 weeks and is mainly by the female alone, although the male occasionally helps. The chicks are fed and cared for by both parents. Fledging takes 2 weeks and the young become independent about 3 weeks afterwards. The age of first breeding is probably one year old. The pair-bond is monogamous and of seasonal duration only, although it may be renewed in subsequent years owing to site-fidelity.

Hints on recognition: It is light brown on the upperparts and pale grey on the underparts, with dark streaks on the throat and breast and white streaks on the forehead. The very upright 'neck-less' stance when it is perched is diagnostic, as is its persistent flycatching.

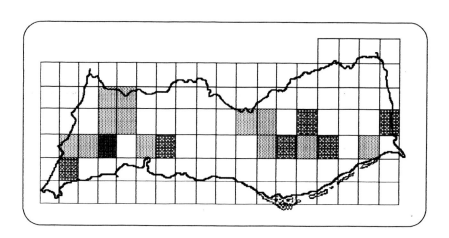

Hints on finding: This quiet and unobtrusive species is difficult to spot. If a bird is seen to repeatedly sally forth from a tree, returning to the same perch or nearby, it could well be a flycatcher, however. It can usually be found at Azinhal (see Where to watch breeding birds, G), in the valley just north of São Braz de Alportel (see Orphean Warbler), and south of the Bravura Reservoir.

Confirmation of breeding:

Number of rectangles in which recorded: 19
Possible breeding: 0
Probable breeding: 6
Confirmed breeding: 13

AEGITHALOS CAUDATUS

LONG-TAILED TIT

Portuguese name: Chapim-rabilongo.

Distribution: The Long-tailed Tit breeds in most of Europe and the temperate latitudes of Asia. It is well-distributed throughout Portugal, but is more common in the north than in the south (CEMPA).

Status in the Western Palearctic: It has increased its range in some parts of northern Europe but decreased in others. Coverley states that this species was fairly common, which would appear to be the position today. It is resident but dispersive.

Preferred habitat: A mixture of scrub and mature broadleaf trees. It will also use pine-trees, eucalyptus plantions, and sequeiros, where there is sufficient scrub. Moist or wet environments (but not saline) are often favoured, owing more to the richer density of scrub and prey than to a need for water.

Food: Mainly arthropods, but also some seeds. It pecks food from twigs, leaves, and buds, in the tops of trees or bushes, but rarely from the ground. It will readily hang upside down, hover, or fly after passing prey, but it does not have a strong enough bill to chisel or dig.

Breeding: Family parties from the previous season join with other parties to feed and roost together during the winter months. By January the juveniles have dispersed and in February the older birds return to the breeding territory of the previous year. Young birds wander away from the natal area and form pairs with other young birds.

The male displays to an unmated female by fluttering upwards for 5-6m, rapidly fanning and closing his tail to show the white edges, then diving back down, twittering. Once formed, the pair searches for an unoccupied nesting area. There would appear to be no aggression involved in finding a mate or a breeding place and, therefore, no territorial song. The pair builds an elongated ball of moss, woven with cobwebs and hair, and covered on the outside with lichen. It is lined with up to 2,000 feathers and has a concealed entrance hole near the top. The nest may be built in a tree-fork or hung amongst the twigs of a bush, such as bramble or gorse. One clutch of 7-11 eggs is laid in April. Incubation takes a little over 2 weeks and is by the female alone. The chicks are fed and cared for by both sexes, the female brooding them for the first week. Elsewhere, the parents are often helped with the feeding by an unpaired bird, but this behaviour has not been reported in the Algarve. Fledging takes 2 to 2 1/2 weeks and the young become independent 2-3 weeks later, although they remain with the parents until the winter. The age of first breeding is probably one year old. The pair bond is monogamous and may last for more than one season.

Hints on recognition: It is small, with a body-size about the same as a Chiffchaff, but with an extremely long tail, making it almost double the body-length. The upperparts are brownish-grey and the underparts are pale buffish-white. The face and crown are a 'dirty' white with a broad dark brown stripe over the eye, reaching across the nape. The race from the Algarve and southern Spain *A.c. irbii* differs from *A.c. taiti* of northern Portugal (Lisbon upwards) in having no pure black or white (being always brown-tinged) and in having no discernible pink on the body or wing.

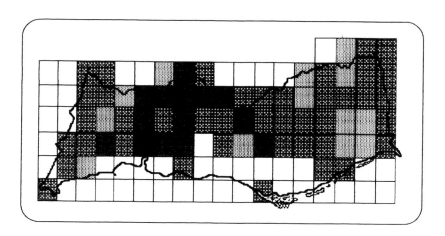

Hints on finding: The rich farmland, with abundant neglected woodland and riverine scrub, between Silves and São Marcos da Serra holds good populations. The repeated contact call "pit" can be heard long before the pair or flock come into view.

Confirmation of breeding:

Number of rectangles in which recorded: 68
Possible breeding: 0
Probable breeding: 3
Confirmed breeding: 65

PARUS CRISTATUS

CRESTED TIT

Portuguese name: Chapim-de-poupa.

Distribution: The Crested Tit is virtually restricted to the Western Palearctic. It is absent from the extreme north, most of Great Britain, Asia Minor, and North Africa. It is evenly distributed throughout Portugal (CEMPA).

Status in the Western Palearctic: It has spread and increased in many parts of Europe following increased afforestation. It would appear from Coverley's accounts that this species used to be common in the north but scarce or totally absent from the south. The BBA found it in more than half the rectangles, perhaps indicating a range expansion in Portugal. It is resident and very sedentary.

Preferred habitat: Mature oakwoods, even small copses of oaks in open countryside. It will also occasionally use pinewoods and in northern Europe it relies exclusively on conifers. It avoids all treeless terrain, even where bushes and nest-holes are plentiful.

Food: Mainly invertebrates, but also seeds. It is a typical tit, foraging agilely by hanging upside down or clinging to vertical surfaces. It will take surface-prey at any height in trees, dislodge bark or lichen, or dig with the bill into crevices for hidden prey. It will actively search the ground or undergrowth for small insects. All kinds of food are commonly stored, each individual item stored separately. The stored item may be simply wedged in a tree or it may be attached with cobwebs or the bird's saliva.

Breeding: Young birds wander during the winter months, searching for a suitable unoccupied territory or an unmated bird with a territory. By February, the males have established their territories and begun to advertise their presence by song, given whilst foraging. When a female approaches, the male flutters towards her and lands close by, crest erect and wings quivering. If she accepts him, she excavates a nest-hole in a dead branch or sometimes adapts an existing hole, including old woodpecker holes. She constructs a nest-cup of moss, lined with hair and wool, in which one clutch (sometimes two) of 4-8 eggs is laid. Incubation takes about 2 weeks and is by the female alone, the male bringing her food. The chicks are fed by both parents, but are brooded and cared for by the female alone. Fledging takes almost 3 weeks and the young become independent 2-3 weeks later, dispersing away from the area about one week after independence. The age of first breeding is one year old. The pair-bond is monogamous and lasts for life.

Hints on recognition: It is similar in size and behaviour to a Blue Tit. The upperparts are medium-brown, the underparts white with buff on the flanks. The head is black and white (see illustration for pattern), and both the crown and the distinctive crest are of black feathers with prominent white tips. The song or call is a harsh tremolo of a few notes down the scale.

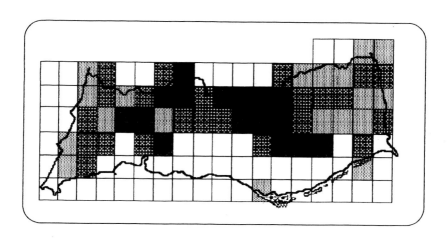

Hints on finding: It is particularly common in the oakwoods around Monchique and towards São Marcos da Serra, as well as in the extensive oakwoods between Barranco do Velho and Ameixal. A distinctive harsh tremolo, running down the scale for a few notes, is often the first indication of its presence.

Confirmation of breeding:

Number of rectangles in which recorded:	58
Possible breeding:	0
Probable breeding:	12
Confirmed breeding:	46

PARUS ATER

COAL TIT

Portuguese name: Chapim-preto.

Distribution: The Coal Tit is to be found in all the temperate latitudes of Europe, Asia, and North Africa. The national atlas found it only in the north of Portugal.

Status in the Western Palearctic: It has spread in many parts of its range, probably as a result of increased afforestation. Coverley mentions its presence near Monchique, but intimates that it was scarce, which corresponds with the findings of the BBA. It is resident and sedentary.

Preferred habitat: Medium-growth oak-woods with plentiful scrub. Elsewhere, it is primarily a bird of the northern conifers and other forest environments. It is fairly tolerant of human disturbance, yet inhabits only remote valleys in the Algarve.

Food: Mainly insects and spiders, but also other invertebrates and seeds. As with other tits, it forages on foliage and branches, often hanging upside down and freely clinging to vertical surfaces. It will take visible prey in trees at any height, tear off bark or lichen to find hidden prey, or flutter over the outermost twigs to pick it off. It commonly stores food of all kinds; each store is visited only once, although several items may be brought. The most commonly used store is an empty bud capsule, but the needles of pine-trees or crevices in bark are also used.

Breeding: Young birds wander during the winter months, often in mixed flocks with other tits, searching for a suitable unoccupied territory or an unmated bird. Older, paired birds also join mixed flocks in the winter, but stay within or close to the breeding territory. By February, all males have established their territories and have begun to advertise and defend their possession by song. A female approaches an unpaired male with a special wheezing call and the male glides down close to her. If they accept one another, the pair inspects every hole in the territory, even hollows which only superficially resemble holes. The final choice may be made by the female, who constructs the nest alone. The nest-cup is made of moss, lined with hair and wool, and may be sited in a hole in a tree, wall, rock crevice, or in the ground. Two clutches of 7-9 eggs are laid. Incubation takes a little over 2 weeks and is by the female alone, the male guarding her and bringing her food. The chicks are fed and cared for by both sexes, the female brooding them at first. Fledging takes 2 1/2 to 3 weeks and the young remain dependent on the parents for several weeks afterwards. The age of first breeding is one year old. The pair-bond is monogamous and lasts for life.

Hints on recognition: It is smaller than a Blue Tit, grey-brown on the upperparts, with two small pale wing-bars. It is creamy on the underparts, with buff flanks. The head is glossy black with a large white patch on the nape; the face is white with a black streak running downwards from the bill and widening to cover the throat. A distant fleeting glimpse of the rear of a Great Tit can appear to have the same head pattern (but see that species).

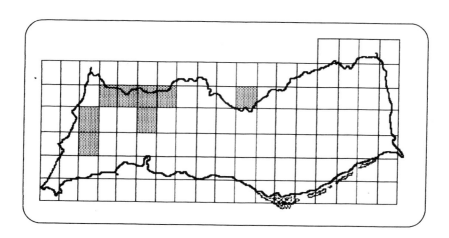

Hints on finding: This species is scarce in the Algarve and therefore little help can be given in this section. A useful access track to the area where it has been found runs to the east from Odeceixe, immediately before the bridge into the Alentejo. This track eventually links with the Monchique to Lisbon road and is drivable by car.

Confirmation of breeding:

Number of rectangles in which recorded:	8
Possible breeding:	1
Probable breeding:	5
Confirmed breeding:	2

PARUS CAERULEUS

BLUE TIT

Portuguese name: Chapim-azul.

Distribution: The Blue Tit is virtually restricted to the Western Palearctic, otherwise extending only into Iran. It is well-distributed and common throughout Portugal (CEMPA).

Status in the Western Palearctic: The population has spread and increased during this century in northern Europe. There has apparently been no recent change in its status in Portugal. It is resident and mostly sedentary.

Preferred habitat: Woodlands which are neither very open nor densely planted, especially in the foothills of the serras. It will accept scattered trees where there is plentiful scrub, but avoids lowland habitats even where they appear to be suitable. Pinewoods and eucalyptus plantations are very rarely used. It is very tolerant of human disturbance and will use man-made nest-sites.

Food: Mainly insects and spiders, but also other invertebrates and small fruits. It actively and methodically searches for visible prey on stone walls and in the branches and foliage of trees. As with other tits, it readily hangs upside down or perches on vertical surfaces. It will also peck galls open and tear buds open in search of hidden prey, and likewise remove bark or lichen, often stopping to listen for the movement of prey.

Breeding: In other parts of its range, the Blue Tit joins with other tits to form mixed foraging flocks during the winter. In the Algarve, the pair remains and defends the nesting territory throughout the year, using the same hole for roosting and nesting every year. Young birds establish a territory in the autumn or early winter and advertise their presence by song, often from an exposed perch. When a female approaches, the male flutters around her, singing, or glides whilst singing towards a suitable nest-hole. If she follows him to the hole, he may display, ruffling his nape to enhance his head pattern, and hopping stiffly, wings drooped. Once the pair-bond is formed, the female either accepts the male's hole or finds another one. She roosts in the chosen hole during the winter months, whilst he roosts in a separate one. In early March, she makes a pad of moss with a nest cup lined with hair, wool, and other fine materials. One clutch of 6-12 eggs is laid. Incubation takes 2 weeks and is by the female alone. The chicks are fed and cared for by both parents, the female brooding them at first. Fledging takes 2 1/2 to 3 weeks and the young become independent some weeks later. The age of first breeding is one year old. The pair-bond is monogamous and often lasts for life.

Hints on recognition: It is smaller than the Great Tit and basically greenish-blue on the upperparts and yellow on the underparts. The cap, wings, and tail are blue, the face white with a very dark blue to black pattern (see illustration). The young Blue Tit has only a little blue on the wing and tail, the remaining upperparts being brownish yellow and the underparts pale yellow, including the face. The head markings are similar to the adult, although yellow and brown, but lack any collar or throat pattern.

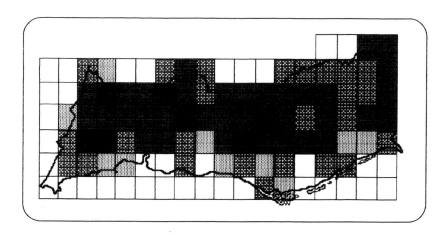

Hints on finding: It can be seen from the distribution map that this species is most common in the foothills of the serras. It is easily found in suitable habitats around the Bravura Reservoir, in the Monchique area, to the north of the Arade Reservoir, and between Salir and Barranco do Velho

Confirmation of breeding:

Number of rectangles in which recorded:	76
Possible breeding:	0
Probable breeding:	5
Confirmed breeding:	71

PARUS MAJOR

GREET TIT

Portuguese name: Chapim-real.

Distribution: The Great Tit is to be found in most of Europe, North Africa, the temperate latitudes of Asia, and much of southern Asia. The national atlas recorded it on every one of their maps, and found it equally common in the north as in the south.

Status in the Western Palearctic: There has been a spread northwards during this century, as well as a general increase in the population over much of Europe. This is possibly because of an increase in the provision of nest-boxes and winter-feeding. It is resident and mainly sedentary.

Preferred habitat: Lowland woodlands, especially sequeiros and pine-woods. It also readily uses farmland and gardens, and will inhabitat oakwoods at the bottom, or near the bottom, of valleys. It is very tolerant of human disturbance and readily adapts to man-made environments.

Food: Mainly insects, but also other invertebrates and fruits or seeds. In a study in Spain, *Lepidoptera* were found to be the principal food item given to nestlings (BWP, 1993). It actively searches for prey on the branches and foliage of bushes or trees at any height and can hang upside down for short periods. This species is far less agile than other Portuguese tits, however. It will tear off bark or lichen for hidden prey, as well as turn over leaf-litter or small stones on the ground. The bill is strong, capable of drilling into bark or nuts. In winter it forages in flocks with other species of tits, together with the Short-toed Treecreeper and the Chiffchaff.

Breeding: When the winter flocks break up in early January, older birds return to their breeding territories of the previous year whilst young birds search for unoccupied territories. The male advertises his presence by song, often given from a prominent perch. When a female approaches, he flutters around her, or he may land near her with wings quivering and tail fanned, his body held horizontally. If she remains, he may show her the nest-holes that he has found. The nest-holes may be in a tree or wall, in a crevice on a cliff, or in the ground but, where available, nest-boxes are preferred. The female inspects each site, finally choosing one for the nest. She constructs a base of moss, in which she forms a cup, thickly lined with hair, wool, dry grass, and sometimes feathers. One clutch (rarely two) of 5-12 eggs is laid in March. Incubation takes 2 weeks and is by the female alone, the male bringing her food. The chicks are fed and cared for by both parents, the female brooding them while they are small. Fledging takes 2 1/2 weeks and the young become independent about a week afterwards. The age of first breeding is one year old. The pair-bond is monogamous and of seasonal duration only, although it may be renewed in subsequent years owing to site-fidelity.

Hints on recognition: Both sexes are greenish-yellow on the upperparts, with grey-blue on the wings and tail, and bright yellow on the underparts. The head is glossy blue-black, with large white cheek patches and a small pale patch on the nape. The male has a broad blue-black stripe running down the underparts from the beak to under the tail, the female has a narrower stripe fading out between the legs.

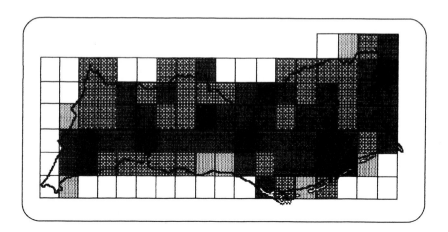

Confirmation of breeding:

Hints on finding: The Great Tit can be found in the sequeiros and farmland of the foothills and the littoral, away from areas of heavy urbanization.

Number of rectangles in which recorded:	85
Possible breeding:	1
Probable breeding:	3
Confirmed breeding:	81

SITTA EUROPAEA

NUTHATCH

Portuguese name: Trepadeira-azul.

Distribution: The Nuthatch is to be found in the temperate latitudes of Europe and Asia, Morocco, and much of southern Asia. It breeds in most parts of Portugal where there is suitable habitat (CEMPA).

Status in the Western Palearctic: It has recently spread and increased in Morocco and parts of Europe, for reasons not perfectly understood. The current status of this species in the Algarve is not known, although it would appear to be stable. It is resident and sedentary.

Preferred habitat: Mature oakwoods, with scant ground cover. It particularly favours copses of well-grown oaks, either holm or cork, which adjoin grassland or streams. It avoids eucalyptus plantations and 'managed' cork forests, as well as all treeless terrain. It is tolerant of limited human disturbance.

Food: Invertebrates and seeds, especially acorns. Surplus seeds are stored in crevices or, sometimes, in the ground. It forages almost entirely within the trees, often hanging upside down on the ends of twigs, but will occasionally feed on the ground. Aerial prey can be caught in the air by hovering. This is the only species in the area which can walk head first down the trunk of a tree.

Breeding: During the autumn months, young birds search for an unoccupied territory or an unmated older bird with a territory, as near to the natal site as possible. The males advertise their presence by song, given from a branch within the canopy of a tree. When a female approaches the male, he circles her with head raised and tail fanned, and both sexes may flutter from one tree to another. Young birds form pair-bonds in the autumn, usually breaking up in the winter to form new bonds with different mates in the early spring. Once the permanent pair-bond has been formed, the male shows the female potential nest-holes in trees, entering them and performing 'symbolic' work or cleaning. If the female accepts a hole, she plasters around the entrance with mud to make it exactly the right size for her to enter. She may also plaster the inside of the cavity, smoothing out irregularities. In late February or early March, she makes a large heap of wood chippings, bark flakes, dry leaves, etc. One nest used 3,350 bark flakes and another nest, including plaster, weighed over 1 kg (BWP, 1993). One clutch of 6-11 eggs is laid. Incubation takes 2 weeks and is by the female alone, the male feeding her through the entrance-hole. The chicks are fed and cared for by both parents, the female brooding them for 1-2 weeks after hatching. Fledging takes a little over 3 weeks and the young become independent 1-2 weeks afterwards. The age of first breeding is probably one year old. The pair-bond is monogamous and lasts for life.

Hints on recognition: *Sitta e.hispaniensis*, which is the race of Nuthatch in the Iberian Peninsular, is pinky-buff on the underparts, contrasting with rich chestnut on the flanks. The upperparts are blue-grey, the throat white, and there is a thick black stripe through the eye from the bill to the side of the neck. It is the only species in the region which can walk head-first down tree-trunks.

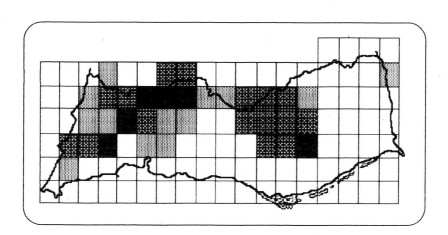

Hints on finding: It is particularly common in the oak-woods between the Serra de Monchique and São Marcos, and in the fragmented oakwoods north of São Braz. It can usually be found in the valley to the north of Alportel, described under Orphean Warbler.

Confirmation of breeding:

Number of rectangles in which recorded: 35
Possible breeding: 3
Probable breeding: 7
Confirmed breeding: 25

CERTHIA BRACHYDACTYLA

SHORT-TOED TREECREEPER

Portuguese name: Trepadeira-comum.

Distribution: The Short-toed Treecreeper is entirely restricted to the Western Palearctic, and specifically to southern and central Europe and the coastal regions of north-west Africa. It is well-distributed throughout Portugal, but is apparently more common in the south than in the north (CEMPA).

Status in the Western Palearctic: It has spread northwards into Denmark recently, but the population would appear to be otherwise stable. There is no evidence of any change in its status in Portugal. It is resident and sedentary.

Preferred habitat: All kinds of mature oak-woods, pine-woods, and sequeiros, including copses of these trees in scrub. It avoids all kinds of treeless terrain and urban development, but is fairly tolerant of human disturbance.

Food: Mainly spiders and the larvae and pupae of insects. It ascends the trunk of a tree, searching for prey, spiralling to cover all sides of the trunk. When it reaches the top, it glides to the lower part of the next trunk and repeats the search pattern. It also searches branches, including the undersides, but not the foliage.

Breeding: During the winter months, young and older birds forage with other species, e.g. tits, Chiffchaff, Firecrest, and Nuthatch. By the end of February, the young male has established a territory which he advertises by song, given from a perch high in a tree or whilst climbing. Older males return to the territory of the previous year. When a female begins roosting in his territory, the male will often make fluttering leaps around her before going to his own roost-site. Eventually, both sexes roost in the same place. The male shows the female prospective nest-sites, going in and out of the holes, flickering his wings, until the female enters and accepts one. The nest-site is usually behind a flap of bark or in a deep crevice on the trunk of a tree, but may be in a building or in the old nest of a woodpecker. The pair constructs a foundation nest of twigs, dry grass, and pieces of bark, which is lined with moss, lichen, plant down, hair, feathers, and other fine material. Two clutches of 5-7 eggs are laid. Incubation takes 2 weeks and is by the female alone. The chicks are fed and cared for by both sexes, the female brooding them when they are small. Fledging takes 2 1/2 weeks and the young become independent shortly afterwards, leaving the territory completely. The age of first breeding is probably one year old. The pair-bond is monogamous and may last for more than one season.

Hints on recognition: The Treecreeper *Certhia familiaris* is very similar to this species but has not been recorded breeding in Portugal or southern Spain. The upper-parts are medium brown, heavily streaked with light brown, and the underparts are buff. It has a long, down-curved beak and a pale supercilium. The method of spiralling up tree-trunks is diagnostic.

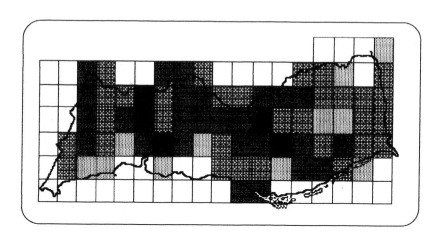

Hints on finding: It is particularly common in the oak-woods between the Serra de Monchique and São Marcos da Serra, as well as in the fragmented oakwoods north of São Braz. It is also readily found in many sequeiros and in the pinewoods around Quinta do Lago and Ludo (see Where to watch breeding birds, E).

Confirmation of breeding:

Number of rectangles in which recorded: 73
Possible breeding: 0
Probable breeding: 11
Confirmed breeding: 62

REMIZ PENDULINUS

PENDULINE TIT

Portuguese name: Chapim-de-faces-pretas.

Distribution: The Penduline Tit is to be found in the temperate latitudes of Europe and Asia. It has a very fragmented distribution and was not proved breeding in Portugal before the BBA.

Status in the Western Palearctic: It has increased and spread in much of northern and western Europe, although it has declined in southern France and Greece. It has apparently expanded markedly in Spain and the new breeding population in the Algarve is presumably a result of that. It was hitherto known only as a winter visitor to Portugal, although Coverley makes no mention at all of this species.

Preferred habitat: The edges of reed-beds, where the habitat is a broken mixture of different riparian vegetations. This species favours almost all kinds of wetland, where there is suitable vegetation, including semi-saline. However, it avoids extensive reed-beds and the centres of even small ones. It is tolerant of limited human disturbance.

Food: Mainly larval insects, but also adults and their eggs. Spiders and seeds are also taken sometimes. It searches from the trunk to the outermost twigs of trees for prey, as well as in bushes, reeds, etc., and will tear the seed-heads of bulrushes or the stems of plants to shreds in order to reach hidden prey.

Breeding: Males arrive at the breeding grounds in April and almost immediately begin to look for nest-sites. When the females arrive, each male will then construct a hanging basket-nest, to which he tries to attract one of the females. Firstly, he twines plant fibres around a fork in a twig and weaves a loop suspended from it. He then weaves a ball-shaped nest onto it with a completely open front. If a female shows interest, he sits inside singing or calling, or flies back and forth in front of it singing. If she accepts the nest, the pair completes the construction by closing the front and forming an entrance tube near the top. The outside of it is interwoven with plant down and hair; the inside is lined with more plant down. Whilst still building, the female lays 6-8 eggs, which either he or she (but not both) will incubate for 2 weeks. If the male is polygynous, he builds another basket-nest as soon as his mate is incubating and attempts to attract another female. He continues building and mating till the end of the season. Often, unpaired males will steal the nest (and occupant female) from another more successful male. Otherwise, the male incubates and the female leaves for another mate, or the male builds a nest for a second clutch (which either sex may incubate) whilst she is incubating the first clutch. The chicks are fed and cared for by either the male or the female, rarely by both. Fledging takes 3 weeks and the young become independent shortly afterwards. The age of first breeding is one year old. The pair-bond is often polygynous or polyandrous and typically lasts 1-2 weeks. Some pairs, however, may be monogamous and remain together for the season, especially where there are few prospective mates available.

Hints on recognition: It is similar to a Blue Tit in shape and manner, but smaller. The upperparts are rich chestnut, pale on the wings, and the underparts are warm buff. The head and neck are very pale grey with a very distinctive jet-black mask.

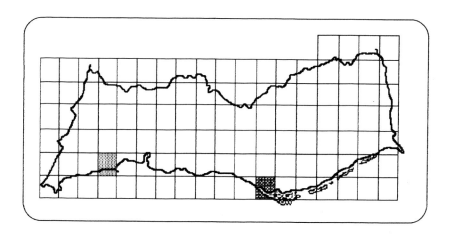

Hints on finding: It was found breeding only at Ludo and Sargaçal (near Lagos) during the course of the BBA. It is possible, however, that it breeds at other sites, such as Boca do Rio (see Where to watch breeding birds, A) and Fontes (between Estômbar and Silves), where it commonly overwinters.

Confirmation of breeding:

Number of rectangles in which recorded:	2
Possible breeding:	0
Probable breeding:	0
Confirmed breeding:	2

ORIOLUS ORIOLUS

GOLDEN ORIOLE

Portuguese name: Papa-figos.

Distribution: The Golden Oriole breeds in the temperate latitudes of the Western Palearctic and western Asia. It is well distributed and fairly common throughout Portugal (CEMPA).

Status in the Western Palearctic: It has recently increased and spread in north-western Europe, but declined in parts of central and eastern Europe. There is apparently no change in its status in the Algarve. It is a summer visitor, probably wintering in West Africa.

Preferred habitat: Woodland edges, including clearings or sides of tracks through eucalyptus plantations. Clusters and lines of mature trees, e.g. along the banks of rivers, are also used. It particularly favours woodland where the trees are close enough together to provide good cover, but far enough apart for it to fly easily between them. It avoids sequeiros near the coast, but readily accepts coastal pine-woods and inland almond groves. The ground beneath the trees is largely immaterial as it rarely visits the ground.

Breeding: Males return to the breeding grounds in early April, a few days before the females or simultaneously with them, and establish their territories. Older birds retake the territories of the previous year. The male advertises his presence by song, which he gives from a prominent perch or whilst fly-ing from tree to tree. The female may be attracted and enter his territory. Often the male follows her outside of his territoy and she chooses her mate from several males courting her. In courtship, the male sings from a perch, then hovers with tail spread before landing near her. She squalls in response and the pair may duet. The pair searches for a nest-site, often close to that of the previous year in the case of older birds, the female making the final choice. The nest-site is in a fork of thin outer branches high in a tree. The pair constructs a hammock-like foundation of dry plant material, suspended below the fork by means of long grass looped over the branch and pulled taught, often gummed with saliva. The female lines the nest with fine grass, wool, feathers, etc. and lays one clutch of 3-4 eggs. Incubation takes 2 1/2 weeks and is mainly by the female, although the male helps whilst she is feeding. The chicks are fed and cared for by both sexes equally, both parents brooding them when they are small. Fledging takes 2 1/2 weeks and the young become independent about 1 1/2 to 3 weeks afterwards, although the family may remain together until migration. Young, unpaired birds often help at the nest of older birds. The age of first breeding is probably at least two years old. The pair-bond is monogamous and may be renewed each year, owing to site-fidelity.

Hints on recognition: It is almost as big as a Blackbird, although it seems larger because of its bright colouring. The male is unmistakable, being brilliant yellow all over except for jet black wings, a little black on the tail, and a bright red beak. The female and juveniles are green on the upperparts, whitish-grey on the underparts, streaked with brown, and yellow on the flanks and under the tail.

F   M

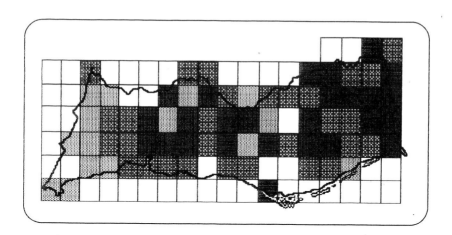

Hints on finding: The loud calls of the Oriole quickly localize its presence in suitable habitat. The repertoire of sounds is large, but of two basic types: whistling or squawking. The former are loud, audible at least 1 1/2 km distant, in short phrases of 3-4 notes or sometimes warbling, fluting, often almost human-sounding. The second are cat-like squalls, harsh, sometimes rattling, sometimes resembling a Kestrel.

Confirmation of breeding:

Number of rectangles in which recorded:	70
Possible breeding:	0
Probable breeding:	15
Confirmed breeding:	55

LANIUS EXCUBITOR

GREAT GREY SHRIKE

Portuguese name: Picanço-real.

Distribution: The Great Grey Shrike has a fragmented distribution covering parts of Europe, northern and south-western Asia as far as India, and the northern half of Africa. In Portugal, it is mainly to be found in the southern half of the country and on the north-eastern border with Spain (CEMPA).

Status in the Western Palearctic: It has expanded its range in some parts of Europe and contracted in others, possibly as a result of habitat changes. There is no evidence of any alteration in its status in Portugal. It is resident and sedentary in the Algarve, .although Coverley suggested that it may be dispersive in the north.

Preferred habitat: Open terrain with scattered trees or large bushes and with little or no ground cover. It particularly favours the open grasslands of the east and the more sheltered areas of heath in the south-west. Barren terrain and woodland are both avoided. It is not tolerant of human disturbance at the nest and avoids habitations.

Food: Large insects, small birds and reptiles (including their eggs), and small mammals. It uses a high vantage point, especially overhead wires or poles, from which to watch and pounce onto prey. Aerial prey is taken in flight, by swooping or by direct pursuit. It hovers readily, being able to maintain it continuously for 20 min (BWP, 1993), and will forage on the ground. It can take mammals up to the size of a stoat, killing them by repeated bites to sever the spinal cord at the neck. Food is sometimes impaled in bushes or on barbed wire for later consumption, giving this species the nick-name of 'butcher bird'.

Breeding: The male advertises his territory, in the autumn and spring, by song, which is given from a prominent perch. The female may also hold a neighbouring territory and sing, having already made contact with the male. During the winter, males and females fly over their territories, often hovering high to display their presence, and sometimes duetting. By February, the female has ceased to sing and has joined her territory to that of the male. The male chooses several nest-sites, in the branches of a tree or bush, from which one is chosen. The pair builds a bulky foundation of twigs and plant material, lined with hair, feathers, plant down, etc. Two clutches of 4-7 eggs are laid. Incubation takes 2 to 2 1/2 weeks and is mainly by the female. The chicks are fed and cared for by both sexes, the female brooding them for at least the first week after hatching. Fledging takes 2 1/2 weeks and the young become independent 3-5 weeks later. The brood is split between the parents, the male leaving the territory with his share and the female leaving with her share. The age of first breeding is one year old. The pair-bond is monogamous and may be renewed in subsequent years.

Hints on recognition: It is about the size of the Blackbird or the Golden Oriole. The Iberian race *Lanius excubitor meridionalis* is medium-grey on the upperparts and pale pink on the underparts. Other races can be light-grey on the upperparts and almost white on the underparts. It has a black mask, contrasting with a white throat and a thin white eye-brow. The wings are black, with a white wing-bar, and tail is black with white side-feathers.

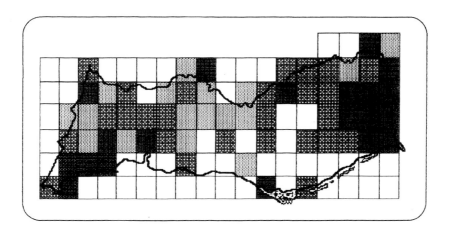

Hints on finding: It can be readily found between Castro Marim and the Beliche Reservoir, as well as between Budens and Sagres away from the main road, perched on overhead wires.

Confirmation of breeding:

Number of rectangles in which recorded: 63
Possible breeding: 0
Probable breeding: 13
Confirmed breeding: 50

LANIUS SENATOR

WOODCHAT SHRIKE

Portuguese name: Picanço-barreteiro.

Distribution: The Woodchat Shrike is mainly confined to the middle latitudes of the Western Palearctic, with a small extension into Iran. In Portugal, it breeds primarily in the southern half of the country and on the north-eastern border with Spain (CEMPA).

Status in the Western Palearctic: There has been a marked contraction and decline in this species in the north and west of Europe during this century, becoming extinct in some areas. It would appear to have been common in the north-west of Portugal in Coverley's time, whereas the national atlas found no proof of breeding there now. It is a summer visitor, wintering between the Sahara and the Equator.

Preferred habitat: Open broadleaf woodland or stands of trees, e.g. along rivers or around horticulture. Orange-groves, which are not too extensive or which have an admixture of other trees, are particularly favoured. It is also common in lowland sequeiros and inland almond or olive groves. It is fairly tolerant of human disturbance.

Food: Invertebrates, especially beetles, but also small vertebrates. It generally perches on an exposed branch, post, or overhead wire and drops onto prey beneath. It will also flycatch and take aerial prey in flight. Prey is often impaled before consumption, in a similar fashion to the impaling by the Great Grey Shrike (for which, see that species). Indigestible items are regurgitated as pellets.

Breeding: Males may arrive at the breeding grounds in April, a few days before the females or sometimes already paired. The male establishes a territory which he defends and advertises by song, given from a prominent perch. If a female approaches, the male lands in front of her, facing her, crown feathers erect, and bobs his head slowly up and down, whilst singing quietly. The female may respond by bobbing, too, and singing in duet. The pair-bond is further strengthened by the male feeding the female. The male chooses the nest-site in the branches of a tree or bush. The pair constructs a cup of plant material and roots, lined with wool, hair, cobwebs, moss, and other fine materials. One clutch (or sometimes two) of 5-6 eggs is laid. Incubation takes 2 weeks and is by the female alone. The chicks are fed and cared for by both sexes, the female brooding them at first. Fledging takes 2 1/2 weeks and the young become independent 3-4 weeks afterwards, although the family may remain together until migration. The age of first breeding is one year old. The pair-bond is monogamous and is probably of seasonal duration only.

Hints on recognition: It is between the House Sparrow and the Blackbird in size, with an upright stance when perched and a fairly long tail. The nape and the top of the head are bright chestnut, contrasting with a wide black band running over the forehead, down the cheeks, and onto the black upperparts. The underparts are creamy. It has a broad white wing-bar, white side-tail feathers, and a creamy rump, which show up strongly in flight. When flying away from the observer, this species appears to be a brilliant mixture of black, white, and chestnut.

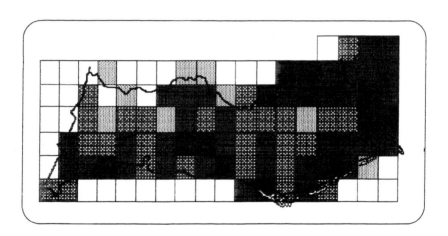

Hints on finding: It can be readily found in lowland farmland and sequeiros, where there are overhead wires for perches. Elsewhere requires more patience, as it is a quiet bird which tends to sit in the crown of trees. The song is an attractive warble and in flight the species is a conspicuous black, white, and chestnut.

Confirmation of breeding:

Number of rectangles in which recorded: 82
Possible breeding: 2
Probable breeding: 4
Confirmed breeding: 76

GARRULUS GLANDARIUS

JAY

Portuguese name: Gaio-comum.

Distribution: The Jay is to be found in most of the Western Palearctic and the temperate latitudes of Asia, reaching S.E. Asia. It is well-distributed and fairly common through-out Portugal (CEMPA).

Status in the Western Palearctic: After some decline in the last century, as a result of persecution, this species has recovered and is continuing to expand slowly to the north and west of Europe (BTO, 1993). There is apparently no change in its status in Portugal since Coverley's time. It is resident.

Preferred habitat: Open broadleaf wood-land in hilly countryside. It particularly favours areas of mixed habitat, with broken scrub and clusters of mature trees, or wood-land with clearings, in gently rolling terrain. It avoids lowland habitats and the tops of mountains, but will use eucalyptus plan-tations and is tolerant of limited human disturbance, where it is not persecuted.

Food: Mainly invertebrates for the young. Adults also take small reptiles, amphibeans, birds (including eggs), grain, acorns, olives, and other small fruits during the winter months. It searches the branches of trees for prey and will also take flying insects in aerial pursuit. Frequently it forages on the ground, turning over leaf-litter and small objects, probing with its bill, scratching with its feet, or bounding with long rapid hops after mov-ing prey. Acorns are often buried in the ground for future consumption, each acorn buried singly. Many of these acorns are not recovered and grow into trees, so that the species' habit of plundering other birds' nests is balanced by its spreading the regeneration of oakwoods.

Breeding: Older birds remain close to the breeding area in winter, although they are not territorial at that time. By February, the males have returned to the territory of the previous year and renewed the pair-bond with their mates. Young birds form social gatherings of up to 20 individuals, which chase one another through the trees. Court-ship involves posturing and the spreading of wings and tail to show the colours to advantage. Those which cannot find a mate and an unoccupied site are obliged to remain within the territories of others. The pair constructs a nest of twigs, mixed with a little mud and lined with rootlets and hair. The site is in the crown or fork of a small tree or a bush. One clutch of 4-7 eggs is laid. Incu-bation takes 2 1/2 weeks and is by the female alone, the male bringing food to her. The chicks are fed and cared for by both sexes, the female brooding them at first. Fledging takes nearly 3 weeks and the young become independent a few weeks after-wards, although the family remains together until at least the autumn. The pair-bond is monogamous and of seasonal duration, although it is usually renewed in subsequent years.

Hints on recognition: It is fairly large, being about 2/3 the size of a Crow. The upperparts are pinkish brown and the underparts pinkish buff. It has a white throat, with a broad black 'moustache', and has white on the rump and under the tail. The crown-feathers are highly mobile and readily erected to a crest. In flight, the wings show patches of blue, black, and white, but in the distance this species often appears all dark with a white rump. As well as its dis-tinctive screech, it can also warble pleasantly and mimic a wide range of other species.

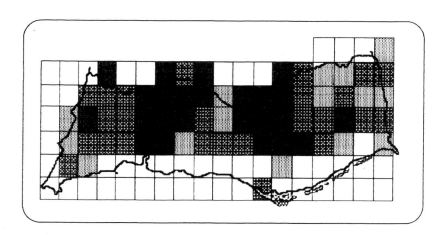

Hints on finding: It can be readily found in suitable habitat between Monchique and São Marcos da Serra, as well as between São Braz and Ameixal (near the northern border with the Alentejo). It is most easily seen in the autumn when it is roaming the countryside for acorns, but its noisy screech is often all that indicates its presence during the breeding season.

Confirmation of breeding:

Number of rectangles in which recorded:	64
Possible breeding:	1
Probable breeding:	11
Confirmed breeding:	52

CYANOPICA CYANA

AZURE-WINGED MAGPIE

Portuguese name: Pega-azul.

Distribution: The Azure-winged Magpie is to be found in the southern Iberian Peninsula and the Far East only. In Portugal, it is primarily restricted to the southern half of the country, extending a little northwards on the eastern border with Spain (CEMPA).

Status in the Western Palearctic: It is apparently increasing and expanding its range northwards in both Portugal and Spain. There is no evidence of any change in its status in the Algarve. It is resident and sedentary.

Preferred habitat: Open oakwoods, with low scrub or herbage and areas of short grass. It particularly favours the foothills of the serras and the parkland of the north-east, but will use lowland pinewoods and the orange-groves of the interior. It avoids wind-swept or cold climates, such as the west coast, the tops of mountains, wetlands, and saline environments, and is rarely found in lowland sequeiros. It will use small plantations of eucalyptus, or the edges of large ones, for nesting, often feeding elsewhere.

Food: Mainly invertebrates, but also acorns and other fruits. Acorns and other seeds are often hidden in the ground for future consumption. Invertebrates are taken from the branches of trees or from the ground and the bird frequently hovers over longer vegetation in search of prey. It is considered a pest by farmers as it feeds on all kinds of commercial fruit, including olives and almonds, and it will pierce oranges with its beak, sucking them dry and leaving the peel hanging on the trees. Occasionally, small vertebrates and carrion are taken.

Breeding: Semi-colonial. Several family groups join together at the end of the breeding season, to form flocks of 30-70 birds which forage over the neighbourhood during the winter. Established pairs remain together within the flock, whilst young birds choose mates during this period. Young males encircle a female, chasing her through the trees and displaying their blue wings and tails to her. They will often flutter around her, head bowed and wings partly open, singing quietly, until she accepts one of them. Individuals tend to nest close to the natal site or the nest-site of the previous year, but rarely use the same tree. Although the flock will nest in a loose colony, individual nests are often widely spread out. The pair constructs a neat cup of twigs, roots, and moss, mixed with a little mud and lined with hair, fur, and fine vegetable matter. The nest-site is in the branches or in a fork in the trunk of a tree. One clutch (occasionally two) of 5-9 eggs is laid, beginning in April. Incubation takes a little over 2 weeks and is by the female alone. The chicks are fed by regurgitation and cared for by both parents, the female brooding them at first. Fledging takes about 3 1/2 weeks and the young remain with the parents until at least the winter, when they join other foraging families. The age of first breeding is probably two years old. The pair-bond is monogamous and lasts for life.

Hints on recognition: The body is mostly pinkish-buff and little larger than that of the Blackbird, but the very long and rounded tail make it appear much bigger. The head and nape are glossy black, the throat whitish, and the wings and tail blue. In flight, it flaps the wings vigorously or glides, calling loudly.

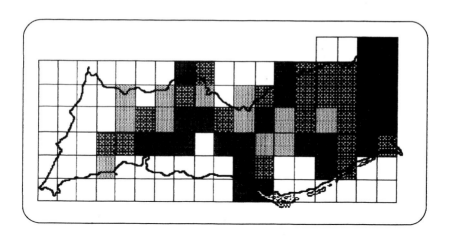

Hints on finding: It can be readily found in suitable habitat along the Odelouca Valley and in the pine-woods between Quinta do Lago and Ludo (see Where to watch breeding birds, D and E), as well as along the Guadiana River. As it is a flocking species, the observer may need to wait for some to arrive and cross an open area, where they are more visible than amongst the trees.

Confirmation of breeding:

Number of rectangles in which recorded: 57
Possible breeding: 0
Probable breeding: 10
Confirmed breeding: 47

P. PYRRHOCORAX

CHOUGH

Portuguese name:
Gralha-de-bico-vermelho.

Distribution: The Chough is to be found in the temperate latitudes of the Western Palearctic and Asia. In Europe, it breeds mainly around the Mediterranean Basin, but there are also colonies on the west coasts of the British Isles. The distribution in Portugal is very broken, there being colonies in the south-west Algarve, the centre of the west coast north of Lisbon, and the extreme north of the country (CEMPA).

Status in the Western Palearctic: It has declined markedly in most of its range during this century, mainly owing to changes in agricultural practices but also to human disturbance and persecution. It has also declined in Portugal and is absent from many places where it used to breed (CEMPA). It is resident.

Preferred habitat: Sea-cliffs, where there are ample crevices and caves for nesting, in close proximity to low-intensity livestock grazing. In the Algarve, this combination is only found on the west coast. Elsewhere in its range, it nests in old buildings, allowing it to breed at inland localities. It is not tolerant of human disturbance.

Food: It is a very specialised feeder, eating mainly soil arthropods, although it will also take earthworms, lizards, and occasionally seeds and fruit. It hunts its prey by searching the ground on foot or probing the ground with its long bill.

Breeding: Colonial. During the winter months, adult and juvenile birds form flocks, often with Jackdaws, and roam the countryside close to the breeding cliffs. Established pairs remain together within the flocks. In February or March, they begin to spend more time around the cliffs, the males performing spectacular aerial displays, using the updraughts to soar and dive, often turning over on their backs with feet in the air. The males also display whilst feeding in the flock, by strutting about and 'clapping' their wings together. They are very noisy at this time, which has led to the term 'a clattering of choughs' for a group of Choughs. When the male and female accept one another and form a pair, they will perform mutual aerial acrobatics. Courtship at the nest-site includes billing and mutual preening of the head feathers, as well as courtship feeding by the male. The nest-site is a crevice or hole in a cliff or cave, although ruins are sometimes used, and the same nest is often used in subsequent years. In April, the pair builds a nest of sticks, lined with wool and hair. One clutch of 3-6 eggs is laid. Incubation takes about 3 weeks and is by the female alone, the male feeding her at the nest. The chicks are fed by regurgitation and cared for by both sexes, being brooded by the female for the first 2-3 weeks. Fledging takes about 5 1/2 weeks, the young flying properly at 6-7 weeks old and becoming independent 2-3 weeks later. The age of first breeding is 2 or 3 years old. The pair-bond is monogamous and probably lasts for life, the pair remaining together even whilst flocking in the winter.

Hints on recognition: It is little larger than the Jackdaw, with which it often feeds, but has a glossy purple-black plumage without any grey on the nape. The red legs and long, down-curved, red bill are diagnostic. When flying, it is graceful and acrobatic and the flight-feathers tend to separate like fingers.

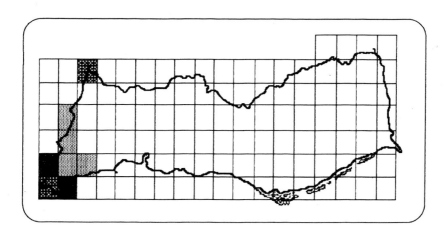

Hints on finding: The only area where this species can be found is the west coast. It feeds in groups on grassland close to the cliffs, often in company with Jackdaws.

Confirmation of breeding:

Number of rectangles in which recorded:	8
Possible breeding:	0
Probable breeding:	2
Confirmed breeding:	6

CORVUS MONEDULA

JACKDAW

Portuguese name: Gralha-de-nuca-cinzenta

Distribution: The Jackdaw is to be found in most of Europe and the western half of Asia. It has recently colonized North Africa. In Portugal, it is mainly confined to the south-west coast of the Algarve and all the borders with Spain (CEMPA).

Status in the Western Palearctic: It is increasing in many parts of its range, including in Portugal, although decreasing in central Europe. Coverley states that, although abundant on the south-west coast of the Algarve, it was scarce elsewhere, whereas the national atlas found it in almost a third of the country. It is resident.

Preferred habitat: Sea-cliffs close to grassland. Unlike the Chough (for which, see that species), the Jackdaw is not restricted to the south-west but commonly breeds on the cliffs as far east as Albufeira. Elsewhere in Portugal it frequently nests in buildings and can be found far from the sea, but this only occurs at Castro Marim in the Algarve.

Food: It will eat almost anything that it finds. It is an opportunist feeder, taking grain or fruit when that is abundant, berries and nuts, potatoes from the fields, larvae of almost any invertebrate when they hatch, young inexperienced vertebrates, eggs, molluscs, carrion, and rubbish. Almost all food is taken from the ground, or by probing into the ground, but it is also taken from the branches and leaves of trees.

Breeding: Colonial, occasionally solitary. During the winter months, young and mature birds of both sexes form flocks, which roam the countryside, sometimes at a considerable distance from the breeding area. In February or March, they return to the breeding grounds, where the males display. They bow, touching their breasts with their beaks, crown feathers raised to show the grey nape, wings and tails spread and quivering. The females join them in displaying, crouching and quivering, until gradually pair-bonds are formed and strengthened by mutual grooming and by the male feeding the female. By the end of March, the pair has constructed an untidy pile of sticks, lined with wool, hair, leaves, and grass, in a crevice or hole in a cliff (or building). If the hole is too large, the birds will fill the surplus space with twigs. One clutch of 3-6 eggs is laid. Incubation takes 2 1/2 weeks and is by the female alone, the male feeding her at the nest. The chicks are fed by regurgitation and cared for by both parents, the female brooding them for the first 2-3 weeks. Fledging takes about 4 weeks, although the young do not fly well until at least 5 weeks old. Newly-fledged young are crèched at first, while the adults forage widely, then they join the adults to form flocks when they can fly strongly. The age of first breeding is two years old, although some attempt to breed at one year old. The pair-bond is monogamous and probably lasts for life.

Hints on recognition: It is about the same size as a Feral Pigeon but entirely black, except for a grey nape and cheeks. This grey on the neck gives it the appearance of having a black cap. It is usually seen in flocks, which fly up with a loud "kyow" or a quieter "jack".

306

Hints on finding: This species can be commonly found on the west coast sea-cliffs, especially on the Cape St. Vincent Peninsula. It feeds in groups on grassland close to the cliffs, often in company with Choughs. It also breeds on almost all the cliffs as far east as Albufeira.

Confirmation of breeding: As this species often feeds away from the nesting-colonies, only rectangles with at least a possibility of breeding are shaded on the map.

Number of rectangles in which recorded: 16
Possible breeding: 0
Probable breeding: 0
Confirmed breeding: 16

CORVUS CORONE

CARRION CROW

Portuguese name: Gralha-preta.

Distribution: The Carrion Crow, together with the conspecific Hooded Crow, is to be found throughout most of Europe, the northern and middle latitudes of Asia, and a few sites in northern Africa. It is well-distributed and fairly common throughout Portugal (CEMPA), except for the Algarve where it is very scarce.

Status in the Western Palearctic: Despite constant persecution by man (it is one of the few non-game species to be legal quarry everywhere), there has been no decrease. In some areas, in fact, it is increasing, as a result of its spread into urban areas. There is apparently no change in its status in Portugal. It is resident.

Preferred habitat: Open terrain with plentiful trees for nesting and grassland or horticulture for feeding. In the Algarve, it was found nesting only in mature oak-woods, but elsewhere in Portugal it prefers pine-woods (CEMPA).

Food: It eats almost anything and is a notorious egg-thief, sometimes taking half the eggs of game-birds on an estate. It will also peck at newborn animals. These habits result in heavy persecution by game-keepers and farmers. Amongst other food items taken are insects and their larvae, grain, wild seeds, fruit, small vertebrates, earthworms, molluscs and crustaceans, spiders, carrion, and rubbish. It feeds mainly on the ground, but will also forage in trees. In the case of hard nuts or prey with shells, such as shellfish, it has learned to carry the food into the air, then drop it onto rocks in order to crack it open.

Breeding: Young birds search for an unoccupied territory during the winter months; mature pairs remain on their territories for life. The male advertises his presence by loud caws, given from a prominent perch, and by display flights, which include tumbling and other aerial acrobatics. When a female approaches, the male lands by her and struts around her, bowing and jerking his head up and down, spreading his wings and tail. The female will often join him in mutual displays, crouching and quivering, and the pair-bond is further strengthened by mutual preening and by courtship feeding of the female by the male. In February or March, the pair builds the nest or refurbishes an old one, high in a tree. It is a bulky structure of sticks and moss, mixed with mud and lined with wool, hair, and sometimes feathers. One clutch of 3-6 eggs is laid in April. Incubation takes 2 1/2 to 3 weeks and is by the female alone, although the male sometimes helps. The chicks are fed and cared for by both sexes, the female brooding them at first. Fledging takes about 5 weeks and the young do not become independent until at least 4 weeks later. They often remain with the parents until the following breeding season. The age of first breeding is three or four years old. The pair-bond is monogamous and probably lasts for life.

Hints on recognition: It is large, about 50% bigger than the Jackdaw, and totally black. It can be confused with the Raven (for which, see that species), which is nearly 50% bigger again. When it is seen on the ground, the smooth outline to the head and throat is diagnostic. In flight, it shows an almost square tip to the tail, just slightly rounded at the 'corners'.

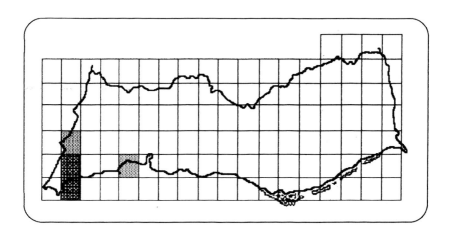

Hints on finding: There are so few records for the Algarve that no help can be given in this section.

Confirmation of breeding:

Number of rectangles in which recorded:	4
Possible breeding:	1
Probable breeding:	1
Confirmed breeding:	2

CORVUS CORAX

RAVEN

Portuguese name: Corvo.

Distribution: The Raven is to be found in most parts of Europe, the middle-to-northern latitudes of Asia, northern Africa, and northern and central America. It is well-distributed throughout Portugal (CEMPA).

Status in the Western Palearctic: It decreased drastically in Europe during the 19th century, as a result of persecution by farmers and gaming interests. Although it is still widely shot, poisoned, and trapped, it has recovered in some areas. It is not likely to regain former numbers, however, because of widespread afforestation of uplands, intensive farming reducing carrion and other prey, and the effects of pesticides. It has apparently declined in Portugal since Coverley's time, probably due to increasing pressures from urbanization and to continued persecution. It is resident.

Preferred habitat: Open countryside, with few habitations but containing trees or cliff-ledges which are difficult to reach by predators. In the Algarve, this habitat preference restricts the species to the mountainous areas and to the west coast. It avoids all contact with man and is not tolerant of human disturbance.

Food: It takes almost anything available, including carrion, small vertebrates, eggs, invertebrates, rubbish from tips, grain, acorns, fruit, etc. It hunts by aerial pursuit or by soaring, pouncing on prey beneath. It will also forage on foot or wait patiently for a sickly animal to die.

Breeding: Males establish their territories during the winter months, advertising them by flying backwards and forwards uttering deep and far-carrying croaks. When a female is attracted, the male performs extravagant aerial acrobatics, including flying upside-down with wings and tail spread. If the female remains, he lands on the ground by the side of her, bowing and stretching, throat feathers ruffled and head feathers erect, then crouching with wings and tail spread. The female responds by crouching and quivering, and often he will preen her face or suddenly leap into the air. When the pair-bond has been formed, the female will join him in aerial acrobatics, which serve to advise other Ravens that the territory has resident occupants. This territory is then held for the rest of their lives, with 2 or 3 nest-sites used in rotation. The pair builds a nest of sticks, cemented with mud and moss and lined with grass, leaves, and moss. It has an inner lining of wool and hair. One clutch of 4-6 eggs is laid in February or early March. Incubation takes 3 weeks and is by the female alone, the male bringing food to her on the nest. The chicks are fed and cared for by both sexes, the female brooding them at first. Fledging takes 5-6 weeks and the young stay with the parents for 6 months. The age of first breeding is probably at least three years old.   The pair-bond is monogamous and lasts for life.

Hints on recognition: It soars in a similar manner to the Buzzard (for which, see that species), but is a little larger. It is entirely black and in flight shows a distinctive wedge-shaped tail and separated flight feathers (like fingers) on the wings. It frequently croaks whilst flying. When perched, it has a 'shaggy', deeply-feathered throat. The similar Carrion Crow (for which, see that species) is also black, but is about 1/3 smaller and has a smoother, less 'shaggy' appearance.

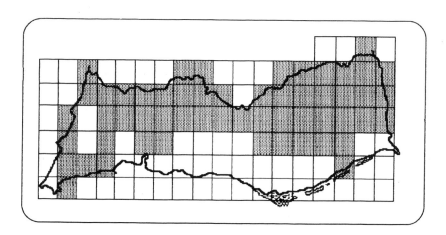

Hints on finding: The sound of a hoarse croaking is often the first indication of this species' presence. It can then be found soaring like a raptor over the mountains or cliffs.

Confirmation of breeding: Because of the size of the territories of this species and the way in which the same pair may use different rectangles, all rectangles in which it has been recorded have been marked equally. This also helps to obscure the whereabouts of nests.

Number of rectangles in which recorded: 55
Confirmed breeding: 15

STURNUS UNICOLOR

SPOTLESS STARLING

Portuguese name: Estorninho-preto.

Distribution: The Spotless Starling is entirely restricted to the western Mediterranean. It is well-distributed throughout Portugal, although more common in the east than in the west (CEMPA).

Status in the Western Palearctic: There is little recorded on the status of this species, but there has apparently been no recent change in Portugal. It is resident, dispersing in flocks during the winter months, although some may migrate to northern Africa in winter.

Preferred habitat: Open woodland mixed with grassland or horticulture. It is to be found in most habitats, but generally avoids extensive eucalyptus plantations and barren terrain. Unlike the Starling *Sturnus vulgaris*, it rarely feeds or nests close to man and is not tolerant of human disturbance.

Food: Almost all kinds of invertebrates, molluscs, fruits, and seeds. It will search for prey on the branches and trunks of trees, or on stone walls and cliffs, and will take flying prey in aerial pursuit. It also forages on the ground, probing with its bill, turning over small obstacles, and following animals or larger birds for disturbed insects.

Breeding: Semi-colonial or solitary. During the winter months, families join with other families to form small foraging parties of about 10 birds, roosting with other parties communally in such places as reed-beds. In mid-winter, the males break away from the flocks and establish territories, which are normally just the area around prospective nest-sites. The male advertises his presence by song given from a prominent perch, often immediately above the nest-hole. The hole may be in a tree, an isolated ruin, or a cliff but, unlike the Starling , it does not nest near man. Sometimes, the male begins the nest by building a base of plant material. If a female is attracted, he lands by her and sidles towards her, plumage ruffled, singing quietly. He shows her the hole by entering it, turning round, and poking his head out of the hole, singing. The female inspects his hole and nest and, if acceptable, she completes the nest by making a cup lined with feathers, hair, and wool. One clutch (sometimes two) of 4 eggs is laid in March or early April. Incubation takes almost 2 weeks and is by the female alone. The chicks are fed and cared for by both sexes, the female brooding them at first. Fledging takes at least 3 weeks and the young become independent about 2 weeks later, although late broods often remain with the parents after independence. The age of first breeding is one year old. The pair-bond is monogamous and of seasonal duration only.

Hints on recognition: It is smaller than the Starling, which is an occasional winter visitor only. It appears to be entirely black, including the eye, with no markings or glossiness. The bill is pale yellow, whitish at the base, and the legs are flesh-coloured. The tail is short compared with a Blackbird's and it tends to walk, not hop. It's most common song is a loud whistle, but it will readily mimic the songs of other birds or even a human whistle.

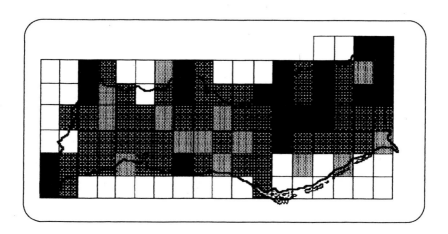

Hints on finding: It nests on almost all the sea-cliffs and stacks. It can be readily found on the Cape St. Vincent Peninsula and the cliffs to the west of Albufeira.

Confirmation of breeding:

Number of rectangles in which recorded: 78
Possible breeding: 2
Probable breeding: 11
Confirmed breeding: 65

PASSER DOMESTICUS

HOUSE SPARROW

Portuguese name: Pardal-comum.

Distribution: The House Sparrow is native throughout Europe, Asia, except the Far East, and northern Africa. It has been widely introduced into many other parts of the world, including North and South America, Australasia, and several regions of Africa. It is well-distributed and abundant throughout Portugal (CEMPA).

Status in the Western Palearctic: It is increasing and spreading throughout its range, owing to its adaptability to humans and its readiness to exploit food sources made available by man. It is resident and sedentary.

Preferred habitat: Close proximity to habitations, with access to food supplies, especially cultivation. It readily accepts man's artefacts for nesting, including old woodpecker holes in telephone poles. It avoids dense forests, even where there are suitable nest-sites, but otherwise uses all types of habitat.

Food: All kinds of seeds including grain, insects and their larvae, and scraps of food discarded by man. It mainly feeds on the ground, where it pecks up food or hops in pursuit of insects, but it will also take seeds from plants and fruit from bushes or trees.

Breeding: Colonial or semi-colonial. Outside of the breeding season, large flocks roam the countryside and roost in concentrations in reed-beds, clumps of trees, etc.

Exceptionally, nesting occurs in every month of the year, but normally the males break away from the flocks in February or March. The male finds a suitable nest-hole, usually in a building, which he defends and advertises by song, given from a prominent perch in the immediate vicinity of the hole. If a female is seen on the ground, several cocks surround her, chirping loudly, tails held vertically, wings drooped and quivering. They strut around her, bowing repeatedly until she flies off, pursued by the whole flock. Eventually, the hen approaches the nest-hole and enters. If she accepts it, the pair builds an untidy nest of dry grass and rubbish, lined with feathers, hair, and wool. Sometimes, nests are made in creepers or the branches of a tree, in which case it is a large domed structure with a side entrance. At least 3 clutches of 3-5 eggs are laid. Incubation takes almost 2 weeks and is mainly by the female. The chicks are fed mostly on insects, by both parents. They are cared for by both sexes, but the female alone broods them at first. Fledging takes a little over 2 weeks and the young become independent shortly afterwards. The age of first breeding is one year old, although the young of early broods can breed towards the end of their year of hatching. The pair-bond can be monogamous or polygynous and is of seasonal duration only.

Hints on recognition: The male is a rich chestnut, streaked with black, on the upperparts, buff on the underparts. The crown is grey, the cheeks white, and the throat and lores black. The female is entirely brown, although darker and streaked with dark brown on the upperparts. She has a dark streak running from the eye to the back of the head. It can only be confused with the Tree Sparrow or the Rock Sparrow (for which, see those species).

F   M

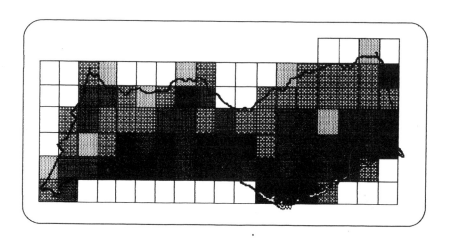

Confirmation of breeding:

Hints on finding: It nests in all the towns of the Algarve.

Number of rectangles in which recorded:	82
Possible breeding:	0
Probable breeding:	0
Confirmed breeding:	82

PASSER MONTANUS

TREE SPARROW

Portuguese name: Pardal-montez.

Distribution: The Tree Sparrow is to be found in most of Europe and Asia, except the extreme north and south. In much of the Orient and south-east Asia, it replaces the House Sparrow and is considered a pest. It has been introduced or has escaped into North America, Australasia, and many Pacific and Asian islands. It is well distributed throughout Portugal, although more common on the littoral than in the interior (CEMPA).

Status in the Western Palearctic: It decreased markedly during the last century and the early part of this century in much of its range, for reasons imperfectly understood. There has been a partial recovery or increase in many places, however. Coverley states that it was scarce in his time and that he had never seen one in Portugal, whereas the national atlas recorded it on almost every map. It is resident but dispersive.

Preferred habitat: Sequeiros or clusters of old trees in grassland or horticulture. Unlike the House Sparrow, it prefers to nest in holes in trees and avoids human habitations in the Algarve.

Food: Mainly weed-seeds, but also grain, broken acorns, spiders, and insects and their larvae. It forages on the ground, pecking up food and hopping after moving prey. It also readily takes seeds from plants and trees.

Breeding: Semi-colonial or solitary. During the winter months, it forages over the countryside in flocks, sometimes with House Sparrows, roosting in considerable numbers in such places as reed-beds. In March, the males break away from the flocks and select nest-holes, which they advertise and defend by song. The hole is usually in an old tree, but may also be in a wall or cliff. When a female approaches, the male lands by her and circles round her, bowing repeatedly, wings spread and quivering, and the crown feathers raised to form a rounded head. He cheeps softly and chases her whenever she tries to leave. He shows her the nest-hole and, if she accepts it, the pair builds a nest of dry grass and twigs, lined with down and feathers. Sometimes, the nest is constructed in the branches of a tree or in a creeper, in which case it is a a completely domed structure. Two or three clutches of 3-6 eggs are laid. Incubation takes 11-14 days and is by both sexes. The chicks are fed and cared for by both parents. Fledging takes about 2 weeks and the young become independent shortly afterwards, although they often remain near the nesting and feeding areas. The age of first breeding is one year old. The pair-bond is monogamous or polygynous and of seasonal duration only.

Hints on recognition: It is slightly smaller and slimmer than the House Sparrow and has more retiring habits. The general colouring is the same as the male House Sparrow (for which, see that species), but the top of the head is entirely chestnut, the black on the throat is small and neatly shaped, and there is a black patch behind the eye on the white cheek. Both sexes look identical.

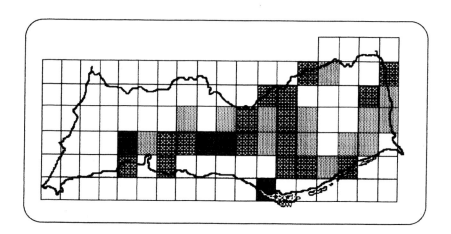

Hints on finding: It can be found in the sequeiros of the foothills, but requires patience as it is a timid bird. A walk along the River Algibre, east of Paderne, is pleasant and should provide good views of this species.

Confirmation of breeding:

Number of rectangles in which recorded:	34
Possible breeding:	1
Probable breeding:	10
Confirmed breeding:	23

317

PETRONIA PETRONIA

ROCK SPARROW

Portuguese name: Pardal-francês.

Distribution: The Rock Sparrow is to be found around the Mediterranean Basin and in the middle latitudes of western Asia. It is sparsely distributed in most regions of Portugal, but mainly absent from the Algarve and the north-west (CEMPA).

Status in the Western Palearctic: The breeding range is decreasing in western Europe as a result of climatic changes, especially the change to more humid and less warm summers. It has become extinct in central Europe and is retreating southwards in France. Coverley states that this species was common in some parts of Portugal, which does not appear to be the case now. He also mentions having heard one at Quarteira, which is unlikely to happen in the urbanizations of today. It is resident and sedentary.

Preferred habitat: Small cliff-faces or the sides of narrow gorges in rocky or relatively scrub-free terrain. Elsewhere in Portugal it nests in old oak-trees and in other parts of its range it uses burrows or holes in walls, which are presumably the prospective nest-sites for the southern Algarve record. It is not generally associated with man.

Food: Insects, seeds, and fruit, which may be pecked from the ground or directly from low plants. The bird forages on the ground in a series of short, rapid runs, like a lark. It will also search crevices in rocks for hidden prey. The young are fed entirely on insects, especially caterpillars.

Breeding: During the winter months, where this species is common, it forms small flocks and roams the countryside looking for food. In the early spring, whilst the birds are still flocking, pair-formation takes place. The males sing from a vantage point, frequently launching themselves into a rolling, gliding flight, still singing, before fluttering to the ground in a parachute-like descent. By mid-April, the pair has left the flock and chosen a nest-site, the immediate viscinity of which will be defended as a nesting-territory. The site may be in a crevice or a hole in rocks, but can also be in an old tree or wall, or even in the ground. In Spain, nests have been found in Bee-eater holes. The female constructs an intidy domed nest from straw, dry grass, rootlets, and wool, lined with feathers, in which two clutches of 4-7 eggs are laid. The first clutch is laid in May and the second in July. Incubation takes 2 weeks and fledging 3 weeks. The chicks are fed and cared for by both parents and become independent 1-2 weeks after leaving the nest. The age of first breeding is probably one year old. The pair-bond is monogamous and of seasonal duration only.

Hints on recognition: Although it resembles a sparrow and is called a sparrow, it is not one in fact. Both sexes have a yellow patch on the lower throat, but this is often difficult to see and, superficially, they both look like a female House Sparrow. At a distance, they can be distinguished by the way they walk and run, not hopping stiffly. Their calls are a continual plaintive double note, a distinctive "tut", a wheezing "chwee" like some finches, and sparrow-like cheeps. At close range, the head can be seen to be distinctly striped, with a pale band along the crown, and the body mottled.

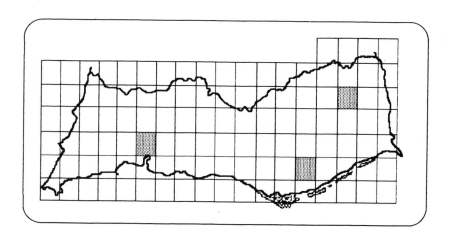

Hints on finding: As this species is so scarce in the Algarve, no help can be given in this section.

Confirmation of breeding: The single confirmed breeding, in the north-eastern Algarve, was of a pair nesting on a small cliff-face at the side of a newly-excavated road.

Number of rectangles in which recorded: 3
Possible breeding: 2
Probable breeding: 0
Confirmed breeding: 1

ESTRILDA ASTRILD

COMMON WAXBILL

Portuguese name: Bico-de-lacre.

Distribution: The Common Waxbill originally came from Africa, south of the Sahara reaching to the Cape. It came to Europe as a cage-bird and was released in Portugal at Óbidos in 1967 (Xavier, 1968). It was also introduced into Brazil, where it has established itself ferally in small numbers. Outside of Africa, it mainly breeds in the western half of southern Portugal (CEMPA).

Status in the Western Palearctic: Since its original introduction at Óbidos in 1967 it has escaped or been released in several other places in Portugal. It has rapidly increased and spread so that by 1987 it was estimated that there were some 10,000 birds in Portugal (Vowles & Vowles, 1987). Since that estimate it has further increased and spread and is still increasing. It is resident and sedentary.

Preferred habitat: Low dense undergrowth in moist situations, with ready access to uncut grassland or weed-seeds. It uses reed-beds for roosting but avoids them for breeding. It is a highly adaptable species and, where there is insufficient preferred habitat, will use any available low undergrowth as long as there is ample food. It is very tolerant of human disturbance.

Food: Invertebrates and seeds. Almost all food is taken directly from plants and this species is agile in obtaining it from the tips of grass fronds.

Breeding: Although it can breed throughout the year, it most commonly nests in spring and autumn. Individuals do not necessarily use the same territory or mate for the two nesting periods. During the winter and summer months, families join together to form flocks, roaming the countryside for food and roosting in large numbers in such places as reed-beds. Shortly before the start of the breeding season, the birds will begin to separate into pairs within the flocks. In March or early September they leave their flocks and establish territories, which will cover a prospective nest-site only. Food may be obtained close to the nest or communally at some distance away. The male sings from a prominent perch to advertise his presence and often begins building the nest by himself in a bush or low undergrowth. Otherwise, the pair constructs a pear-shaped nest of dry grass, with a protruding side-entrance, the male bringing the material whilst the female weaves it. The nest is lined with feathers and fine grasses, and on top of the nest a further cup-nest is often built, which is also lined and sometimes even contains an egg. Two clutches of 4-6 eggs are laid in the spring and one clutch in the autumn. Incubation takes 10-11 days and is by the female alone. The chicks are brooded and cared for by both parents. They are fed by means of regurgitation by both sexes. Fledging takes 2 weeks, but the young remain with the parents for several weeks, the last brood remaining until the next breeding period. The young of the first brood of the spring often breed in the autumn of the same year. The pair-bond is monogamous and of seasonal duration only.

Hints on recognition: It is light brownish-grey on the upperparts and pinkish-grey on the underparts, all finely barred with dark brown. The throat is pure white, contrasting with a red bill and mask. The male has a considerable amount of red on the breast, as well as a red tinge to the rump, and is jet black under the tail. The female is similar, but she has less red in the plumage and is dark brown under the tail.

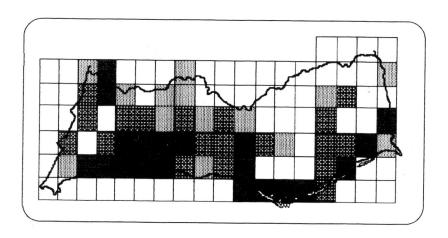

Hints on finding: Between breeding periods, this species can easily be found in any reed-bed, especially early in the morning or in the evening. Otherwise, the nasal call of "zzz-zzz-zzz" as it moves through dank vegetation draws attention to its presence.

Confirmation of breeding:

Number of rectangles in which recorded:	53
Possible breeding:	1
Probable breeding:	10
Confirmed breeding:	42

FRINGILLA COELEBS

CHAFFINCH

Portuguese name: Tentilhão-comum.

Distribution: The Chaffinch is to be found in most of Europe, northern Africa, and western Asia, as far east as western Siberia. It is well distributed and fairly common throughout Portugal (CEMPA).

Status in the Western Palearctic: This species has increased and spread in recent years, as a result of afforestation. There is apparently no change in its status in Portugal. It is resident but dispersive; migrants from further north overwinter in the Algarve.

Preferred habitat: Open woodlands or the edges of more extensive forests. Other habitats with trees, such as sequeiros and the banks of rivers or streams, are also accepted. It avoids all terrain with few or no trees, but is tolerant of some human disturbance.

Food: Outside of the breeding season, it takes mainly seeds, pecked from the ground, and some grain. In the breeding season, however, it becomes an isectivore. It picks small beetles and other insects from the ground and takes flying prey in aerial pursuit, but the young are fed mainly on caterpillars gleened from the leaves of trees and bushes.

Breeding: During the winter months, some Chaffinches form flocks with other finches, such as Goldfinches and Serins, and roam the countryside in search of food. Others stay on territory all the year round, if there is ample food. Older birds, which have flocked during the winter, return to their territories of the previous year in late January or early February and renew the pair-bond with their mates. The male advertises and defends the territory by song, given from a conspicuous perch. A young male will search for an unoccupied territory late in February and, quietly and unobtrusively, he checks for suitable nest-sites in the crutches between the branches and side-branches of trees. If no male challenges him, he begins to sing a juvenile song. The full song has to be learnt by listening to the males on adjoining territories, which leads to strong 'dialects' between regions. If a female approaches, he sleeks his feathers so that the white wing-flashes are exposed and flies beneath her. He crouches with his body turned away from her, raising the wing nearest her to expose his red flank and belly. Once the pair has accepted one another, the female examines the nest-sites and chooses one in which to build the nest. The nest is constructed of 4 layers: a shell of lichen and spider-silk, decorated with bark flakes; a mixture of moss and grass; fine dry grass; and a lining of thin roots, wool, and feathers. Cobwebs are often used to attach the nest to a twig. One or two clutches of 3-5 eggs are laid. Incubation takes almost 2 weeks and is by the female alone. Both sexes feed and care for the chicks, the female brooding them at first. Fledging takes 2 weeks and the young become independent 3 weeks later, often with the brood divided between the parents. The age of first breeding is one year old. The pair-bond is monogamous and may last for life.

Hints on recognition: It looks about the same size as the House Sparrow. The male is colourful, with a pinkish-chestnut face, underparts, and back. His head is grey, he has two prominent white wing-bars, and his rump is greenish-yellow. The female is light brown on the upperparts, buff on the underparts, with slightly less-prominent white wing-bars than the male. The alarm-call is a sharp "chink".

322

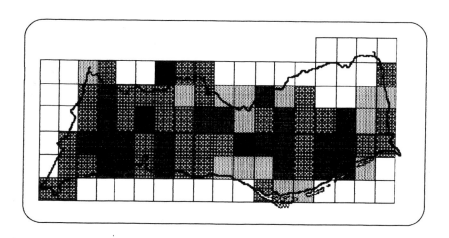

Hints on finding: It can be readily found in suitable habitat in the foothills of the western Serras as well as the Caldeirão. Inland sequeiros north of Tavira and between Portimão and Burgau are also worth searching.

Confirmation of breeding:

Number of rectangles in which recorded:	74
Possible breeding:	0
Probable breeding:	16
Confirmed breeding:	58

SERINUS SERINUS

SERIN

Portuguese name: Chamariz.

Distribution: The Serin is to be found as a resident around the Mediterranean Basin and as a summer visitor to most of Europe as far north as the Baltic Sea. It is well-distributed throughout Portugal, being recorded on every map by the national atlas, and is thought to be the commonest breeding species in the country (CEMPA).

Status in the Western Palearctic: It was originally restricted to the Mediterranean. During the 1800s it began spreading rapidly northwards, reaching Scandinavia and Great Britain this century. It is resident and sedentary in the Algarve, although Coverley refers to it as a summer migrant in the north of Portugal.

Preferred habitat: Lowland orange groves and sequeiros. Gardens and open broad-leaf or pine woodlands are also used, where there is access to a good food source. It avoids all types of treeless terrain and wind-swept or cold places. It is very tolerant of human disturbance.

Food: Primarily seeds, although buds and insects are sometimes taken. Food is pecked from the ground or taken directly from plants. As the food-source may change from week to week, the Serin often flies 3 kms or more from the nest to obtain it, storing the seeds in an expandable gullet. The chicks also have expandable gullets, so that they may slowly digest the food between visits by the parents.

Breeding: As the food-source is not part of the territory of a pair, the Serin feeds in flocks throughout the year. Nests are often grouped together in small loose colonies and are rarely at the same site for more than one brood, the birds moving with seed availability. Whilst in winter flocks, males and females form pairs and then, in early February, search for nest-sites. The female actively inspects prospective sites, in small forks towards the ends of branches in trees or large bushes, whilst the male follows and watches. Only the immediate vicinity of the nest is defended and advertised by the song of the male. He either sings from the top of the nesting-tree or whilst fluttering erratically over it, descending as though parachuting to the same tree or a neighbouring one. The female constructs a neat nest-cup of vegetation, moss and lichen, bound with spider-silk and lined with hair, feathers, and plant down. One clutch of 3-5 eggs is laid in that nest, although 2-3 further clutches are laid later in new nests, often in a completely different area. Incubation takes nearly 2 weeks and is by the female alone. Both parents feed and care for the chicks. Fledging takes 2 weeks and the young become independent shortly afterwards, although they often remain together when they leave the area. The age of first breeding is one year old. The pair-bond is monogamous and of seasonal duration only.

Hints on recognition: It is small, about the same size as the Blue Tit, and can only be confused with the Siskin (for which, see that species). It is primarily yellow, streaked with brown, with a stubby bill and a plain greyish-brown tail. In flight, it shows a prominent yellow rump. Unlike the Siskin, it has no black in its plumage, nor has it any obvious wing-bars.

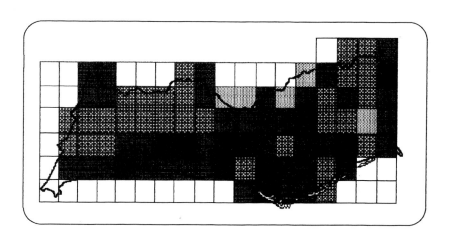

Hints on finding: It can be readily found in suitable habitat throughout the lowlands of the Algarve. The monotonous jingling song is a feature of any agricultural area where there are trees.

Confirmation of breeding:

Number of rectangles in which recorded:	82
Possible breeding:	0
Probable breeding:	4
Confirmed breeding:	78

CARDUELIS CHLORIS

GREENFINCH

Portuguese name: Verdilhão-comum.

Distribution: The Greenfinch is to be found all over Europe, except the extreme north, as well as in northern Africa, S.W. Asia, and Central Asia. It has been introduced into the Azores, Uruguay, and Australasia. It is well-distributed throughout Portugal, but is most common on the western and southern littoral (CEMPA).

Status in the Western Palearctic: It has increased recently in much of northern Europe. There has been a general move away from agricultural land to towns and villages, possibly due to the trend in urban feeding of birds during the winter. There is apparently no recent change in its status in Portugal. It is resident but dispersive.

Preferred habitat: Broken woodland, in close proximity to an abundant food-source. It particularly favours orange-groves, sequeiros, and mature gardens, avoiding all treeless habitats.

Food: Grain and large weed-seeds, which are picked directly from the plants or the ground. This species often forages in farmyards or follows the plough, pecking up fallen seeds. Where possible, it chooses large seeds, ignoring small ones. It has an expandable gullet in which to store the seeds and carry them to its nest. The chicks have a similar gullet, so that they may digest the food whilst the parents are away.

Breeding: During the winter months, flocks of Greenfinches roam over the countryside in search of food, often in company with other finches. In January, the males begin to pursue the females, hopping around them and attempting to touch bills. The male perches obliquely or laterally to the female's body, wings drooped and tail spread to show his markings more clearly. At first the male courts several females, but gradually a pair-bond is formed. The female becomes dominant and takes the male's food, as well as being fed by the male by regurgitation. After pair-formation, the pair visits prospective nest-sites, the female leading and the male following, watching and singing quietly. As the nesting-area is often separate from the feeding-area, only the area immediately around the nest is defended. The male sings from a conspicuous perch or from erratic flight, weaving between the trees, whilst the female builds the nest. The nest may be sited in a fork in the branches of a tree or bush and is constructed from grass and moss, lined with plant material, hair, and sometimes feathers. In February or early March, the first of 2 or 3 clutches of 4-6 eggs is laid. Incubation takes nearly 2 weeks and is by the female alone. Both parents care for the chicks and feed them by regurgitation. The young leave the nest at about 2 weeks old, before they can fly well, and are often tended by the male alone while the female re-lays. The age of first breeding is one year old. The pair-bond is monogamous and of seasonal duration only.

Hints on recognition: It is the size of a House Sparrow, with a heavy conical bill, brightly coloured greenish-yellow. The male has mainly yellow underparts and rump, a broad yellow bar along the wing, and prominent yellow patches on each side of a dark tail. The female is similar but slightly less bright. The northern European race *Carduelis chloris chloris* is browner and duller, lacking the bright green and yellow of the southern race *C.c. aurantiiventris*.

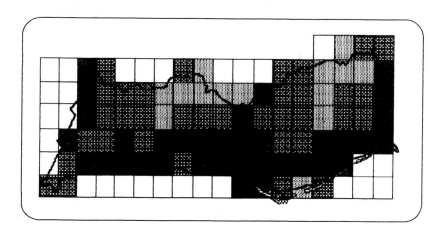

Hints on finding: It can be readily found in farmland throughout the lowlands of the Algarve. The monotonous nasal song of "zweee" is a feature of any agricultural area where there are trees.

Confirmation of breeding:

Number of rectangles in which recorded:	85
Possible breeding:	0
Probable breeding:	13
Confirmed breeding:	72

CARDUELIS CARDUELIS

GOLDFINCH

Portuguese name: Pintassilgo.

Distribution: The Goldfinch was originally confined to the Western Palearctic and adjoining Central Asia. It has, however, been introduced into South America, Bermuda, and Australasia, and has become a pest in New Zealand. It is well-distributed throughout Portugal but is particularly common in the Algarve (CEMPA).

Status in the Western Palearctic: It has increased in some of the northern regions of Europe. This is possibly resulting partly from legislation against trapping and partly from this species' spread into urban areas and its use of bird-table food in winter. There is apparently no change in its status in Portugal. It is a summer visitor to much of northern Europe, wintering in the Iberian Peninsula, but is mainly resident or dispersive in the Algarve.

Preferred habitat: Lowland fallow-fields, horticulture, sequeiros, and other habitats with a mixture of weeds and trees. It is very tolerant of human disturbance and readily uses gardens and orange-groves close to man.

Food: Primarily weed-seeds, for which the Goldfinch will travel many kilometres per day. When food is scarce, however, they will eat small insects and tree-seeds, including pine-nuts. Food is almost entirely taken directly from the plants or trees.

Breeding: The Goldfinch habitually feeds in flocks throughout the year, even during the breeding season. In January or February, the males begin to sing, whilst perching close to the females. At first, each male courts several females, but gradually the flock becomes a group of pairs. During courtship, both sexes crouch then swing from side to side, using their legs as pivots, wings lowered to show the yellow pattern. The red face is expanded and the tail spread. Once the pair-bond is formed, the pair searches for a suitable nest-site, the female leading and the male following. As most feeding is carried out in a flock, only the nest-site is defended and other Goldfinches feeding near the nest are ignored. The nest is sited high in the outermost fine twigs of a tree, where it sways and rocks with every wind. For this reason, the female makes the cup very deep and compact. It is made of moss, lichens, wool, and cobwebs, and is lined with plant down. Three clutches of 4-6 eggs are laid between February and the dry season, when seeds begin to become scarce. Incubation takes almost 2 weeks and is by the female alone, the male feeding her at the nest. Throughout these activities the male sings, from a prominent perch or in erratic flight over the nest-tree. Each male has a slightly different song and it is important that the female learns it, so that she may recognize her mate even in a large flock. The chicks are fed and cared for by both parents, leaving the nest at about 2 weeks old but not becoming self-sufficient until at least 10 days afterwards. The age of first breeding is one year old. The pair-bond is monogamous and of seasonal duration only.

Hints on recognition: There is no other species with which this can be confused. It is basically pinkish brown on the upperparts and creamy on the underparts. The 'face' around the bill is bright red, surrounded by white except for a black cap. The rump is whitish, contrasting with the black tail, and the wings are black with a broad, strikingly vivid, yellow wing-bar.

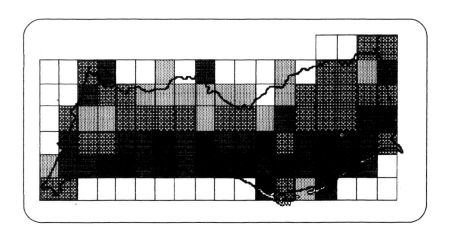

Hints on finding: It can be readily found in farmland throughout the lowlands of the Algarve. The liquid call "swit-wit-swit" can be heard in any part of the littoral where there are trees.

Confirmation of breeding:

Number of rectangles in which recorded: 83
Possible breeding: 1
Probable breeding: 10
Confirmed breeding: 72

329

CARDUELIS SPINUS

SISKIN

Portuguese name: Pintassilgo-verde.

Distribution: The Siskin breeds in two separate areas: one is northern and eastern Europe and the other is the Far East. It was not known to breed south of the Pyrenees before the BBA.

Status in the Western Palearctic: This species has increased markedly in much of northern Europe, probably owing to changes in forestry and to the provision in gardens of winter food. It is primarily a common winter visitor to the western Algarve. It is not known whether the current breeding population in the Algarve originates from wintering birds remaining to breed or from escaped cage-birds. It may be significant that all breeding records are from the west, where it most commonly overwinters.

Preferred habitat: Pinewoods, with easy access to a good food-source. Outside of the breeding season, all habitats with plentiful seeds are used.

Food: The preferred food is the pine-nut, but, where this is not available, other seeds are taken. It is an agile feeder, readily hanging upside down like a tit, and takes most seeds directly from the plant or tree. The young are often fed on insects.

Breeding: During the winter months, flocks of Siskins roam suitably weedy areas, often in company with other finches and with Chiffchaffs. Early in spring, the males begin to sing and court the females. A male lands near a female, black crown feathers erect, wings drooped to display the yellow on his wing and rump, and tail fanned to show the tail markings. He fluffs up his breast and utters a long creaking note. As courtship progresses, the female frequently adopts a submissive posture, calling with wings quivering, and the male regurgitates seeds from his gullet into the female's open beak. The pair, the female leading and the male following, searches for a suitable nest-site towards the end of a branch high in a conifer. As with other seed-eaters, this species does not always use the same area for feeding and nesting. The male advertises and defends his possession of a nest-site by song, given from a conspicuous perch or from brief erratic flights. The female builds a neat cup of small twigs, grass, and moss, lined with hair, wool, plant down, and feathers. Two clutches of 3-5 eggs are laid, beginning in April. Incubation takes nearly 2 weeks and is by the female alone, the male bringing her food. The chicks are brooded and fed by the female for the first week after hatching, the male provisioning the nest. Later, both parents feed the young by regurgitation. Fledging takes 2 weeks and the young become independent about a week later. The age of first breeding is one year old. The pair-bond is monogamous and of seasonal duration only.

Hints on recognition: The only species with which it is likely to be confused is the Serin (for which, see that species). It is yellow-green and about the same size as the Serin, but has a longer more pointed bill. The male has blackish streaks on the upper-parts and a blackish cap, bib, wings, and tail. The wings have two conspicuous yellow bars, the rump is bright yellow, and there are bright yellow patches on each side of the tail. The female is similar but shows less black.

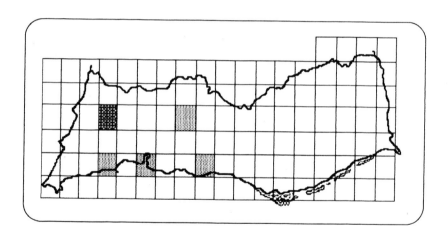

Hints on finding: In winter, it can be readily found with other finches in weedy orchards and orange groves, especially in the Barlavento. It is so scarce in the Algarve in the breeding season, however, that no help can be given for that period.

Confirmation of breeding: The two areas with confirmed breeding were 1) coastal pine-woods and 2) alder with other broad-leaf trees and a few pines on the banks of a river.

Number of rectangles in which recorded:	5
Possible breeding:	0
Probable breeding:	3
Confirmed breeding:	2

331

CARDUELIS CANNABINA

LINNET

Portuguese name: Pinta-rôxa-comum.

Distribution: The Linnet is to be found in most of the Western Palearctic and the adjoining regions of Asia. It is well-distributed and common throughout Portugal (CEMPA).

Status in the Western Palearctic: This species declined during the last century in the north of Europe, possibly because of the pressures of commercial bird-catching. It has recovered since then, following protection. There is no apparent change in its status in Portugal. It is resident in the Algarve, but large numbers from further north overwinter in the region.

Preferred habitat: In the winter, salt-marshes and all lowland weedy areas are favoured. In the breeding season, low bushes are required for nesting. These may be found in the same place as the wintering grounds, or in the hilly scrubland and coastal heathland the west. It is not tolerant of human disturbance near the nest, but is otherwise not shy.

Food: Mainly weed-seeds, which the bird takes directly from the plant by clinging to the stem. Unlike other finches, it avoids berries and fruit and rarely takes tree-seeds. Some insects, especially caterpillars, are fed to the young.

Breeding: During the winter months, it roams the countryside in flocks searching for food. The advantages of flocking for seed-eaters are (1) the food-source varies from day to day as plants grow or die, so when some birds find new seeds the rest quickly follow and (2) vegetarians have to feed almost non-stop with their heads down and are, therefore, vulnerable to predators, so a group on the alert wastes less feeding-time than a solitary bird. In January or February, the males begin to sing and to court the females. The male will approach a receptive female, his red crown feathers raised, wings drooped and tail spread to show the markings to advantage, whilst singing quietly. When a pair is established, it leaves the flock and searches for a suitable nest-site, the female in the lead. She builds a nest of dry grass, moss, and fine twigs, lined with hair or wool, in a low bush. Three clutches of 4-6 eggs are laid, beginning in early March. Incubation takes about 11-14 days and is by the female alone. The chicks are brooded by the female and fed by the male at first, then fed by both parents. Fledging takes about 2 weeks, but the young do not become self-sufficient until at least 2 weeks afterwards, being able to follow their parents at about 3 weeks old. The age of first breeding is one year old. The pair-bond is monogamous and of seasonal duration only.

Hints on recognition: It is very slightly bigger than a Goldfinch, brown on the upperparts and buff on the underparts. Both sexes have a white rump, white patches on each side of the tail, and a white streak down the wing, which shows as a white wing-bar in flight. In addition, the male has a pinkish red forehead and breast, whilst the female has pale circles or half-circles around the eyes and a pale 'bunting-like' throat pattern (see illustration). No similar species is known to occur in Portugal.

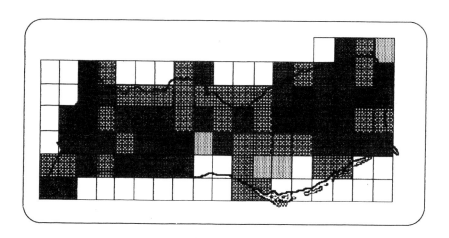

Hints on finding: In winter, it can be readily found with other finches in weedy places, especially along the coast on salt-marshes. In the breeding season, many move to higher ground, where there is suitable scrub for nesting. The foothills of the western and eastern serras are easy to walk and hold good populations.

Confirmation of breeding:

Number of rectangles in which recorded: 80
Possible breeding: 0
Probable breeding: 5
Confirmed breeding: 75

PYRRHULA PYRRHULA

BULLFINCH

Portuguese name: Dom-Fafe.

Distribution: The Bullfinch breeds in most of Europe, except the extreme north, and in the temperate latitudes of Asia. Although it is not shown in guide-books as being present in southern Iberia, it is not uncommon on the Coto de Doñana (García 1989). It was known as a breeding species only along the northern border of Portugal with Spain (CEMPA) and as a passage migrant in Traz-os-Montes (Coverley). The BBA shows that the species also occurs in the Algarve.

Status in the Western Palearctic: It is fairly common throughout its breeding range and has increased in many northern areas. The first known record of this species in the Algarve was of one male in the autumn of 1986, near the Odelouca River. Since then, the annual records for the Algarve have increased substantially - mainly as an autumn migrant but also as a breeding species. The first breeding record for the region was in 1988 near the Odelouca. It is resident and sedentary in most of Europe. The Algarvian population would appear to be migratory, leaving the area in April/May after breeding and returning in October, but it is not known where they pass the summer months.

Preferred habitat: Small, overgrown side-valleys in the foothills. It particularly favours gullies with almost impenetrable scrub on the slopes and thick bramble on the bottom, although it is tolerant of a little tree-cover.

Food: Mainly seeds or fruit, which it holds lengthwise in the bill and turns with the tongue against the edge of the lower jaw so that the skin or flesh of a fruit is peeled off.

Small snails are crushed and de-shelled in the same way (Newton 1972). It will also eat flower-buds, when supplies of the main food are low, which results in its being regarded as an agricultural pest in some areas. The young are fed mainly on cater-pillars, but other insects and spiders are also eaten. Food is taken to the young in special pouches in the adults' mouths, which develop for this purpose during the breeding season.

Breeding: Pair-bonds may be formed during the winter months or in the spring. The male advertises his territory by a very soft song, barely audible more than a few metres distant. The female builds a flat structure of small twigs, with an inner cup of fine roots and hair, just inside the canopy of a dense bush, e.g. a bramble. One clutch of 4-5 eggs is laid in February or early March. Incubation is by the female alone and takes nearly 2 weeks. The female broods the young for the first week, the male bringing all the food, then both parents feed and care for them. Fledging takes 2 to 2 1/2 weeks, after which the family stays together until migration. The pair-bond is monogamous and may last for life, but, owing to how recently this migratory population has colonized the Algarve, there is no data on the duration of the pair-bond. It is possible, however, that the pair may breed again on its summer grounds, as elsewhere in its range the species has more than one clutch and does not normally begin breeding until May.

Hints on recognition: The male is a hand-some bird, with rosy-pink breast and jet black cap, wings, and tail. The female is more drab, with a beige breast and a grey tone to the black parts. It is about the same size as a House Sparrow, but appears to be 'rounder' owing to its very short and almost invisible neck. In flight, a prominent white rump and wing-bar are particularly notice-able.

334

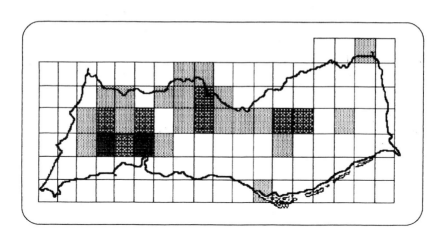

Hints on finding: It is a quiet bird, rarely showing itself as it moves through the bushes. The pure, single-note whistle, which is the contact call between the male and the female, will betray its presence, however. Overgrown side-valleys, leading from remote valleys in the western serras are the most rewarding localities.

Breeding confirmation: The first breeding record was in 1988. The population grew rapidly to a peak in 1990, which is reflected in this map, since when it has declined.

Number of rectangles in which recorded: 28
Possible breeding: 1
Probable breeding: 13
Confirmed breeding: 14

C. COCCOTHRAUSTES

HAWFINCH

Portuguese name: Bico-grossudo.

Distribution: The Hawfinch is virtually restricted to the middle latitudes of the Western Palearctic. It is probably thinly distributed throughout Portugal (CEMPA).

Status in the Western Palearctic: As a result of the difficulty in detecting this species, there are few accurate estimates of its abundance or status. It would appear to have decreased in parts of its range, however, including Portugal (CEMPA).

Preferred habitat: Broadleaf woodland and inland sequeiros, especially almond groves.

Food: Mainly the seeds and fruits of trees, especially olive and almond. The huge bill and massive head and jaw muscles of this species enable it to crack and open large or hard fruit-stones. Apparently, a load of up to 72kg could be required for this 55gm bird to crack an olive stone (Newton, 1972). It also takes buds, shoots, and insects, especially larvae.

Breeding: During the winter months, it roams the countryside in flocks, searching for food. Early in the year, the males begin to court the females with elaborate rituals, designed to reduce aggressiveness where one peck could cripple the other bird. The male cautiously approaches the female, feathers fluffed, holding himself erect with wings drooped and tail spread. If she does not attack him, he bows deeply, hiding his offensive weapon, the bill. He then lowers the wing nearest her, showing the wing pattern, and reaches forward while maintaining as much distance as possible, to touch the tip of the hen's bill with his. Later, if she accepts him, he displays by holding himself erect, pivoting from side to side, with wings quivering and spread at right angles to the body. He fluffs his feathers and patters to and fro, braying, in front of the female, and often she does the same, the two birds appearing to dance together. In March, the male leaves the flock periodically and chooses a nest-site, at which he builds the foundation for the nest from twigs. When the female joins him, she completes the nest with a cup of grass and fine roots, sometimes lining it with hair. The male has a very quiet song, which cannot be heard more than a few metres away, and does not have a conspicuous song-flight, although he often flutters over the place where the hen is perched. One clutch (or sometimes two) of 4-6 eggs is laid. Incubation takes nearly 2 weeks and is by the female alone. The chicks are fed by both parents on seeds or insects regurgitated into their bills. The young leave the nest at 11-14 days, before they are able to fly properly, and remain dependent on the parents for at least a further 2 weeks. The age of first breeding is probably one year old. The pair-bond is monogamous and of seasonal duration, but may be renewed in subsequent years owing to site-fidelity.

Hints on recognition: Even in flight, the huge bill makes this bird unmistakable. The head is also large and the body rounded, making it appear very chunky. It is almost entirely pinkish-brown, but has a black throat and black wings with a wide prominent white bar. In flight, it appears to have two broad white-bars. The loud explosive "tick" call is diagnostic.

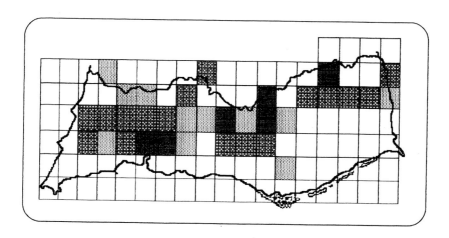

Hints on finding: Except when they are courting, these birds are quiet and difficult to see amongst the foliage of trees. The explosive "tick" call, however, is unmistakable once learnt. The oakwoods around Barranco do Velho and north of São Braz are worthwhile searching, but by ear rather than by eye.

Confirmation of breeding: As this species is so difficult to detect, it has probably been under-recorded.

Number of rectangles in which recorded: 34
Possible breeding: 1
Probable breeding: 11
Confirmed breeding: 22

EMBERIZA CIRLUS

CIRL BUNTING

Portuguese name:
Escrevedeira-de-garganta-preta.

Distribution: The Cirl Bunting is primarily a bird of the northern and western Mediterranean, but reaches as far north as Great Britain and Belgium. It has been introduced into New Zealand. It is thinly distributed throughout Portugal, except for the south-east (CEMPA).

Status in the Western Palearctic: During the 19th century, it spread northwards and reached Great Britain. Since that time, it has declined drastically and is still declining throughout the northern part of its range, possibly because of habitat and climatic changes. Coverley refers to it as the most common bunting in the north, whereas the national atlas found only small numbers. It is resident but dispersive.

Preferred habitat: Horticulture and pasture with plentiful trees. It particularly favours the temperate climate of the north-western Algarve and avoids the areas with hot dry summers. It is sometimes to be found in gardens, especially around Monchique.

Food: Mainly weed and grass seeds, but also cereal seeds and wild fruit. It will occasionally take insects such as beetles, grasshoppers and caterpillars. The young are fed almost entirely on invertebrates.

Breeding: During the winter months, it feeds in small flocks in places where weed seeds are plentiful. Early in February, the males break away from the flocks and establish territories. The cock advertises and defends his territory by song, given from a prominent perch such as an overhead wire or the top of a tree. When a female is attracted, he lands by her, singing quietly, throat feathers fluffed to accentuate his striking pattern, and quivers his wings. He will also chase her, pursuing her at great speed in and out of the trees. It is not known which sex chooses the nest-site, but it is the hen alone who builds. She constructs a bulky, untidy nest of grass and roots, lined with hair and fine grass, on a foundation of moss. It is usually sited in a bush or in the low branches of a tree, but sometimes it may be on the ground. Two or three clutches of 3-4 eggs are laid from March onwards. Incubation takes almost 2 weeks and is by the female alone, the male feeding her at the nest. The chicks are fed and cared for by both parents, although the female broods them at first and may provide the greater share of the food. The young leave the nest at almost 2 weeks old, often before they can fly properly, but do not become independent for at least a further 2 weeks. The age of first breeding is one year old. The pair-bond is usually monogamous and of seasonal duration, but may persist outside of the breeding season.

Hints on recognition: The only species with which this may be confused is the Yellowhammer *Emberiza citrinella*, which is a very rare visitor to the Algarve. The male is mainly yellow on the underparts and streaked chestnut on the upperparts. He has a grey collar across the chest and a distinctive black and yellow face pattern (see illustration). The female is streaked brown and buff and is similar to other female and juvenile buntings, so that identification is advisable only in conjunction with the male. There is always some yellow on her throat and belly, however.

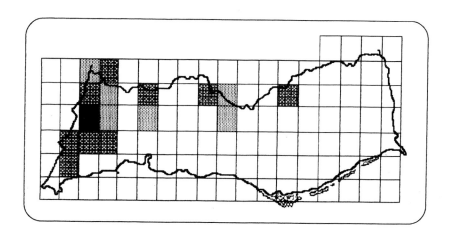

Hints on finding: The track running eastwards from Odeceixe, just before the border bridge to the Alentejo, is a good place to search. The area with the greatest abundance is the valley running south-east from Aljezur to Monte Novo, turning right about 2km from Aljezur on the old road to Marmelete.

Confirmation of breeding: This species is so thinly distributed that it has probably been under-recorded, especially in the São Marcos da Serra area where it might be reasonably expected.

Number of rectangles in which recorded: 16
Possible breeding: 0
Probable breeding: 4
Confirmed breeding: 12

339

EMBERIZA CIA

ROCK BUNTING

Portuguese name: Cia.

Distribution: The Rock Bunting is virtually confined to the Mediterranean Basin, but reaches Germany in the north and extends into south-west Asia. It breeds in the north, the interior of the centre, and the south of Portugal, but is totally absent from the western centre (CEMPA).

Status in the Western Palearctic: There has apparently been no recent change in its status in Europe in general or in Portugal in particular. It has remained stable in the Algarve for at least the past two decades. It is resident and sometimes dispersive.

Preferred habitat: Sloping ground with sparse scrub and numerous trees. In the western Algarve, it readily uses the sides of tracks through eucalyptus plantations and the broken edges of coastal cliffs. In the eastern Algarve, it is restricted to rocky slopes, such as the sides of gorges, and the presence of trees does not appear to be important. Apparently, either rocks or trees must be present, but not necessarily both.

Food: Mainly invertebrates, but it will also take seeds and berries. It actively searches for prey on the ground, turning over leaf-litter with its bill or probing under small stones. It will also peck small insects from vegetation or the foliage of trees, as well as take flying prey by flycatching or by leaping from the ground.

Breeding: In February, the male seeks an unoccupied territory, creeping along the ground and occasionally singing from cover to find out whether there is already a male in possession. If no male responds to him, he moves to a conspicuous perch, such as the top of a tree or a large boulder, and resumes singing. Although he may sing whilst flying from perch to perch, he has no display flight. If a female is seen on the ground, he will land by her and parade around her, hopping stiffly with tail spread and wings touching the ground. If she tries to leave, he chases her vigorously. He may show her prospective nest-sites, but the female has the final choice. The favourite nest-site is a small but very dense bush on a bank, but a cavity under a rock may be used in more barren habitats. The nest-cup is made mainly from grass, lined with finer grass and sometimes hair. Two clutches of 4-6 eggs are laid, beginning in March or April. Incubation takes nearly 2 weeks and is by the female alone. The chicks are fed and cared for by both parents, fledging at 10-13 days old. The young become independent about a week later and breed for the first time at one year old. The pair-bond is monogamous. It may be of seasonal duration, when the birds are dispersive, or may last for life, when the pair remains on territory throughout the year.

Hints on recognition: It is reddish-chestnut, streaked with dark brown on the upperparts and plain on the underparts, and is a little larger than a House Sparrow. The head is boldly patterned with stripes of black and very light grey, both sexes being almost identical, although some guide-books show the female's head as brownish. In flight, it shows prominent white side-tail feathers. The call is a very high, thin "seep", which can be heard only when the observer is very close.

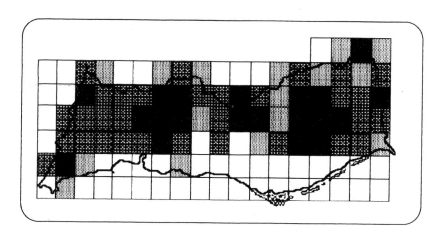

Hints on finding: This species can usually be found with patience in suitable habitat. It is very quiet and generally remains hidden, but the very high-pitched "seep" call betrays its presence. Among many worthwhile places to search are the gorges around Vaqueiros (see Where to watch breeding birds, H) and the small gullies running inland from the cliffs to the north of Vila do Bispo and between Aljezur and Odeceixe.

Confirmation of breeding:

Number of rectangles in which recorded: 67

Possible breeding:	0
Probable breeding:	15
Confirmed breeding:	52

EMBERIZA SCHOENICLUS

REED BUNTING

Portuguese name:
Escrevedeira-dos-caniços.

Distribution: The Reed Bunting is to be found in most of the Palearctic, excluding North Africa and some parts of the Far East. The national atlas found it thinly distributed along the west coast from the northern border to just above Lisbon, but none were found breeding in the Algarve.

Status in the Western Palearctic: It has increased and spread its range in many parts of northern Europe. This has been mainly because of its adaptability to dry habitats, following the destruction of wetlands and the removal of unused wet farmland by modern intensive farming. From Coverley's accounts, it would appear to be more common in Portugal today than in his time. It is mainly resident, although a few individuals from elsewhere overwinter in the Algarve.

Preferred habitat: As its name would suggest, it prefers reed-beds and similar wet habitats. In parts of its range it has moved into dry habitats such as young conifer plantations, sand-dunes, and the rough edges of farmland. The latter habitat was used by three of the Algarve records, the fourth being in traditional wetland.

Food: Mainly seeds, but also invertebrates, such as snails, beetles, caterpillars, and other insects. It will take food either directly from the vegetation or from the ground, and will also flycatch or make short flights in pursuit of aerial prey.

Breeding: Elsewhere in its range, it roams the countryside in flocks during the winter months, searching for food, and often forms pairs during this time. It is so scarce in the Algarve, however, that this is unlikely to happen and probably pair-formation occurs on territory. In March, the male establishes a territory, which he defends and advertises by song. Although he will sing in short, jerky flight, he normally delivers his song from an exposed perch, whilst constantly flicking his tail. If a female approaches, he ruffles his throat and neck feathers, to show the striking pattern to advantage, and struts or flutters around her. Courtship often develops into fast sexual chases, followed by 'rough-and-tumbles' on the ground. The female builds a nest cup of grass and moss, lined with fine grass and hair, in a tussock or on the ground in vegetation. Occasionally, the nest may be sited in a bush. Two or three clutches of 3-5 eggs are laid, beginning in April. Incubation takes 2 weeks and is mainly by the female. The chicks are fed and cared for by both parents and leave the nest at 10-12 days, before they can fly well. The young become independent 1-2 weeks afterwards and breed for the first time at one year old. Elsewhere, the pair-bond is often polygynous and of seasonal duration. With a shortage of mates in the Algarve, the pair-bond is probably monogamous and may last for more than one season.

Hints on recognition: The male is unmistakable, with his jet black head and throat, contrasting with his white moustachial streak joining with a white collar across the back of the neck. The upperparts are chestnut with dark streaks and the underparts white. The female is mostly steaked brown and should only be identified in conjunction with the male.

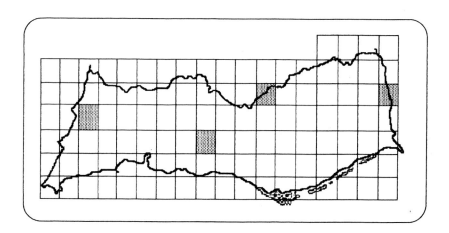

Confirmation of breeding:

Hints on finding: This species is so scarce in the Algarve that no help can be given in this section.

Number of rectangles in which recorded:	4
Possible breeding:	0
Probable breeding:	2
Confirmed breeding:	2

343

MILIARIA CALANDRA

CORN BUNTING

Portuguese name: Trigueirão.

Distribution: The Corn Bunting is to be found in the middle and lower latitudes of Europe, Central and S.W. Asia, and north-western Africa. It is mainly absent from the north-west of Portugal, but is well-distributed elsewhere in the country (CEMPA).

Status in the Western Palearctic: It has decreased markedly in much of northern Europe. This has probably been caused by changes in agricultural practices, including harvesting during the breeding season, pesticides reducing the food supplies for the chicks, and drainage of ditches. In Portugal, however, there appears to be no change in its status. It is resident and sedentary.

Preferred habitat: Cereal crops, ungrazed grassland, horticulture with rough weedy areas, and fallow fields, preferably with song-posts such as scattered trees or bushes, overhead wires, or fencing, and with access to water. It avoids all arboreal habitats and areas with very short herbage.

Food: Weed seeds, leaves, grass, wild fruit, and sometimes grain. It will also take invertebrates, such as insects, spiders, snails, and earthworms, and the chicks are fed almost entirely on these. Food is taken directly from plants or from the ground.

Breeding: As with other seed-eaters, it ranges the countryside in flocks during the winter months, searching for food. In the breeding season, it becomes mainly insectivorous and so leaves the flock and settles on a territory. The male establishes his territory in February, advertising and defending it by song. He may sing either from a prominent perch, such as the top of a tree, or from song-flight. In the latter case, he ascends from a high perch, singing and fluttering with legs dangling, before returning to the same perch or a neighbouring one. As males and females look identical, the male greets all birds which enter his territory with aggression. Only by the female's submissive posture and lack of song does he recognize her sex. If she attempts to leave, he chases her vigorously. Once the pair accepts one another, the female builds an untidy nest of dry grass, lined with hair and fine grass, on the ground in thick herbage or up to 1m in a bush. Two or three clutches of 3-6 eggs are laid, beginning in March. Incubation takes nearly 2 weeks and is by the female alone. The chicks are mainly fed and cared for by the female and leave the nest at 9-11 days old, before they can fly. The young are able to fly at 2 1/2 weeks old and become independent shortly afterwards. The age of first breeding is one year old. The pair-bond is of seasonal duration only and may be either monogamous or polygynous, with as many as 11 hens recorded for one male (BTO, 1993).

Hints on recognition: The Corn Bunting is entirely streaked brown with no obvious distinguishing markings, although many have a black patch on the breast which often causes confusion with the Calandra Lark *Melanocorypha calandra*. It is somewhat larger than a House Sparrow and very chunky. It can be seen on a perch, pouring forth its song, beak in the air and tail pulled well under it for balance, giving it a hump-backed outline.

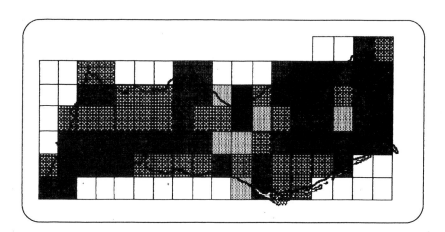

Hints on finding: This species is particularly common in the rolling grasslands of the north-east, where its monotonous jangling song can be heard hour after hour. It can also be readily found in almost any suitable habitat anywhere in the Algarve, especially in the fields of the southwest littoral.

Confirmation of breeding:

Number of rectangles in which recorded: 84
Possible breeding: 0
Probable breeding: 5
Confirmed breeding: 79

APPENDIX I

PROBABLE AND POSSIBLE BREEDING SPECIES

All those species which were recorded as probably breeding at less than three sites during the course of fieldwork for the BBA are included in this appendix. Also included are species which bred in the Algarve outside of the period covered by this book.

BOTAURUS STELLARIS
BITTERN
A male held territory in the reed-beds at Fontes, between Estômbar and Silves, until 1990. No proof of breeding was obtained and it has not been recorded subsequently in the Algarve.

ARDEOLA RALLOIDES
SQUACCO HERON
A pair built a nest in 1992 and 1993 on a sea-stack near Praia da Marinha, in a colony of Cattle and Little Egrets. It could not be determined whether eggs were laid, but certainly no chicks hatched.

PHOENICOPTERUS RUBER
GREATER FLAMINGO
Flightless chicks were reported at Castro Marim in 1986, prior to the start of field-work for the BBA, although there is no confirmed evidence. Adults are to be observed in the Algarve throughout the year so that future breeding is possible.

AYTHYA FERINA
POCHARD
Pairs were observed in the Quinta do Lago to Ludo area every year of fieldwork for the BBA, although no evidence of breeding was found. The national atlas proved nesting of this species near Lisbon and breeding in the Algarve is likely in the near future.

VANELLUS VANELLUS
LAPWING
One pair bred at Castro Marim in 1993, the year after completion of the field-work for the BBA.

SCOLOPAX RUSTICOLA
WOODCOCK
One pair held territory near Silves in 1989 and was strongly suspected to have bred, at least to the stage of incubating eggs. No evidence was found, however.

TRINGA TOTANUS
REDSHANK
The national atlas strongly suspected breeding at several sites in the south-east. The BBA confirms that suspicion, as well as suspecting breeding near Aljezur. No evidence was found, however.

CHLIDONIAS NIGER
BLACK TERN
Several pairs attempted to breed in 1984 and 1985 at Castro Marim, Tavira, and Ludo. Copulating and the formation of nest-scrapes was observed. The pairs occupied the scrapes for approx. 5 weeks, during which time the observers were unable to check for eggs. After the departure of the birds, no evidence of breeding was found at those nests which could be reached.

STREPTOPELIA DECAOCTO
COLLARED DOVE
Breeding was suspected near Messines and near Burgau during the course of fieldwork for the BBA, but no proof was obtained. Since the completion of this work, breeding has been proved near Sagres.

ASIO OTUS
LONG-EARED OWL
This species breeds just over the border in Spain. Individuals are heard or seen every year in the Algarve, but no proof of breeding has yet been obtained.

CHERSOPHILUS DUPONTI
DUPONT'S LARK
A male held territory near Faro in 1992. No evidence of breeding was found. This species breeds in Spain and is spreading, so that breeding may be expected in the future.

SAXICOLA RUBETRA
WHINCHAT
In 1991, several males held territory throughout the breeding season in the western Algarve. It is not known whether any unobserved males obtained mates and bred. One female Whinchat mated with a male Stonechat near Bordeira in that year.

TURDUS PHILOMELOS
SONG THRUSH
A male, which had been shot in one wing, held territory near Silves in 1986. It successfully obtained a mate and fledged 4 chicks. It has not been recorded in subsequent years.

LOCUSTELLA LUSCINIOIDES
SAVI'S WARBLER
A male held territory throughout the breeding season near Silves in 1990 and brief song has been heard at other localities in other' years. No proof of breeding has been obtained.

ACROCEPHALUS MELANOPOGON
MOUSTACHED WARBLER
A male held territory at Quinta do Lago in 1993 and 1994. This species breeds in southern Spain almost to the border with Portugal, but no evidence of breeding in the Algarve has yet been obtained.

SYLVIA COMMUNIS
WHITETHROAT
The national atlas proved breeding in the south-west Algarve. Although no records of breeding were obtained during the course of fieldwork for the BBA, this species could easily nest again in the future.

FICEDULA HYPOLEUCA
PIED FLYCATCHER
In the spring of 1984, several pairs held territory for April and Mary, copulating and building nests. None of the pairs under observation produced eggs, but it is not known whether other pairs nested successfully.

APPENDIX II

FERAL SPECIES

Caged birds are kept extensively in Portugal, often in outside cages and aviaries, so that escapes or deliberate releases often occur. In addition, several hunting reserves breed alien game-birds which wander outside the confines of the estate. The Algarvian climate is so well-suited to many of these species that they successfully adapt to a new habitat and food-source and breed ferally. Although some species have established themselves in viable numbers, they tend to move from one place to another from year to year. For this reason, all the feral species recorded during fieldwork for the BBA are discussed in this appendix, without maps, with the exception of the Partridge, the Pheasant, and the Common Waxbill (for which species, see Chapter 5).

Game and aviary species are so interbred and manipulated for form or colour, that it was not possible for BBA fieldworkers to identify some species. In addition, new species are escaping or being released, establishing new populations since this book was published. It should, therefore, be realized that there are many more non-European birds breeding wild in the region than are in this list and the reader can reasonably expect to find new breeding birds for the Algarve. The Macdonald Encyclopedia of Cage and Aviary Birds, by Matthew M. Vriends, is an excellent book for the general identification of these species.

FRANCOLINUS FRANCOLINUS
BLACK FRANCOLIN
Originates from the eastern Mediterranean and south-western Asia. Established in hilly grassland in the north-eastern Algarve. These game-birds are similar to the Partridge and Red-legged Partridge (for which, see those species) in general shape, but the male has a black breast, chestnut collar, and white cheeks.

NUMIDA MELEAGRIS
HELMETED GUINEAFOWL
Originates from Africa, south of the Sahara. Established in dry abandoned valleys in the north-east. It is a common in farm-yard fowl, grey with white spots.

COLUMBA LIVIA
FERAL PIGEON
Originates from the Rock Dove (for which, see that species), with various colours introduced into the plumage. Most towns have populations of Feral Pigeons and many farms and villages have flocks of pigeons which are allowed to fly free, some of which do not return to their cotes.

STREPTOPELIA RISORIA
BARBARY DOVE
Originates from the African Collared Dove *Streptopelia roseofrisea*, breeding in Africa between the Sahara and the Equator. This species is commonly kept by country people and allowed to fly free. It is similar to the Collared Dove (see Appendix I), but paler, and has given rise to many false reports of the latter breeding in the Algarve.

PLOCEUS CUCULLATUS
VILLAGE WEAVER
Originates from Senegal to central Africa. Colonies have become established on the Arade. It is small, brown and yellow on the upperparts, with a bright yellow head and underparts, black face and throat, and red eyes.

EUPLECTES AFRA
NAPOLEON WEAVER
Originates from Africa south of the Sahara. Colonies have become established on the Arade which may lead to hybridisation in the future. It is similar to the Village Weaver, but the black extends onto the breast and the eye is dark brown.

EUPLECTES HORDEACEA
CRIMSON-CROWNED BISHOP
Originates from Africa. Individuals have been reported from a wide range of habitats between Faro and Sagres. It is a little larger than the House Sparrow, mainly black including a black face, with a brilliant red head, breast and mantle.

ESTRILDA MELPODA
ORANGE-CHEEKED WAXBILL
Originates from western and central Africa. It has been recorded from Albufeira westwards. It is similar in size to the Common Waxbill (for which, see that species), with which it readily cross-breeds, producing intermediate forms. It is plain grey on the head and underparts, brown on the back and wings, with a bright orange patch on each cheek.

ESTRILDA RHODOPYGA
ROSY-RUMPED WAXBILL
Originates from eastern Africa. Individuals have been recorded from Faro to Portimão. It is similar in size to the Common Waxbill (for which, see that species), with which it readily cross-breeds, producing intermediate forms. It is buff and brown all over, reddish rump, with a small red patch behind the eye and on the wing.

ESTRILDA TROGLODYTES
BLACK-RUMPED or GREY WAXBILL
Originates from Senegal to the Sudan and northern Ethiopia. It has been recorded throughout the Algarve. It readily cross-breeds with, and is similar in size to, the Common Waxbill (for which, see that species), producing intermediate forms. The colouring is similar to the Common Waxbill, but the tail and rump are entirely black.

AMANDAVA AMANDAVA
RED AVADAVAT
Originates from India eastwards. It is breeding abundantly in Spain and small numbers have become established ferally near Faro, Silves, and Portimão. It is small, reddish-brown all over with large white spots on the underparts.

LONCHURA MAJA
WHITE-HEADED MUNIA
Originates from Malaysia and Indonesia. Breeding colonies have become established on the Arade between Silves and Portimão. It is small with a wedge-shaped pale blue bill. The upperparts are mauvish-brown and the underparts dark, whilst the head is entirely white.

LONCHURA MALACCA
BLACK-HEADED MUNIA
Originates from India eastwards to the Philippines. Breeding colonies have become established on the Arade between Silves and Portimão. It is small with a wedge-shaped pale blue bill, bright chestnut upperparts, white belly, and a black head.

POEPHILA (TAENIOPYGIA) GUTTATA
ZEBRA FINCH
Originates from Australia. Breeding colonies have become established on the Arade between Portimão and Silves, and near Faro. It is small and greyish, with orange cheeks and a black and white moustache. It has chestnut flanks with large white spots, and a black and white striped tail.

BUCANETES GITHAGINEUS
TRUMPETER FINCH
Originates from north Africa. It has recently become established naturally in S.E. Spain and could occur naturally in Portugal. Small numbers are breeding between Portimão and Silves. It is slightly smaller than the House Sparrow, pinkish brown on the upperparts, greyish pink on the underparts, with a red bill. The call strongly resembles a trumpet being blown.

EMBERIZA STRIOLATA
HOUSE BUNTING
Originates from North Africa and the Middle East and could occur naturally in the Algarve. Small numbers breed in the hills between Portimão and Monchique. It is a typical bunting, entirely rufous-brown with whole head, neck and upper breast grey, lightly flecked with dark grey.

APPENDIX III

LIST OF ANIMALS MENTIONED IN THE TEXT

Ants	Formicidae
Aphids	Hemiptera
Badger	Meles meles
Bats	Chiroptera
Bees	Aculeata
Beetles	Coleoptera
Butterflies	Lepidoptera
Calf	Bos taurus
Cricket	Orthoptera
Dragonflies	Odonata
Earthworms	Lumbricidae
Fox	Vulpes vulpes
Frog	Rana
Grasshoppers	Orthoptera
Hare	Lepus capensis
Lamb	Ovis aries
Mice	Muridae
Midwife toad	Alytes obstetricans
Mites	Acari
Processionary moth	Thaumetopoea pityocampa
Rabbit	Oryctolagus cuniculus
Roe Deer	Capreolus capreolus
Scorpion	Scorpiones
Snails	Gastropoda
Spiders	Araneae
Springtails	Collembola
Stoat	Mustela erminea
Tadpoles	Rana temporaria
Voles	Microtidae
Wasps	Aculeata
Wild Boar	Sus scrofa
Woodlice	Isopoda

PLANTS MENTIONED IN THE TEXT

Alder	Alnus
Almond	Prunus dulcis
Bamboo	Arundo donax
Bramble	Rubus fruticosus *agg*
Broad bean	Vicia faba
Bulrush	Scirpus
Carob	Ceratonia siliqua
Cork oak	Quercus suber
Eucalyptus	Eucalyptus
Fig	Ficus carica
Furze	Ulex
Gorse	Ulex
Heather	Erica/Calluna
Holm oak	Quercus ilex
Juniper	Juniperus
Kermes oak	Quercus coccifera
Lavender	Lavandula
Mastic	Pistacia lentiscus
Oleander	Nerium oleander
Olive	Olea europaea
Prickly pear	Opuntia
Reed	Phragmites
Reedmace	Typha
Rock Rose	Cistaceae
Rosemary	Rosmarinus
Rush	Juncus
Sedge	Carex
Strawberry tree	Arbutus unedo
Tamarisk	Tamarix
Thyme	Thymus
Umbrella pine	Pinus pinea
Willow	Salix
Yellow lupin	Lupinus luteus

APPENDIX IV

CHECKLIST OF THE BREEDING BIRDS OF THE ALGARVE
CONFIRMED AND POSSIBLE BREEDING SPECIES

English Name	Scientific Name	Check	List		
Little Grebe	Tachybaptus ruficollis				
Great Crested Grebe	Podiceps cristatus				
Black-necked Grebe	P. nigricollis				
Shag	Phalacrocorax aristotelis				
Bittern	Botaurus stellaris				
Little Bittern	Ixobrychus minutus				
Night Heron	Nycticorax nycticorax				
Squacco Heron	Ardeola ralloides				
Cattle Egret	Bubulcus ibis				
Little Egret	Egretta garzetta				
Grey Heron	Ardea cinerea				
Purple Heron	A. purpurea				
White Stork	Ciconia ciconia				
Greater Flamingo	Phoenicopterus ruber				
Gadwall	Anas strepera				
Mallard	A. platyrhynchos				
Red-crested Pochard	Netta rufina				
Pochard	Aythya ferina				
Black-winged Kite	Elanus caeruleus				
Black Kite	Milvus migrans				
Short-toed Eagle	Circaetus gallicus				
Hen Harrier	Circus cyaneus				
Montagu's Harrier	C. pygargus				
Goshawk	Accipiter gentilis				
Sparrowhawk	A. nisus				
Buzzard	Buteo buteo				
Steppe Eagle	Aquila rapax				
Imperial Eagle	A. heliaca				
Golden Eagle	A. chrysaetos				

English Name	Scientific Name	Check		List	
Booted Eagle	Hieraaetus pennatus				
Bonelli's Eagle	H. fasciatus				
Osprey	Pandion haliaetus				
Lesser Kestrel	Falco naumanni				
Kestrel	F. tinnunculus				
Peregrine	F. peregrinus				
Red-legged Partridge	Alectoris rufa				
Partridge	Perdix perdix				
Quail	Coturnix coturnix				
Pheasant	Phasianus colchicus				
Water Rail	Rallus aquaticus				
Baillon's Crake	Porzana pusilla				
Moorhen	Gallinula chloropus				
Purple Gallinule	Porphyrio porphyrio				
Coot	Fulica atra				
Little Bustard	Tetrax tetrax				
Great Bustard	Otis tarda				
Black-winged Stilt	Himantopus himantopus				
Avocet	Recurvirostra avosetta				
Stone Curlew	Burhinus oedicnemus				
Collared Pratincole	Glareola pratincola				
Little Ringed Plover	Charadrius dubius				
Kentish Plover	C. alexandrinus				
Lapwing	Vanellus vanellus				
Woodcock	Scolopax rusticola				
Redshank	Tringa totanus				
Common Sandpiper	Actitis hypoleucos				
Herring Gull	Larus argentatus				
Little Tern	Sterna albifrons				
Black Tern	Chlidonias niger				
Rock Dove	Columba livia				
Stock Dove	C. oenus				
Woodpigeon	C. palumbus				
Collared Dove	Streptopelia decaocto				
Turtle Dove	S. turtur				
Great Spotted Cuckoo	Clamator glandarius				

English Name	Scientific Name	Check	List		
Cuckoo	Cuculus canorus				
Barn Owl	Tyto alba				
Scops Owl	Otus scops				
Eagle Owl	Bubo bubo				
Little Owl	Athene noctua				
Tawny Owl	Strix aluco				
Long-eared Owl	Asio otus				
Nightjar	Caprimulgus europaeus				
Red-necked Nightjar	C. ruficollis				
Swift	Apus apus				
Pallid Swift	A. pallidus				
Alpine Swift	A. melba				
Kingfisher	Alcedo atthis				
Bee-eater	Merops apiaster				
Hoopoe	Upupa epops				
Wryneck	Jynx torquilla				
Green Woodpecker	Picus viridis				
Great Spotted Woodpecker	Dendrocopos major				
Lesser Spotted Woodpecker	D. minor				
Dupont's Lark	Chersophilus duponti				
Short-toed Lark	Calandrella brachydactyla				
Lesser Short-toed Lark	C. rufescens				
Crested Lark	Galerida cristata				
Thekla Lark	G. theklae				
Woodlark	Lullula arborea				
Skylark	Alauda arvensis				
Sand Martin	Riparia riparia				
Crag Martin	Ptonoprogne rupestris				
Swallow	Hirundo rustica				
Red-rumped Swallow	H. daurica				
House Martin	Delichon urbica				
Tawny Pipit	Anthus campestris				
Yellow Wagtail	Motacilla flava				
Grey Wagtail	M. cinerea				
White Wagtail	M. alba				
Wren	Troglodytes troglodytes				

English Name	Scientific Name	Check	List		
Rufous Bush Chat	Cercotrichas galactotes				
Robin	Erithacus rubecula				
Nightingale	Luscinia megarhynchos				
Black Redstart	Phoenicurus ochruros				
Redstart	P. phoenicurus				
Whinchat	Saxicola rubetra				
Stonechat	Saxicola torquata				
Wheatear	Oenanthe oenanthe				
Black-eared Wheatear	O. hispanica				
Black Wheatear	O. leucura				
Blue Rock Thrush	Monticola solitarius				
Blackbird	Turdus merula				
Song Thrush	T. philomelos				
Mistle Thrush	T. viscivorus				
Cetti's Warbler	Cettia cetti				
Fan-tailed Warbler	Cisticola juncidis				
Savi's Warbler	Locustella luscinioides				
Moustached Warbler	Acrocephalus melanopogon				
Reed Warbler	A. scirpaceus				
Great Reed Warbler	A. arundinaceus				
Olivaceous Warbler	Hippolais pallida				
Melodious Warbler	H. polyglotta				
Dartford Warbler	Sylvia undata				
Spectacled Warbler	S. conspicillata				
Subalpine Warbler	S. cantillans				
Sardinian Warbler	S. melanocephala				
Orphean Warbler	S. hortensis				
Whitethroat	S. communis				
Garden Warbler	S. borin				
Blackcap	S. atricapilla				
Bonelli's Warbler	Phylloscopus bonelli				
Chiffchaff	P. collybita				
Willow Warbler	P. trochilus				
Firecrest	Regulus ignicapillus				
Spotted Flycatcher	Muscicapa striata				
Pied Flycatcher	Ficedula hypoleuca				

English Name	Scientific Name	Check	List		
Long-tailed Tit	Aegithalos caudatus				
Crested Tit	Parus cristatus				
Coal Tit	P. ater				
Blue Tit	P. caeruleus				
Great Tit	P. major				
Nuthatch	Sitta europaea				
Short-toed Treecreeper	Certhia brachydactyla				
Penduline Tit	Remiz pendulinus				
Golden Oriole	Oriolus oriolus				
Great Grey Shrike	Lanius excubitor				
Woodchat Shrike	L. senator				
Jay	Garrulus glandarius				
Azure-winged Magpie	Cyanopica cyana				
Chough	Pyrrhocorax pyrrhocorax				
Jackdaw	Corvus monedula				
Carrion Crow	C. corone				
Raven	C. corax				
Spotless Starling	Sturnus unicolor				
House Sparrow	Passer domesticus				
Tree Sparrow	P. montanus				
Rock Sparrow	Petronia petronia				
Common Waxbill	Estrilda astrild				
Chaffinch	Fringilla coelebs				
Serin	Serinus serinus				
Greenfinch	Carduelis chloris				
Goldfinch	C. carduelis				
Siskin	C. spinus				
Linnet	C. cannabina				
Bullfinch	Pyrrhula pyrrhula				
Hawfinch	C. coccothraustes				
Cirl Bunting	Emberiza cirlus				
Rock Bunting	E. cia				
Reed Bunting	E. schoeniclus				
Corn Bunting	Miliaria calandra				

FERAL SPECIES

These species are listed in alphabetical order

English Name	Scientific Name	Check	List
Avadavat, Red	Amandava amandava		
Bishop, Crimson-crowned	Euplectes hordeacea		
Bunting, House	Emberiza striolata		
Dove, Barbary	Streptopelia risoria		
Finch, Trumpeter	Bucanetes githagineus		
Finch, Zebra	Poephila guttata		
Feral Pigeon	Columba livia		
Francolin, Black	Francolinus francolinus		
Guineafowl, Helmeted	Numida meleagris		
Munia, Black-headed	Lonchura malacca		
Munia, White-headed	Lonchura maja		
Waxbill, Black-rumped	Estrilda troglodytes		
Waxbill, Orange-cheeked	E. melpoda		
Waxbill, Rosy-rumped	E. rhodopyga		
Weaver, Napoleon	Euplectes afra		
Weaver, Village	Ploceus cucullatus		

APPENDIX V

BIBLIOGRAPHY

Araújo, A. & Pina, J.P. (1984) Boletim da LPN 18 (3): 37-47.
Beven, G. (1970) British Birds 63, 294-9.
Blondel, J. and Badan, O. (1976) Nos oiseaux 33, 189-219.
Bourne, W.R.P. (1955) Ibis 97.
Brown, L.H. (1976) British birds of prey. London.
BTO (1976), The Atlas of Breeding Birds in Britain and Ireland.
BTO (1993), The New Atlas of Breeding Birds in Britain and Ireland: 1988-1991.
BWP:
      Cramp, S. (ed.) (1977) The Birds of the Western Palearctic, Vol. I.
      Cramp, S. (ed.) (1980) The Birds of the Western Palearctic, Vol. II.
      Cramp, S. (ed.) (1983) The Birds of the Western Palearctic, Vol. III.
      Cramp, S. (ed.) (1985) The Birds of the Western Palearctic, Vol. IV.
      Cramp, S. (ed.) (1988) The Birds of the Western Palearctic, Vol. V.
      Cramp, S. (ed.) (1992) The Birds of the Western Palearctic, Vol. VI.
      Cramp, S. (ed.) (1993) The Birds of the Western Palearctic, Vol. VII.
Ferguson-Lees, I.J. (1967) British Birds 60, 80-4.
Finlayson, J.C. (1979) D Phil Thesis. Oxford University.
García, L. et al (1989) Las Aves de Doñana y su Entorno. Estación Biológica de Doñana.
Glutz von Blotzheim, U.N. and Bauer, K.M. (1980) Handbuch der Vögel Mitteleuropas 9,
    Wiesbaden.
Herrera, C.M. (1974) Ardeola 19, 359-94.
Herrera, C.M. (1974) Ardeola 20, 287-306.
Herrera, C.M. and Hiraldo, F. (1976) Ornis scand. 7, 29-41.
Hiraldo, G, Fernandez, F, and Amores, F (1975) Doñana Acta Vert.2, 25-55.
Lowe, F.A. (1954) The Heron. London.
Melchior, E (1988) Regulus Suppl.9, 53-8.
Newton, I. (1972) Finches. London.
Perez Mellado, V. (1980) Ardeola 25, 93-112.
Pinheiro, M.F.V. (1970) Estudos e Divulgação Técnica Grupo a Secção Zoologia Florestal e
    Cenegética, 1-24.
Santos Jr., J.R. (1960) Ocorrência da Hirundo daurica do norte de Portugal. Publ. Inst.
    Zoologia "Dr. Augusto Nobre" No.72.
Tait, W.C. (1924) The birds of Portugal. London.
Teixeira, A.M. (1984) Boletim da LPN 18 (3), 105-115.
Vowles, G.A. & Vowles, R.S. (1987) Ringing and Migration 8: 119-120.
Vowles, G.A. & Vowles, R.S. (1993) Ringing and Migration 14: 143-147.
Xavier, A. (1968) Cyanopica I(1):77-81.

APPENDIX VI

ACKNOWLEDGEMENTS

We should like to thank the large number of people, both resident and holidaymaker, who have given freely of their time to gather data for this book and who have made available all their notes. Without their combined efforts this book would not have been possible. We should like, however, without any lessening of our gratitude to all the other contributors, to particularly thank for the many months of tireless infilling on rectangles:

> Dr. Graham Foggitt
> Norman Llewellyn
> John and Madge Measures
> Paul Mellins

for making available extensive information on raptors:

> Luís Palma

and for the many hours of painstaking proof-reading:

> Nigel Cleere
> John Cooper
> Les Milton

INDEX TO BIRD SPECIES

Page numbers in **bold** indicate main species' text.

NOTES

NOTES

NOTES

NOTES